THE BODLEY HEAD
FORD MADOX FORD
VOLUME I

THE BODLEY HEAD

FORD MADOX FORD

VOLUME I

THE GOOD SOLDIER

SELECTED MEMORIES

POEMS

THE BODLEY HEAD

LONDON

DATES OF ORIGINAL PUBLICATION

The Good Soldier, 1915

The Heart of the Country, 1906
Ancient Lights, 1911
Return to Yesterday, 1931
Mightier than the Sword, 1938

All rights reserved
Printed and bound in Great Britain for
The Bodley Head Ltd
10 Earlham Street, London WC2
by William Clowes and Sons Ltd, Beccles
Set in Linotype Plantin
First published in this edition 1962

CONTENTS

INTRODUCTION

I

FORD MADOX HUEFFER, the name under which he was first known, was born in 1873 and died, in France, in 1939. His first book was published in 1892, his last in 1939, and between those dates some seventy-five books appeared, novels, poems, reminiscences, essays, biographies, histories, books of travel, topography, criticism, sociology. I have chosen for the present selection his finest novel—and perhaps one of the finest novels of our century—*The Good Soldier*, passages from his volumes of reminiscence (the headings and divisions are my own*), a few poems, and his historical trilogy *The Fifth Queen* which has never before been published in one volume. There is a conspicuous absentee which is sometimes known as the Tietjens Saga, after the name of its principal character—the series of war-novels, *Some Do Not, No More Parades, A Man Could Stand Up* and *Last Post*, but those books have already been published in one volume in the United States, and, remarkable though they are, they do not stand up to the erosion of time so satisfactorily as *The Good Soldier*.

Ford was not a man who loved fools or bad writing, and his enemies have been almost as persistent as his friends have been loyal. He was a great editor: in *The English Review* before 1914 he published Conrad, Hudson, Hardy; in the years between the wars in Paris he edited *the transatlantic review* in which he published Gertrude Stein, the early Hemingway, E. E. Cummings. The better the editor, the more numerous his enemies. He was a man too of a passionate nature; his marriage, a Catholic one, was unsuccessful, but divorce was impossible; his long love-affair with the novelist Violet Hunt, of which the reflection is to be found in his poem *On Heaven*, came to a confused and miserable end. On one occasion he tried to leave his country for good and to become a German citizen (that strange episode is recounted in *The Desirable Alien*, a

* The dots which break out like a rash in his later work, for example in *The Pines, Putney*, are Ford's own and do not indicate omissions by the editor.

collaboration with Violet Hunt published ominously in 1913). When war broke out, in spite of his age he joined the army and saw service on the Western Front. Finally he came through the troubled years with his appetite for life undiminished, and was happy in his final relationship. My only memory of him dates from about 1938, a stout sanguine man walking over the fields with the air of a country gentleman—which always, with one side of his nature, he had wanted to be, though the nearest he came to realizing his ambition was on the small property he owned in Provence.

II

Ford had once described himself, before the great disaster of 1914; 'I may humbly write myself down a man in his early forties a little mad about good letters.' By the very nature of his birth and early years he was condemned to the life of an artist. Son of Hueffer, the distinguished musical critic of *The Times* and grandson of Ford Madox Brown, the famous Victorian painter, brought up in the strange mansion in Fitzroy Square immortalized by Thackeray in *The Newcomes*, with small Rossetti cousins tumbling downstairs at his feet and Swinburne, as like as not, lying drunk in the bath on the top floor, he had little choice: one might have prophesied almost anything for him from a staggered laudanum death to membership of the Royal Academy.

One would have been wrong about the details, but not about the fact that, in the age of Kipling, Haggard, and Wells, an age of increasing carelessness among good writers, he was an artist. No one in our century except James has been more attentive to the craft of letters. He was not only a designer; he was a carpenter: you feel in his work the love of the tools and the love of the material. He may sometimes have been over-elaborate, an accusation which after he had spent more than forty years in writing fiction can be brought against his last novels. But who else, except James, has shown such a capacity for growth, even misguided growth, over so long a span of years? Ford's first novel was published in 1892 and his last in 1937. Even so, when he died, he had not reached the limit of his technical experiments.

How seldom a novelist chooses the material nearest to his hand; it is almost as if he were driven to earn experience the hard way. Ford, whom we might have expected to become a novelist of artistic bohemia, a kind of English Murger, did indeed employ the material of Fitzroy Square incomparably well in his volumes of reminiscence—and some people might regard those as his finest novels, for he brought to his dramatizations of people he had known—James, Conrad, Crane, Hudson, Hardy—the same astonishing knack he showed with his historical figures. Most writers dealing with real people find their invention confined, but that was not so with Ford. 'When it has seemed expedient to me I have altered episodes that I have witnessed, but I have been careful never to distort the character of the episode. *The accuracies I deal in are the accuracies of my impressions.* If you want factual accuracies you must go to . . . but no, no, don't go to anyone, stay with me.' (The italics are mine: it is a phrase worth bearing in mind in reading all his works.)

In fact as a novelist Ford began to move further and further from bohemia for his material. His first period as an historical novelist, which he began by collaborating with Conrad in that underrated novel *Romance*, virtually closed with his Tudor trilogy. There were to be two or three more historical novels, until in *Ladies Whose Bright Eyes* . . . he came half out into the contemporary world and began to find his true subject. It could even be argued that in *The Fifth Queen* he was nearest as a novelist to Fitzroy Square. There is the sense of saturation: something is always happening on the stairs, in the passages the servants come and go on half explained errands, and the great King may at any moment erupt upon the scene, half kindly, half malevolent, rather as we feel the presence of Madox Brown in the gas-lit interstices of No. 37.

Most historical novelists use real characters only for purposes of local colour—Lord Nelson passes up a Portsmouth street or Doctor Johnson enters ponderously to close a chapter, but in *The Fifth Queen* we have virtually no fictional characters—the King, Thomas Cromwell, Katharine Howard, they are the principals; we are nearer to the historical plays of Shakespeare than to the fictions of such historical writers as Miss Irwin or Miss Heyer.

'The accuracies I deal in are the accuracies of my impressions.' In *The Fifth Queen* Ford tries out the impressionist method which he was later to employ with triumphant ease in the great confused armistice-day scene of *A Man Could Stand Up*. The whole story of the struggle between Katharine and Cromwell for the King seems told in shadows—shadows which flicker with the flames of a log-fire, diminish suddenly as a torch recedes, stand calm awhile in the candlelight of a chapel: a cresset flares and all the shadows leap together. Has a novel ever before been lit as carefully as a stage production? Nicolas Udal's lies, which play so important a part in the first volume, take their substance from the lighting: they are monstrously elongated or suddenly shrivel: one can believe anything by torchlight. (The power of a lie—that too was a subject he was to pursue through all his later books: the lies of Sylvia Tietjens which ruined her husband's army-career and the monstrous lie of 'poor Florence' in *The Good Soldier* which brought death to three people and madness to a fourth.)

If *The Fifth Queen* is a magnificent bravura piece—and you could say that it was a better painting than ever came out of Fitzroy Square with all the mingled talents there of Madox Brown and Morris, Rossetti and Burne-Jones—in *The Good Soldier* Ford triumphantly found his true subject and oddly enough, for a child of the Pre-Raphaelites, his subject was the English 'gentleman,' the 'black and merciless things' which lie behind that façade.

Edward Ashburnham was the cleanest looking sort of chap;—an excellent magistrate, a first rate soldier, one of the best landlords, so they said, in Hampshire, England. To the poor and to hopeless drunkards, as I myself have witnessed, he was like a painstaking guardian. And he never told a story that couldn't have gone into the columns of the *Field* more than once or twice in all the nine years of my knowing him. He didn't even like hearing them; he would fidget and get up and go out to buy a cigar or something of that sort. You would have said that he was just exactly the sort of chap that you could have trusted your wife with. And I trusted mine and it was madness.

The Good Soldier, which Ford had wished to call *The Saddest Story*, concerns the ravages wrought by a passionate man who had all the virtues but continence. The narrator is the betrayed husband, and it is through his eyes alone that we watch the complications and involvements left by Ashburnham's blind urge towards satisfaction. Technically the story is undoubtedly Ford's masterpiece: the book is simultaneously a study of the way memory works. The time-shifts are valuable not merely for purposes of suspense—they lend veracity to the appalling events. This is just how memory does work, and we become involved with the narrator's memory as though it were our own. Ford's apprenticeship with Conrad had borne its fruit, but he improved on the Master.

I have, I am aware, told this story in a very rambling way so that it may be difficult for anyone to find their path through what may be a sort of maze. I cannot help it. I have stuck to my idea of being in a country cottage with a silent listener, hearing between the gusts of the wind and amidst the noises of the distant sea, the story as it comes. And when one discusses an affair—a long, sad affair—one goes back, one goes forward. One remembers points that one has forgotten and one explains them all the more minutely since one recognizes that one has forgotten to mention them in their proper places and that one may have given, by omitting them, a false impression. I console myself with thinking that this is a real story and that, after all, real stories are probably told best in the way a person telling a story would tell them. They will then seem most real.

A short enough book it is to contain two suicides, two ruined lives, a death, and a girl driven insane: it may seem odd to find the keynote of the book is restraint, a restraint which is given it by the gentle character of the narrator ('I am only an ageing American with very little knowledge of life') who never loses his love and compassion for the characters concerned. 'Here were two noble people—for I am convinced that both Edward and Leonora had noble natures—here, then, were two noble natures, drifting down life, like fireships afloat on a lagoon and causing miseries, heartaches, agony of the mind and death. And they themselves steadily deteriorated. And why? For what purpose? To point what lesson? It is all a darkness.' He condemns no one; in extremity he doesn't even condemn human nature, and I find one of the most moving under-statements in literature his summing up of Leonora's attitude to her husband's temporary infatuation for the immature young woman, Maisie Maidan: 'I think she would really have welcomed it if he could have come across the love of his life. It would have given her a rest.'

I don't know how many times in nearly forty years I have come back to this novel of Ford's, every time to discover a new aspect to admire, but I think the impression which will be left most strongly on the reader is the sense of Ford's involvement. A novelist is not a vegetable absorbing nourishment mechanically from soil and air: material is not easily or painlessly gained, and one cannot help wondering what agonies of frustration and error lay behind *The Saddest Story*.

GRAHAM GREENE

THE GOOD SOLDIER

A TALE OF PASSION

PART ONE

I

THIS is the saddest story I have ever heard. We had known the Ashburnhams for nine seasons of the town of Nauheim with an extreme intimacy—or, rather with an acquaintanceship as loose and easy and yet as close as a good glove's with your hand. My wife and I knew Captain and Mrs Ashburnham as well as it was possible to know anybody, and yet, in another sense, we knew nothing at all about them. This is, I believe, a state of things only possible with English people of whom, till to-day, when I sit down to puzzle out what I know of this sad affair, I knew nothing whatever. Six months ago I had never been to England, and, certainly, I had never sounded the depths of an English heart. I had known the shallows.

I don't mean to say that we were not acquainted with many English people. Living, as we perforce lived, in Europe, and being, as we perforce were, leisured Americans, which is as much as to say that we were un-American, we were thrown very much into the society of the nicer English. Paris, you see, was our home. Somewhere between Nice and Bordighera provided yearly winter quarters for us, and Nauheim always received us from July to September. You will gather from this statement that one of us had, as the saying is, a 'heart,' and, from the statement that my wife is dead, that she was the sufferer.

Captain Ashburnham also had a heart. But, whereas a yearly month or so at Nauheim tuned him up to exactly the right pitch for the rest of the twelvemonth, the two months or so were only just enough to keep poor Florence alive from year to year. The reason for his heart was, approximately, polo, or too much hard sportsmanship in his youth. The reason for poor Florence's broken years was a storm at sea upon our first crossing to Europe, and the immediate reasons for our imprisonment in that continent were doctors' orders. They said that even the short Channel crossing might well kill the poor thing.

When we all first met, Captain Ashburnham, home on sick leave from an India to which he was never to return, was thirty-three; Mrs Ashburnham—Leonora—was thirty-one. I was thirty-six and poor Florence thirty. Thus to-day Florence would have been thirty-nine and Captain Ashburnham forty-two; whereas I am forty-five and Leonora forty. You will perceive, therefore, that our friendship has been a young-middle-aged affair, since we were all of us of quite quiet dispositions, the Ashburnhams being more particularly what in England it is the custom to call 'quite good people.'

They were descended, as you will probably expect, from the Ashburnham who accompanied Charles I to the scaffold, and, as you must also expect with this class of English people, you would never have noticed it. Mrs Ashburnham was a Powys; Florence was a Hurlbird of Stamford, Connecticut, where, as you know, they are more old-fashioned than even the inhabitants of Cranford, England, could have been. I myself am a Dowell of Philadelphia, Pa., where, it is historically true, there are more old English families than you would find in any six English counties taken together. I carry about with me, indeed—as if it were the only thing that invisibly anchored me to any spot upon the globe—the title deeds of my farm, which once covered several blocks between Chestnut and Walnut Streets. These title deeds are of wampum, the grant of an Indian chief to the first Dowell, who left Farnham in Surrey in company with William Penn. Florence's people, as is so often the case with the inhabitants of Connecticut, came from the neighbourhood of Fordingbridge, where the Ashburnhams' place is. From there, at this moment, I am actually writing.

You may well ask why I write. And yet my reasons are quite many. For it is not unusual in human beings who have witnessed the sack of a city or the falling to pieces of a people to desire to set down what they have witnessed for the benefit of unknown heirs or of generations infinitely remote; or, if you please, just to get the sight out of their heads.

Some one has said that the death of a mouse from cancer is the whole sack of Rome by the Goths, and I swear to you that the breaking up of our little four-square coterie was such another unthinkable event. Supposing that you should come upon us sitting together at one of the little tables in front of the club house, let us say, at Homburg, taking tea of an afternoon and watching the miniature golf, you would have said that, as human affairs go, we were an extraordinarily safe castle. We were, if you will, one of those tall ships with the white sails upon a blue sea, one of those things that seem the proudest and the safest of all the beautiful and safe things that God has permitted the mind of men to frame. Where better could one take refuge? Where better?

Permanence? Stability? I can't believe it's gone. I can't believe that that long, tranquil life, which was just stepping a minuet, vanished in four crashing days at the end of nine years and six weeks. Upon my word, yes, our intimacy was like a minuet, simply because on every possible occasion and in every possible circumstance we knew where to go, where to sit, which table we unanimously should choose; and we could rise and go, all four together, without a signal from any one of us, always to the music of the Kur orchestra, always in the temperate sunshine, or, if it rained, in discreet shelters. No, indeed, it can't be gone. You can't kill a minuet de la cour. You may shut up the music-book, close the harpsichord; in the cupboard and presses the rats may destroy the white satin favours. The mob may sack Versailles; the Trianon may fall, but surely the minuet—the minuet itself is dancing itself away into the furthest stars, even as our minuet of the Hessian bathing places must be stepping itself still. Isn't there any heaven where old beautiful dances, old beautiful intimacies prolong themselves? Isn't there any Nirvana pervaded by the faint thrilling of instruments that have fallen into the dust of wormwood but that yet had frail, tremulous, and everlasting souls?

No, by God, it is false! It wasn't a minuet that we stepped; it was a prison—a prison full of screaming hysterics, tied down so that they might not outsound the rolling of our carriage wheels as we went along the shaded avenues of the Taunus Wald.

And yet I swear by the sacred name of my creator that it was true. It was true sunshine; the true music; the true splash of the fountains from the mouth of stone dolphins. For, if for me we were four people with the same tastes, with the same desires, acting—or, no, not acting—sitting here and there unanimously, isn't that the truth? If for nine years I have possessed a goodly apple that is rotten at the core and discover its rottenness only in nine years and six months less four days, isn't it true to say that for nine years I possessed a goodly apple? So it may well be with Edward Ashburnham, with Leonora his wife and with poor dear Florence. And, if you come to think of it, isn't it a little odd that the physical rottenness of at least two pillars of our four-square house never presented itself to my mind as a menace to its security? It doesn't so present itself now though the two of them are actually dead. I don't know . . .

I know nothing—nothing in the world—of the hearts of men. I only know that I am alone—horribly alone. No hearthstone will ever again witness, for me, friendly intercourse. No smoking-room will ever be other than peopled with incalculable simulacra amidst smoke wreaths. Yet, in the name of God, what should I know if I don't know the life of the hearth and of the smoking-room, since my whole life has been passed in those places? The warm hearthside! —Well, there was Florence: I believe that for the twelve years her life lasted, after the storm that seemed irre-

trievably to have weakened her heart—I don't believe that
for one minute she was out of my sight, except when she
was safely tucked up in bed and I should be downstairs,
talking to some good fellow or other in some lounge or
smoking-room or taking my final turn with a cigar before
going to bed. I don't, you understand, blame Florence.
But how can she have known what she knew? How could
she have got to know it? To know it so fully. Heavens!
There doesn't seem to have been the actual time. It must
have been when I was taking my baths, and my Swedish
exercises, being manicured. Leading the life I did, of the
sedulous, strained nurse, I had to do something to keep
myself fit. It must have been then! Yet even that can't
have been enough time to get the tremendously long conversations full of worldly wisdom that Leonora has reported to me since their deaths. And is it possible to
imagine that during our prescribed walks in Nauheim and
the neighbourhood she found time to carry on the protracted negotiations which she did carry on between
Edward Ashburnham and his wife? And isn't it incredible
that during all that time Edward and Leonora never spoke
a word to each other in private? What is one to think of
humanity?

For I swear to you that they were the model couple. He
was as devoted as it was possible to be without appearing
fatuous. So well set up, with such honest blue eyes, such
a touch of stupidity, such a warm goodheartedness! And
she—so tall, so splendid in the saddle, so fair! Yes,
Leonora was extraordinarily fair and so extraordinarily the
real thing that she seemed too good to be true. You don't,
I mean, as a rule, get it all so superlatively together. To be
the county family, to look the county family, to be so
appropriately and perfectly wealthy; to be so perfect in
manner—even just to the saving touch of insolence that
seems to be necessary. To have all that and to be all that!
No, it was too good to be true. And yet, only this afternoon, talking over the whole matter she said to me:—
'Once I tried to have a lover but I was so sick at the heart,

so utterly worn out that I had to send him away.' That struck me as the most amazing thing I had ever heard. She said 'I was actually in a man's arms. Such a nice chap! Such a dear fellow! And I was saying to myself, fiercely, hissing it between my teeth, as they say in novels—and really clenching them together: I was saying to myself: "Now, I'm in for it and I'll really have a good time for once in my life—for once in my life!" It was in the dark, in a carriage, coming back from a hunt ball. Eleven miles we had to drive! And then suddenly the bitterness of the endless poverty, of the endless acting—it fell on me like a blight, it spoilt everything. Yes, I had to realize that I had been spoilt even for the good time when it came. And I burst out crying and I cried and I cried for the whole eleven miles. Just imagine *me* crying! And just imagine me making a fool of the poor dear chap like that. It certainly wasn't playing the game, was it now?'

I don't know; I don't know; was that last remark of hers the remark of a harlot, or is it what every decent woman, county family or not county family, thinks at the bottom of her heart? Or thinks all the time for the matter of that? Who knows?

Yet, if one doesn't know that at this hour and day, at this pitch of civilization to which we have attained, after all the preachings of all the moralists, and all the teachings of all the mothers to all the daughters *in saecula saeculorum* ... but perhaps that is what all mothers teach all daughters, not with lips but with the eyes, or with heart whispering to heart. And, if one doesn't know as much as that about the first thing in the world, what does one know and why is one here?

I asked Mrs Ashburnham whether she had told Florence that and what Florence had said and she answered:—
'Florence didn't offer any comment at all. What could she say? There wasn't anything to be said. With the grinding poverty we had to put up with to keep up appearances, and the way the poverty came about—*you* know what I mean—any woman would have been justified in taking a

lover and presents too. Florence once said about a very similar position—she was a little too well-bred, too American, to talk about mine—that it was a case of perfectly open riding and the woman could just act on the spur of the moment. She said it in American of course, but that was the sense of it. I think her actual words were:—"That it was up to her to take it or leave it..." '

I don't want you to think that I am writing Teddy Ashburnham down a brute. I don't believe he was. God knows, perhaps all men are like that. For as I've said what do I know even of the smoking-room? Fellows come in and tell the most extraordinarily gross stories—so gross that they will positively give you a pain. And yet they'd be offended if you suggested that they weren't the sort of person you could trust your wife alone with. And very likely they'd be quite properly offended—that is if you can trust anybody alone with anybody. But that sort of fellow obviously takes more delight in listening to or in telling gross stories—more delight than in anything else in the world. They'll hunt languidly and dress languidly and dine languidly and work without enthusiasm and find it a bore to carry on three minutes' conversation about anything whatever and yet, when the other sort of conversation begins, they'll laugh and wake up and throw themselves about in their chairs. Then, if they so delight in the narration, how is it possible that they can be offended—and properly offended—at the suggestion that they might make attempts upon your wife's honour? Or again: Edward Ashburnham was the cleanest looking sort of chap;—an excellent magistrate, a first rate soldier, one of the best landlords, so they said, in Hampshire, England. To the poor and to hopeless drunkards, as I myself have witnessed, he was like a painstaking guardian. And he never told a story that couldn't have gone into the columns of the *Field* more than once or twice in all the nine years of my knowing him. He didn't even like hearing them; he would fidget and get up and go out to buy a cigar or something of that sort. You would have said that he was just exactly the sort

of chap that you could have trusted your wife with. And
I trusted mine and it was madness.

And yet again you have me. If poor Edward was
dangerous because of the chastity of his expressions—and
they say that that is always the hall-mark of a libertine—
what about myself? For I solemnly avow that not only
have I never so much as hinted at an impropriety in my
conversation in the whole of my days; and more than that,
I will vouch for the cleanness of my thoughts and the absolute chastity of my life. At what, then, does it all work out?
Is the whole thing a folly and a mockery? Am I no better
than a eunuch or is the proper man—the man with the
right to existence—a raging stallion forever neighing after
his neighbour's womankind?

I don't know. And there is nothing to guide us. And if
everything is so nebulous about a matter so elementary as
the morals of sex, what is there to guide us in the more
subtle morality of all other personal contacts, associations,
and activities? Or are we meant to act on impulse alone?
It is all a darkness.

II

I don't know how it is best to put this thing down—
whether it would be better to try and tell the story from
the beginning, as if it were a story; or whether to tell it
from this distance of time, as it reached me from the lips
of Leonora or from those of Edward himself.

So I shall just imagine myself for a fortnight or so at one
side of the fireplace of a country cottage, with a sympathetic soul opposite me. And I shall go on talking, in a
low voice while the sea sounds in the distance and overhead the great black flood of wind polishes the bright stars.
From time to time we shall get up and go to the door and
look out at the great moon and say:—'Why, it is nearly as
bright as in Provence!' And then we shall come back to
the fireside, with just the touch of a sigh because we are
not in that Provence where even the saddest stories are

gay. Consider the lamentable history of Peire Vidal. Two
years ago Florence and I motored from Biarritz to Las
Tours, which is in the Black Mountains. In the middle of
a tortuous valley there rises up an immense pinnacle and
on the pinnacle are four castles—Las Tours, the Towers.
And the immense mistral blew down that valley which was
the way from France into Provence so that the silver grey
olive leaves appeared like hair flying in the wind, and the
tufts of rosemary crept into the iron rocks that they might
not be torn up by the roots.

It was, of course, poor dear Florence who wanted to go
to Las Tours. You are to imagine that, however much her
bright personality came from Stamford, Connecticut, she
was yet a graduate of Poughkeepsie. I never could imagine
how she did it—the queer, chattery person that she was.
With the far-away look in her eyes—which wasn't, however, in the least romantic—I mean that she didn't look as
if she were seeing poetic dreams, or looking through you,
for she hardly ever did look at you!—holding up one hand
as if she wished to silence any objection—or any comment
for the matter of that—she would talk. She would talk
about William the Silent, about Gustave the Loquacious,
about Paris frocks, about how the poor dressed in
1337, about Fantin-Latour, about the Paris-Lyons-
Méditerranée train-de-luxe, about whether it would be
worth while to get off at Tarascon and go across the
windswept suspension-bridge, over the Rhone to take
another look at Beaucaire.

We never did take another look at Beaucaire, of course
—beautiful Beaucaire, with the high, triangular white
tower, that looked as thin as a needle and as tall as the
Flatiron, between Fifth and Broadway—Beaucaire with
the grey walls on the top of the pinnacle surrounding an
acre and a half of blue irises, beneath the tallness of the
stone pines. What a beautiful thing the stone pine is!...

No, we never did go back anywhere. Not to Heidelberg,
not to Hamelin, not to Verona, not to Mont Majour—not
so much as to Carcassonne itself. We talked of it, of course,

but I guess Florence got all she wanted out of one look at a place. She had the seeing eye.

I haven't, unfortunately, so that the world is full of places to which I want to return—towns with the blinding white sun upon them; stone pines against the blue of the sky; corners of gables, all carved and painted with stags and scarlet flowers and crowstepped gables with the little saint at the top; and grey and pink palazzi and walled towns a mile or so back from the sea, on the Mediterranean, between Leghorn and Naples. Not one of them did we see more than once, so that the whole world for me is like spots of colour in an immense canvas. Perhaps if it weren't so I should have something to catch hold of now.

Is all this digression or isn't it digression? Again I don't know. You, the listener, sit opposite me. But you are so silent. You don't tell me anything. I am, at any rate, trying to get you to see what sort of life it was I led with Florence and what Florence was like. Well, she was bright; and she danced. She seemed to dance over the floors of castles and over seas and over and over the salons of modistes and over the *plages* of the Riviera—like a gay tremulous beam, reflected from water upon a ceiling. And my function in life was to keep that bright thing in existence. And it was almost as difficult as trying to catch with your hand that dancing reflection. And the task lasted for years.

Florence's aunts used to say that I must be the laziest man in Philadelphia. They had never been to Philadelphia and they had the New England conscience. You see, the first thing they said to me when I called in on Florence in the little ancient, colonial, wooden house beneath the high, thin-leaved elms—the first question they asked me was not how I did but what did I do. And I did nothing. I suppose I ought to have done something, but I didn't see any call to do it. Why does one do things? I just drifted in and wanted Florence. First I had drifted in on Florence at a Browning tea, or something of the sort in Fourteenth Street, which was then still residential. I don't know why I had gone to New York; I don't know why I had gone to

the tea. I don't see why Florence should have gone to that
sort of spelling bee. It wasn't the place at which, even then,
you expected to find a Poughkeepsie graduate. I guess
Florence wanted to raise the culture of the Stuyvesant
crowd and did it as she might have gone in slumming.
Intellectual slumming, that was what it was. She always
wanted to leave the world a little more elevated than she
found it. Poor dear thing, I have heard her lecture Teddy
Ashburnham by the hour on the difference between a
Franz Hals and a Wouvermans and why the Pre-
Mycenaean statues were cubical with knobs on the top.
I wonder what he made of it? Perhaps he was thankful.

I know I was. For do you understand my whole attentions, my whole endeavours were to keep poor dear
Florence on to topics like the finds at Cnossos and the
mental spirituality of Walter Pater. I had to keep her at it,
you understand, or she might die. For I was solemnly informed that if she became excited over anything or if her
emotions were really stirred her little heart might cease to
beat. For twelve years I had to watch every word that any
person uttered in any conversation and I had to head it off
what the English call 'things'—off love, poverty, crime,
religion and the rest of it. Yes, the first doctor that we had
when she was carried off the ship at Havre assured me that
this must be done. Good God, are all these fellows monstrous idiots, or is there a freemasonry between all of them
from end to end of the earth?... That is what makes me
think of that fellow Peire Vidal.

Because, of course, his story is culture and I had to head
her towards culture and at the same time it's so funny and
she hadn't got to laugh, and it's so full of love and she
wasn't to think of love. Do you know the story? Las Tours
of the Four Castles had for chatelaine Blanche Somebody-
or-other who was called as a term of commendation, La
Louve—the She-Wolf. And Peire Vidal the Troubadour
paid his court to La Louve. And she wouldn't have anything to do with him. So, out of compliment to her—the
things people do when they're in love!—he dressed himself

up in wolfskins and went up into the Black Mountains. And the shepherds of the Montagne Noire and their dogs mistook him for a wolf and he was torn with the fangs and beaten with clubs. So they carried him back to Las Tours and La Louve wasn't at all impressed. They polished him up and her husband remonstrated seriously with her. Vidal was, you see, a great poet and it was not proper to treat a great poet with indifference.

So Peire Vidal declared himself Emperor of Jerusalem or somewhere and the husband had to kneel down and kiss his feet though La Louve wouldn't. And Peire set sail in a rowing boat with four companions to redeem the Holy Sepulchre. And they struck on a rock somewhere, and, at great expense, the husband had to fit out an expedition to fetch him back. And Peire Vidal fell all over the Lady's bed while the husband, who was a most ferocious warrior, remonstrated some more about the courtesy that is due to great poets. But I suppose La Louve was the more ferocious of the two. Anyhow, that is all that came of it. Isn't that a story?

You haven't an idea of the queer old-fashionedness of Florence's aunts—the Misses Hurlbird, nor yet of her uncle. An extraordinarily lovable man, that Uncle John. Thin, gentle, and with a 'heart' that made his life very much what Florence's afterwards became. He didn't reside at Stamford; his home was in Waterbury where the watches come from. He had a factory there which, in our queer American way, would change its functions almost from year to year. For nine months or so it would manufacture buttons out of bone. Then it would suddenly produce brass buttons for coachmen's liveries. Then it would take a turn at embossed tin lids for candy boxes. The fact is that the poor old gentleman, with his weak and fluttering heart, didn't want his factory to manufacture anything at all. He wanted to retire. And he did retire when he was seventy. But he was so worried at having all the street boys in the town point after him and exclaim:—'There goes the laziest man in Waterbury!' that he tried taking a tour round the world. And Florence and a young man called Jimmy went with him. It appears from what Florence told me that Jimmy's function with Mr Hurlbird was to avoid exciting topics for him. He had to keep him, for instance, out of political discussions. For the poor old man was a violent Democrat in days when you might travel the world over without finding anything but a Republican. Anyhow, they went round the world.

I think an anecdote is about the best way to give you an idea of what the old gentleman was like. For it is perhaps important that you should know what the old gentleman was; he had a great deal of influence in forming the character of my poor dear wife.

Just before they set out from San Francisco for the South Seas old Mr Hurlbird said he must take something with him to make little presents to people he met on the voyage. And it struck him that the things to take for that purpose were oranges—because California is the orange country—and comfortable folding chairs. So he bought I don't know how many cases of oranges—the great cool California oranges, and half-a-dozen folding chairs in a special case that he always kept in his cabin. There must have been half a cargo of fruit.

For, to every person on board the several steamers that they employed—to every person with whom he had so much as a nodding acquaintance, he gave an orange every morning. And they lasted him right round the girdle of this mighty globe of ours. When they were at North Cape, even, he saw on the horizon, poor dear thin man that he was, a lighthouse. 'Hello,' says he to himself, 'these fellows must be very lonely. Let's take them some oranges.' So he had a boatload of his fruit out and had himself rowed to the lighthouse on the horizon. The folding chairs he lent to any lady that he came across and liked or who seemed tired and invalidish on the ship. And so, guarded against his heart and, having his niece with him, he went round the world . . .

He wasn't obtrusive about his heart. You wouldn't have

known he had one. He only left it to the physical laboratory at Waterbury for the benefit of science, since he considered it to be quite an extraordinary kind of heart. And the joke of the matter was that, when, at the age of eighty-four, just five days before poor Florence, he died of bronchitis there was found to be absolutely nothing the matter with that organ. It had certainly jumped or squeaked or something just sufficiently to take in the doctors, but it appears that that was because of an odd formation of the lungs. I don't much understand about these matters.

I inherited his money because Florence died five days after him. I wish I hadn't. It was a great worry. I had to go out to Waterbury just after Florence's death because the poor dear old fellow had left a good many charitable bequests and I had to appoint trustees. I didn't like the idea of their not being properly handled.

Yes, it was a great worry. And just as I had got things roughly settled I received the extraordinary cable from Ashburnham begging me to come back and have a talk with him. And immediately afterwards came one from Leonora saying, 'Yes, please do come. You could be so helpful.' It was as if he had sent the cable without consulting her and had afterwards told her. Indeed, that was pretty much what had happened, except that he had told the girl and the girl told the wife. I arrived, however, too late to be of any good if I could have been of any good. And then I had my first taste of English life. It was amazing. It was overwhelming. I never shall forget the polished cob that Edward, beside me, drove; the animal's action, its high-stepping, its skin that was like satin. And the peace! And the red cheeks! And the beautiful, beautiful old house.

Just near Branshaw Teleragh it was and we descended on it from the high, clear, windswept waste of the New Forest. I tell you it was amazing to arrive there from Waterbury. And it came into my head—for Teddy Ashburnham, you remember, had cabled to me to 'come and have a talk' with him—that it was unbelievable that anything essentially calamitous could happen to that place and those people. I tell you it was the very spirit of peace. And Leonora, beautiful and smiling, with her coils of yellow hair, stood on the top doorstep, with a butler and footman and a maid or so behind her. And she just said:—'So glad you've come,' as if I'd run down to lunch from a town ten miles away, instead of having come half the world over at the call of two urgent telegrams.

The girl was out with the hounds, I think.

And that poor devil beside me was in an agony. Absolute, hopeless, dumb agony such as passes the mind of man to imagine.

III

It was a very hot summer, in August, 1904; and Florence had already been taking the baths for a month. I don't know how it feels to be a patient at one of those places. I never was a patient anywhere. I daresay the patients get a home feeling and some sort of anchorage in the spot. They seem to like the bath attendants, with their cheerful faces, their air of authority, their white linen. But, for myself, to be at Nauheim gave me a sense—what shall I say? —a sense almost of nakedness—the nakedness that one feels on the sea-shore or in any great open space. I had no attachments, no accumulations. In one's own home it is as if little, innate sympathies draw one to particular chairs that seem to enfold one in an embrace, or take one along particular streets that seem friendly when others may be hostile. And, believe me, that feeling is a very important part of life. I know it well, that have been for so long a wanderer upon the face of public resorts. And one is too polished up. Heaven knows I was never an untidy man. But the feeling that I had when, whilst poor Florence was taking her morning bath, I stood upon the carefully swept steps of the Englischer Hof, looking at the carefully arranged trees in tubs upon the carefully arranged gravel whilst carefully arranged people walked past in carefully calculated gaiety, at the carefully calculated hour, the tall trees of the public gardens, going up to the right; the reddish stone of the baths—or were they white half-timber châlets? Upon my word I have forgotten, I who was there so often. That will give you the measure of how much I was in the landscape. I could find my way blindfolded to the hot rooms, to the douche rooms, to the fountain in the centre of the quadrangle where the rusty water gushes out. Yes, I could find my way blindfolded. I know the exact distances. From the Hotel Regina you took one hundred and eighty-seven paces, then, turning sharp, lefthanded, four hundred and twenty took you straight down to the fountain. From the Englischer Hof, starting on the sidewalk, it was ninety-seven paces and the same four hundred and twenty, but turning lefthanded this time.

And now you understand that, having nothing in the world to do—but nothing whatever! I fell into the habit of counting my footsteps. I would walk with Florence to the baths. And, of course, she entertained me with her conversation. It was, as I have said, wonderful what she could make conversation out of. She walked very lightly, and her hair was very nicely done, and she dressed beautifully and very expensively. Of course she had money of her own, but I shouldn't have minded. And yet you know I can't remember a single one of her dresses. Or I can remember just one, a very simple one of blue figured silk— a Chinese pattern—very full in the skirts and broadening out over the shoulders. And her hair was copper-coloured, and the heels of her shoes were exceedingly high, so that she tripped upon the points of her toes. And when she came to the door of the bathing place, and when it opened to receive her, she would look back at me with a little coquettish smile, so that her cheek appeared to be caressing her shoulder.

I seem to remember that, with that dress, she wore an immensely broad Leghorn hat—like the Chapeau de Paille of Rubens, only very white. The hat would be tied with a lightly knotted scarf of the same stuff as her dress. She knew how to give value to her blue eyes. And round her neck would be some simple pink, coral beads. And her complexion had a perfect clearness, a perfect smoothness . . .

Yes, that is how I most exactly remember her, in that dress, in that hat, looking over her shoulder at me so that the eyes flashed very blue—dark pebble blue . . .

And, what the devil! For whose benefit did she do it? For that of the bath attendant? of the passers-by? I don't know. Anyhow, it can't have been for me, for never, in all the years of her life, never on any possible occasion, or in any other place did she so smile to me, mockingly, invitingly. Ah, she was a riddle; but then, all other women are riddles. And it occurs to me that some way back I began a sentence that I have never finished . . . It was about the feeling that I had when I stood on the steps of my hotel every morning before starting out to fetch Florence back from the bath. Natty, precise, well-brushed, conscious of being rather small amongst the long English, the lank Americans, the rotund Germans, and the obese Russian Jewesses, I should stand there, tapping a cigarette on the outside of my case, surveying for a moment the world in the sunlight. But a day was to come when I was never to do it again alone. You can imagine, therefore, what the coming of the Ashburnhams meant for me.

I have forgotten the aspect of many things, but I shall never forget the aspect of the dining-room of the Hotel Excelsior on that evening—and on so many other evenings. Whole castles have vanished from my memory, whole cities that I have never visited again, but that white room, festooned with papier-maché fruits and flowers; the tall windows; the many tables; the black screen round the door with three golden cranes flying upward on each panel; the palm-tree in the centre of the room; the swish of the waiter's feet; the cold expensive elegance; the mien of the diners as they came in every evening—their air of earnestness as if they must go through a meal prescribed by the Kur authorities and their air of sobriety as if they must seek not by any means to enjoy their meals—those things

I shall not easily forget. And then, one evening, in the
twilight, I saw Edward Ashburnham lounge round the
screen into the room. The head waiter, a man with a face
all grey—in what subterranean nooks or corners do people
cultivate those absolutely grey complexions?—went with
the timorous patronage of these creatures towards him and
held out a grey ear to be whispered into. It was generally
a disagreeable ordeal for newcomers but Edward Ashburnham bore it like an Englishman and a gentleman. I could
see his lips form a word of three syllables—remember I
had nothing in the world to do but to notice these niceties
—and immediately I knew that he must be Edward Ashburnham, Captain, Fourteenth Hussars, of Branshaw
House, Branshaw Teleragh. I knew it because every evening just before dinner, whilst I waited in the hall, I used,
by the courtesy of Monsieur Schontz, the proprietor, to
inspect the little police reports that each guest was expected to sign upon taking a room.

The head waiter piloted him immediately to a vacant
table, three away from my own—the table that the Gren-
falls of Falls River, N.J., had just vacated. It struck me that
that was not a very nice table for the newcomers, since the
sunlight, low though it was, shone straight down upon it,
and the same idea seemed to come at the same moment
into Captain Ashburnham's head. His face hitherto had, in
the wonderful English fashion, expressed nothing whatever. Nothing. There was in it neither joy nor despair;
neither hope nor fear; neither boredom nor satisfaction.
He seemed to perceive no soul in that crowded room; he
might have been walking in a jungle. I never came across
such a perfect expression before and I never shall again.
It was insolence and not insolence; it was modesty and not
modesty. His hair was fair, extraordinarily ordered in a
wave, running from the left temple to the right; his face
was a light brick-red, perfectly uniform in tint up to the
roots of the hair itself; his yellow moustache was as stiff
as a toothbrush and I verily believe that he had his black
smoking jacket thickened a little over the shoulder-blades

so as to give himself the air of the slightest possible stoop. It would be like him to do that; that was the sort of thing he thought about. Martingales, Chiffney bits, boots; where you got the best soap, the best brandy, the name of the chap who rode a plater down the Khyber cliffs; the spreading power of number three shot before a charge of number four powder . . . by heavens, I hardly ever heard him talk of anything else. Not in all the years that I knew him did I hear him talk of anything but these subjects. Oh, yes, once he told me that I could buy my special shade of blue ties cheaper from a firm in Burlington Arcade than from my own people in New York. And I have bought my ties from that firm ever since. Otherwise I should not remember the name of the Burlington Arcade. I wonder what it looks like. I have never seen it. I imagine it to be two immense rows of pillars, like those of the Forum at Rome, with Edward Ashburnham striding down between them. But it probably isn't—the least like that. Once also he advised me to buy Caledonian Deferred, since they were due to rise. And I did buy them and they did rise. But of how he got the knowledge I haven't the faintest idea. It seemed to drop out of the blue sky.

And that was absolutely all that I knew of him until a month ago—that and the profusion of his cases, all of pigskin and stamped with his initials, E. F. A. There were guncases, and collar cases, and shirt cases, and letter cases and cases each containing four bottles of medicine; and hat cases and helmet cases. It must have needed a whole herd of the Gadarene swine to make up his outfit. And, if I ever penetrated into his private room it would be to see him standing, with his coat and waistcoat off and the immensely long line of his perfectly elegant trousers from waist to boot heel. And he would have a slightly reflective air and he would be just opening one kind of case and just closing another.

Good God, what did they all see in him? for I swear there was all there was of him, inside and out; though they said he was a good soldier. Yet, Leonora adored him with a passion that was like an agony, and hated him with an agony that was as bitter as the sea. How could he arouse anything like a sentiment, in anybody?

What did he even talk to them about—when they were under four eyes?—Ah, well, suddenly, as if by a flash of inspiration, I know. For all good soldiers are sentimentalists—all good soldiers of that type. Their profession, for one thing, is full of the big words, courage, loyalty, honour, constancy. And I have given a wrong impression of Edward Ashburnham if I have made you think that literally never in the course of our nine years of intimacy did he discuss what he would have called 'the graver things.' Even before his final outburst to me, at times, very late at night, say, he has blurted out something that gave an insight into the sentimental view of the cosmos that was his. He would say how much the society of a good woman could do towards redeeming you, and he would say that constancy was the finest of the virtues. He said it very stiffly, of course, but still as if the statement admitted of no doubt.

Constancy! Isn't that the queer thought? And yet, I must add that poor dear Edward was a great reader—he would pass hours lost in novels of a sentimental type—novels in which typewriter girls married Marquises and governesses Earls. And in his books, as a rule, the course of true love ran as smooth as buttered honey. And he was fond of poetry, of a certain type—and he could even read a perfectly sad love story. I have seen his eyes filled with tears at reading of a hopeless parting. And he loved, with a sentimental yearning, all children, puppies, and the feeble generally . . .

So, you see, he would have plenty to gurgle about to a woman—with that and his sound common sense about martingales and his—still sentimental—experiences as a county magistrate; and with his intense, optimistic belief that the woman he was making love to at the moment was the one he was destined, at last, to be eternally constant to . . . Well, I fancy he could put up a pretty good deal of talk when there was no man around to make him feel shy. And I was quite astonished, during his final burst out to me—at the very end of things, when the poor girl was on her way to that fatal Brindisi and he was trying to persuade himself and me that he had never really cared for her—I was quite astonished to observe how literary and how just his expressions were. He talked like quite a good book—a book not in the least cheaply sentimental. You see, I suppose he regarded me not so much as a man. I had to be regarded as a woman or a solicitor. Anyhow, it burst out of him on that horrible night. And then, next morning, he took me over to the Assizes and I saw how, in a perfectly calm and business-like way, he set to work to secure a verdict of not guilty for a poor girl, the daughter of one of his tenants, who had been accused of murdering her baby. He spent two hundred pounds on her defence . . . Well, that was Edward Ashburnham.

I had forgotten about his eyes. They were as blue as the sides of a certain type of box of matches. When you looked at them carefully you saw that they were perfectly honest, perfectly straightforward, perfectly, perfectly stupid. But the brick pink of his complexion, running perfectly level to the brick pink of his inner eyelids, gave them a curious, sinister expression—like a mosaic of blue porcelain set in pink china. And that chap, coming into a room, snapped up the gaze of every woman in it, as dexterously as a conjurer pockets billiard balls. It was most amazing. You know the man on the stage who throws up sixteen balls at once and they all drop into pockets all over his person, on his shoulders, on his heels, on the inner side of his sleeves; and he stands perfectly still and does nothing. Well, it was like that. He had rather a rough, hoarse voice.

And, there he was, standing by the table. I was looking at him, with my back to the screen. And, suddenly, I saw two distinct expressions flicker across his immobile eyes. How the deuce did they do it, those unflinching blue eyes with the direct gaze? For the eyes themselves never moved, gazing over my shoulder towards the screen. And the gaze was perfectly level and perfectly direct and perfectly un-changing. I suppose that the lids really must have rounded themselves a little and perhaps the lips moved a little too, as if he should be saying:—'There you are, my dear.' At any rate, the expression was that of pride, of satisfaction, of the possessor. I saw him once afterwards, for a moment, gaze upon the sunny fields of Branshaw and say:—'All this is my land!'

And then again, the gaze was perhaps more direct, harder if possible—hardy too. It was a measuring look; a challenging look. Once when we were at Wiesbaden watching him play in a polo match against the Bonner Hussaren I saw the same look come into his eyes, balancing the possibilities, looking over the ground. The German Cap-tain, Count Baron Idigon von Lelöffel, was right up by their goal posts, coming with the ball in an easy canter in that tricky German fashion. The rest of the field were just anywhere. It was only a scratch sort of affair. Ashburnham was quite close to the rails not five yards from us and I heard him saying to himself:—'Might just be done!' And he did it. Goodness! he swung that pony round with all its four legs spread out, like a cat dropping off a roof. . . .

Well, it was just that look that I noticed in his eyes:— 'It might,' I seem even now to hear him muttering to himself, 'just be done.'

I looked round over my shoulder and saw, tall, smiling brilliantly and buoyant—Leonora. And, little and fair, and as radiant as the track of sunlight along the sea—my wife.

That poor wretch! to think that he was at that moment in a perfect devil of a fix, and there he was, saying at the back of his mind:—'It might just be done.' It was like a chap in the middle of the eruption of a volcano, saying that he might just manage to bolt into the tumult and set fire to a haystack. Madness? Predestination? Who the devil knows?

Mrs Ashburnham exhibited at that moment more gaiety than I have ever since known her to show. There are certain classes of English people—the nicer ones when they have been to many spas, who seem to make a point of becoming much more than usually animated when they are introduced to my compatriots. I have noticed this often. Of course, they must first have accepted the Americans. But that once done, they seem to say to themselves: 'Hallo, these women are so bright. We aren't going to be outdone in brightness.' And for the time being they certainly aren't. But it wears off. So it was with Leonora—at least until she noticed me. She began, Leonora did—and perhaps it was that that gave me the idea of a touch of insolence in her character, for she never afterwards did any one single thing like it—she began by saying in quite a loud voice and from quite a distance:

'Don't stop over by that stuffy old table, Teddy. Come and sit by these nice people!'

And that was an extraordinary thing to say. Quite extraordinary. I couldn't for the life of me refer to total strangers as nice people. But, of course, she was taking a line of her own in which I at any rate—and no one else in the room, for she too had taken the trouble to read through the list of guests—counted any more than so many clean, bull terriers. And she sat down rather brilliantly at a vacant table, beside ours—one that was reserved for the Guggenheimers. And she just sat absolutely deaf to the remonstrances of the head waiter with his face like a grey ram's. That poor chap was doing his steadfast duty too. He knew that the Guggenheimers of Chicago, after they had stayed there a month and had worried the poor life out of him, would give him two dollars fifty and grumble at the tipping system. And he knew that Teddy Ashburnham and his wife would give him no trouble whatever except what the smiles of Leonora might cause in his apparently unimpressionable bosom—though you never can tell what may go on behind even a not quite spotless plastron!— And every week Edward Ashburnham would give him a solid, sound, golden English sovereign. Yet this stout

fellow was intent on saving that table for the Guggenheimers of Chicago. It ended in Florence saying:

'Why shouldn't we all eat out of the same trough?—
that's a nasty New York saying. But I'm sure we're all nice
quiet people and there can be four seats at our table. It's
round.'

Then came, as it were, an appreciative gurgle from the
Captain and I was perfectly aware of a slight hesitation—
a quick sharp motion in Mrs Ashburnham, as if her horse
had checked. But she put it at the fence all right, rising
from the seat she had taken and sitting down opposite me,
as it were, all in one motion.

I never thought that Leonora looked her best in evening
dress. She seemed to get it too clearly cut, there was no
ruffling. She always affected black and her shoulders were
too classical. She seemed to stand out of her corsage as a
white marble bust might out of a black Wedgwood vase.
I don't know.

I loved Leonora always and, to-day, I would very cheerfully lay down my life, what is left of it, in her service. But
I am sure I never had the beginnings of a trace of what is
called the sex instinct towards her. And I suppose—no I
am certain that she never had it towards me. As far as I
am concerned I think it was those white shoulders that did
it. I seemed to feel when I looked at them that, if ever I
should press my lips upon them that they would be slightly
cold—not icily, not without a touch of human heat, but,
as they say of baths, with the chill off. I seemed to feel
chilled at the end of my lips when I looked at her ...

No, Leonora always appeared to me at her best in a blue
tailor-made. Then her glorious hair wasn't deadened by
her white shoulders. Certain women's lines guide your eyes
to their necks, their eyelashes, their lips, their breasts. But
Leonora's seemed to conduct your gaze always to her wrist.
And the wrist was at its best in a black or a dog-skin glove
and there was always a gold circlet with a little chain sup-
porting a very small golden key to a dispatch box. Perhaps

it was that in which she locked up her heart and her feelings.

Anyhow, she sat down opposite me and then, for the first time, she paid any attention to my existence. She gave me, suddenly, yet deliberately, one long stare. Her eyes too were blue and dark and the eyelids were so arched that they gave you the whole round of the irises. And it was a most remarkable, a most moving glance, as if for a moment a lighthouse had looked at me. I seemed to perceive the swift questions chasing each other through the brain that was behind them. I seemed to hear the brain ask and the eyes answer with all the simpleness of a woman who was a good hand at taking in qualities of a horse—as indeed she was. 'Stands well; has plenty of room for his oats behind the girth. Not so much in the way of shoulders,' and so on. And so her eyes asked: 'Is this man trustworthy in money matters; is he likely to try to play the lover; is he likely to let his women be troublesome? Is he, above all, likely to babble about my affairs?'

And, suddenly, into those cold, slightly defiant, almost defensive china blue orbs, there came a warmth, a tenderness, a friendly recognition . . . oh, it was very charming and very touching—and quite mortifying. It was the look of a mother to her son, of a sister to her brother. It implied trust; it implied the want of any necessity for barriers. By God, she looked at me as if I were an invalid—as any kind woman may look at a poor chap in a bath chair. And, yes, from that day forward she always treated me and not Florence as if I were the invalid. Why, she would run after me with a rug upon chilly days. I suppose, therefore, that her eyes had made a favourable answer. Or, perhaps, it wasn't a favourable answer. And then Florence said: 'And so the whole round table is begun.' Again Edward Ashburnham gurgled slightly in his throat; but Leonora shivered a little, as if a goose had walked over her grave. And I was passing her the nickel-silver basket of rolls. Avanti! . . .

IV

So began those nine years of uninterrupted tranquillity. They were characterized by an extraordinary want of any communicativeness on the part of the Ashburnhams to which we, on our part, replied by leaving out quite as extraordinarily, and nearly as completely, the personal note. Indeed, you may take it that what characterized our relationship was an atmosphere of taking everything for granted. The given proposition was, that we were all 'good people.' We took for granted that we all liked beef under-done but not too underdone; that both men preferred a good liqueur brandy after lunch; that both women drank a very light Rhine wine qualified with Fachingen water—that sort of thing. It was also taken for granted that we were both sufficiently well off to afford anything that we could reasonably want in the way of amusements fitting to our station—that we could take motor cars and carriages by the day; that we could give each other dinners and dine our friends and we could indulge if we liked in economy. Thus, Florence was in the habit of having the *Daily Telegraph* sent to her every day from London. She was always an Anglo-maniac, was Florence; the Paris edition of the New York *Herald* was always good enough for me. But when we discovered that the Ashburnhams' copy of the London paper followed them from England, Leonora and Florence decided between them to suppress one sub-scription one year and the other the next. Similarly it was the habit of the Grand Duke of Nassau Schwerin, who came yearly to the baths, to dine once with about eighteen families of regular Kur guests. In return he would give a dinner of all the eighteen at once. And, since these dinners were rather expensive (you had to take the Grand Duke and a good many of his suite and any members of the diplomatic bodies that might be there)—Florence and Leonora, putting their heads together, didn't see why we shouldn't give the Grand Duke his dinner together. And so we did. I don't suppose the Serenity minded that economy, or even noticed it. At any rate, our joint dinner to the Royal Personage gradually assumed the aspect of a yearly function. Indeed, it grew larger and larger, until it became a sort of closing function for the season, at any rate, as far as we were concerned.

I don't in the least mean to say that we were the sort of persons who aspired to mix 'with royalty.' We didn't; we hadn't any claims; we were just 'good people.' But the Grand Duke was a pleasant, affable sort of royalty, like the late King Edward VII, and it was pleasant to hear him talk about the races and, very occasionally, as a bonne bouche, about his nephew, the Emperor; or to have him pause for a moment in his walk to ask after the progress of our cures or to be benignantly interested in the amount of money we had put on Lelöffel's hunter for the Frankfurt Welter Stakes.

But upon my word, I don't know how we put in our time. How does one put in one's time? How is it possible to have achieved nine years and to have nothing whatever to show for it? Nothing whatever, you understand. Not so much as a bone penholder, carved to resemble a chessman and with a hole in the top through which you could see four views of Nauheim. And, as for experience, as for knowledge of one's fellow beings—nothing either. Upon my word, I couldn't tell you offhand whether the lady who sold the so expensive violets at the bottom of the road that leads to the station, was cheating me or no; I can't say whether the porter who carried our traps across the station at Leghorn was a thief or no when he said that the regular tariff was a lira a parcel. The instances of honesty that one comes across in this world are just as amazing as the instances of dishonesty. After forty-five years of mixing with one's kind, one ought to have acquired the habit of being able to know something about one's fellow beings. But one doesn't.

I think the modern civilized habit—the modern English habit of taking every one for granted is a good deal to blame for this. I have observed this matter long enough to know the queer, subtle thing that it is; to know how the faculty, for what it is worth, never lets you down.

Mind, I am not saying that this is not the most desirable type of life in the world; that it is not an almost unreasonably high standard. For it is really nauseating, when you detest it, to have to eat every day several slices of thin, tepid, pink india rubber, and it is disagreeable to have to drink brandy when you would prefer to be cheered up by warm, sweet Kümmel. And it is nasty to have to take a cold bath in the morning when what you want is really a hot one at night. And it stirs a little of the faith of your fathers that is deep down within you to have to have it taken for granted that you are an Episcopalian when really you are an old-fashioned Philadelphia Quaker.

But these things have to be done; it is the cock that the whole of this society owes to Æsculapius.

And the odd, queer thing is that the whole collection of rules applies to anybody—to the anybodies that you meet in hotels, in railway trains, to a less degree, perhaps, in steamers, but even, in the end, upon steamers. You meet a man or a woman and, from tiny and intimate sounds, from the slightest of movements, you know at once whether you are concerned with good people or with those who won't do. You know, that is to say, whether they will go rigidly through with the whole programme from the underdone beef to the Anglicanism. It won't matter whether they be short or tall; whether the voice squeak like a marionette or rumble like a town bull's; it won't matter whether they are Germans, Austrians, French, Spanish, or even Brazilians—they will be the Germans or Brazilians who take a cold bath every morning and who move, roughly speaking, in diplomatic circles.

But the inconvenient—well, hang it all, I will say it— the damnable nuisance of the whole thing is, that with all the taking for granted, you never really get an inch deeper than the things I have catalogued.

I can give you a rather extraordinary instance of this. I can't remember whether it was in our first year—the first year of us four at Nauheim, because, of course, it would have been the fourth year of Florence and myself—but it must have been in the first or second year. And that gives the measure at once of the extraordinariness of our discussion and of the swiftness with which intimacy had grown up between us. On the one hand we seemed to start out on the expedition so naturally and with so little preparation, that it was as if we must have made many such excursions before; and our intimacy seemed so deep. . . .

Yet the place to which we went was obviously one to which Florence at least would have wanted to take us quite early, so that you would almost think we should have gone there together at the beginning of our intimacy. Florence was singularly expert as a guide to archaeological expeditions and there was nothing she liked so much as taking people round ruins and showing you the window from which some one looked down upon the murder of some one else. She only did it once; but she did it quite magnificently. She could find her way, with the sole help of Baedeker, as easily about any old monument as she could about any American city where the blocks are all square and the streets all numbered, so that you can go perfectly easily from Twenty-fourth to Thirtieth.

Now it happens that fifty minutes away from Nauheim, by a good train, is the ancient city of M——, upon a great pinnacle of basalt, girt with a triple road running sideways up its shoulder like a scarf. And at the top there is a castle —not a square castle like Windsor, but a castle all slate gables and high peaks with gilt weathercocks flashing bravely—the castle of St Elizabeth of Hungary. It has the disadvantage of being in Prussia; and it is always disagreeable to go into that country; but it is very old and there are many double-spired churches and it stands up like a pyramid out of the green valley of the Lahn. I don't suppose the Ashburnhams wanted especially to go there and I didn't especially want to go there myself. But, you understand, there was no objection. It was part of the cure to make an excursion three or four times a week. So that we were all quite unanimous in being grateful to Florence for providing the motive power. Florence, of course, had a motive of her own. She was at that time engaged in educating Captain Ashburnham—oh, of course, quite pour le bon motif! She used to say to Leonora: 'I simply can't understand how you can let him live by your side and be so ignorant!' Leonora herself always struck me as being remarkably well educated. At any rate, she knew beforehand all that Florence had to tell her. Perhaps she got it up out of Baedeker before Florence was up in the morning. I don't mean to say that you would ever have known that Leonora knew anything, but if Florence started to tell us how Ludwig the Courageous wanted to have three wives at once—in which he differed from Henry VIII, who wanted them one after the other, and this caused a good deal of trouble—if Florence started to tell us this, Leonora would just nod her head in a way that quite pleasantly rattled my poor wife.

She used to exclaim: 'Well, if you knew it, why haven't you told it all already to Captain Ashburnham? I'm sure he finds it interesting!' And Leonora would look reflectively at her husband and say: 'I have an idea that it might injure his hand—the hand, you know, used in connection with horses' mouths...' And poor Ashburnham would blush and mutter and would say: 'That's all right. Don't you bother about me.'

I fancy his wife's irony did quite alarm poor Teddy; because one evening he asked me seriously in the smoking-room if I thought that having too much in one's head would really interfere with one's quickness in polo. It struck him, he said, that brainy Johnnies generally were rather muffs when they got on to four legs. I reassured him as best I could. I told him that he wasn't likely to take in enough to upset his balance. At that time the Captain was quite evidently enjoying being educated by Florence. She used to do it about three or four times a week under the approving eyes of Leonora and myself. It wasn't, you

understand, systematic. It came in bursts. It was Florence
clearing up one of the dark places of the earth, leaving the
world a little lighter than she had found it. She would tell
him the story of Hamlet; explain the form of a symphony,
humming the first and second subjects to him, and so on;
she would explain to him the difference between Arminians
and Erastians; or she would give him a short lecture on the
early history of the United States. And it was done in a
way well calculated to arrest a young attention. Did you
ever read Mrs Markham? Well, it was like that . . .

But our excursion to M—— was a much larger, a much
more full dress affair. You see, in the archives of the
Schloss in that city there was a document which Florence
thought would finally give her the chance to educate the
whole lot of us together. It really worried poor Florence
that she couldn't, in matters of culture, ever get the better
of Leonora. I don't know what Leonora knew or what she
didn't know, but certainly she was always there whenever
Florence brought out any information. And she gave,
somehow, the impression of really knowing what poor
Florence gave the impression of having only picked up.
I can't exactly define it. It was almost something physical.
Have you ever seen a retriever dashing in play after a
greyhound? You see the two running over a green field,
almost side by side, and suddenly the retriever makes a
friendly snap at the other. And the greyhound simply isn't
there. You haven't observed it quicken its speed or strain
a limb; but there it is, just two yards in front of the
retriever's outstretched muzzle. So it was with Florence
and Leonora in matters of culture.

But on this occasion I knew that something was up. I
found Florence some days before, reading books like
Ranke's *History of the Popes*, Symonds' *Renaissance*,
Motley's *Rise of the Dutch Republic*, and Luther's *Table
Talk*.

I must say that, until the astonishment came, I got
nothing but pleasure out of the little expedition. I like
catching the two-forty; I like the slow, smooth roll of the

great big trains—and they are the best trains in the world! I like being drawn through the green country and looking at it through the clear glass of the great windows. Though, of course, the country isn't really green. The sun shines, the earth is blood red and purple and red and green and red. And the oxen in the ploughlands are bright varnished brown and black and blackish purple; and the peasants are dressed in the black and white of magpies; and there are great flocks of magpies too. Or the peasants' dresses in another field where there are little mounds of hay that will be grey-green on the sunny side and purple in the shadows —the peasants' dresses are vermilion with emerald green ribbons and purple skirts and white shirts and black velvet stomachers. Still, the impression is that you are drawn through brilliant green meadows that run away on each side to the dark purple fir-woods; the basalt pinnacles; the immense forests. And there is meadow-sweet at the edge of the streams, and cattle. Why, I remember on that afternoon I saw a brown cow hitch its horns under the stomach of a black and white animal and the black and white one was thrown right into the middle of a narrow stream. I burst out laughing. But Florence was imparting information so hard and Leonora was listening so intently that no one noticed me. As for me, I was pleased to be off duty; I was pleased to think that Florence for the moment was indubitably out of mischief—because she was talking about Ludwig the Courageous (I think it was Ludwig the Courageous but I am not an historian) about Ludwig the Courageous of Hessen who wanted to have three wives at once and patronized Luther—something like that!—I was so relieved to be off duty, because she couldn't possibly be doing anything to excite herself or set her poor heart a-fluttering—that the incident of the cow was a real joy to me. I chuckled over it from time to time for the whole rest of the day. Because it does look very funny, you know, to see a black and white cow land on its back in the middle of a stream. It is so just exactly what one doesn't expect of a cow.

I suppose I ought to have pitied the poor animal; but I just didn't. I was out for enjoyment. And I just enjoyed myself. It is so pleasant to be drawn along in front of the spectacular towns with the peaked castles and the many double spires. In the sunlight gleams come from the city—gleams from the glass of windows; from the gilt signs of apothecaries; from the ensigns of the student corps high up in the mountains; from the helmets of the funny little soldiers moving their stiff little legs in white linen trousers. And it was pleasant to get out in the great big spectacular Prussian station with the hammered bronze ornaments and the paintings of peasants and flowers and cows; and to hear Florence bargain energetically with the driver of an ancient droschka drawn by two lean horses. Of course, I spoke German much more correctly than Florence, though I never could rid myself quite of the accent of the Pennsylvania Duitsch of my childhood. Anyhow, we were drawn in a sort of triumph, for five marks without any trinkgeld, right up to the castle. And we were taken through the museum and saw the firebacks, the old glass, the old swords, and the antique contraptions. And we went up winding corkscrew staircases and through the Rittersaal, the great painted hall where the Reformer and his friends met for the first time under the protection of the gentleman that had three wives at once and formed an alliance with the gentleman that had six wives, one after the other (I'm not really interested in these facts but they have a bearing on my story). And we went through chapels, and music rooms, right up immensely high in the air to a large old chamber, full of presses, with heavily-shuttered windows all round. And Florence became positively electric. She told the tired, bored custodian what shutters to open; so that the bright sunlight streamed in palpable shafts into the dim old chamber. She explained that this was Luther's bedroom and that just where the sunlight fell had stood his bed. As a matter of fact, I believe that she was wrong and that Luther only stopped, as it were, for lunch, in order to evade pursuit. But, no doubt, it would have been his bedroom if he could have been persuaded to stop the night. And then, in spite of the protest of the custodian, she threw open another shutter and came tripping back to a large glass case.

'And there,' she exclaimed with an accent of gaiety, of triumph, and of audacity. She was pointing at a piece of paper, like the half-sheet of a letter with some faint pencil scrawls that might have been a jotting of the amounts we were spending during the day. And I was extremely happy at her gaiety, in her triumph, in her audacity. Captain Ashburnham had his hands upon the glass case. 'There it is—the Protest.' And then, as we all properly stage-managed our bewilderment, she continued: 'Don't you know that is why we were all called Protestants? That is the pencil draft of the Protest they drew up. You can see the signatures of Martin Luther, and Martin Bucer, and Zwingli, and Ludwig the Courageous...'

I may have got some of the names wrong, but I know that Luther and Bucer were there. And her animation continued and I was glad. She was better and she was out of mischief. She continued, looking up into Captain Ashburnham's eyes: 'It's because of that piece of paper that you're honest, sober, industrious, provident, and clean-lived. If it weren't for that piece of paper you'd be like the Irish or the Italians or the Poles, but particularly the Irish...'

And she laid one finger upon Captain Ashburnham's wrist.

I was aware of something treacherous, something fright-ful, something evil in the day. I can't define it and can't find a simile for it. It wasn't as if a snake had looked out of a hole. No, it was as if my heart had missed a beat. It was as if we were going to run and cry out; all four of us in separate directions, averting our heads. In Ashburnham's face I know that there was absolute panic. I was horribly frightened and then I discovered that the pain in my left wrist was caused by Leonora's clutching it:

'I can't stand this,' she said with a most extraordinary passion; 'I must get out of this.'

I was horribly frightened. It came to me for a moment, though I hadn't time to think it, that she must be a madly jealous woman—jealous of Florence and Captain Ashburnham, of all people in the world! And it was a panic in which we fled! We went right down the winding stairs, across the immense Rittersaal to a little terrace that overlooks the Lahn, the broad valley and the immense plain into which it opens out.

'Don't you see?' she said, 'don't you see what's going on?' The panic again stopped my heart. I muttered, I stuttered—I don't know how I got the words out:

'No! What's the matter? Whatever's the matter?'

She looked me straight in the eyes; and for a moment I had the feeling that those two blue discs were immense, were overwhelming, were like a wall of blue that shut me off from the rest of the world. I know it sounds absurd; but that is what it did feel like.

'Don't you see,' she said, with a really horrible bitterness, with a really horrible lamentation in her voice. 'Don't you see that that's the cause of the whole miserable affair; of the whole sorrow of the world? And of the eternal damnation of you and me and them . . .'

I don't remember how she went on; I was too frightened; I was too amazed. I think I was thinking of running to fetch assistance—a doctor, perhaps, or Captain Ashburnham. Or possibly she needed Florence's tender care, though, of course, it would have been very bad for Florence's heart. But I know that when I came out of it she was saying: 'Oh, where are all the bright, happy, innocent beings in the world? Where's happiness? One reads of it in books!'

She ran her hand with a singular clawing motion upwards over her forehead. Her eyes were enormously distended; her face was exactly that of a person looking into the pit of hell and seeing horrors there. And then suddenly she stopped. She was, most amazingly, just Mrs

Ashburnham again. Her face was perfectly clear, sharp, and defined; her hair was glorious in its golden coils. Her nostrils twitched with a sort of contempt. She appeared to look with interest at a gypsy caravan that was coming over a little bridge far below us.

'Don't you know,' she said, in her clear hard voice, 'don't you know that I'm an Irish Catholic?'

V

Those words gave me the greatest relief that I have ever had in my life. They told me, I think, almost more than I have ever gathered at any one moment—about myself. I don't think that before that day I had ever wanted anything very much except Florence. I have, of course, had appetites, impatiences . . . Why, sometimes at a table d'hôte, when there would be, say, caviare handed round, I have been absolutely full of impatience for fear that when the dish came to me there should not be a satisfying portion left over by the other guests. I have been exceedingly impatient at missing trains. The Belgian State Railway has a trick of letting the French trains miss their connections at Brussels. That has always infuriated me. I have written about it letters to *The Times* that *The Times* never printed; those that I wrote to the Paris edition of the New York *Herald* were always printed, but they never seemed to satisfy me when I saw them. Well, that was a sort of frenzy with me.

It was a frenzy that now I can hardly realize. I can understand it intellectually. You see, in those days I was interested in people with 'hearts.' There was Florence, there was Edward Ashburnham—or, perhaps, it was Leonora that I was more interested in. I don't mean in the way of love. But, you see, we were both of the same profession—at any rate as I saw it. And the profession was that of keeping heart patients alive.

You have no idea how engrossing such a profession may

become. Just as the blacksmith says: 'By hammer and hand all Art doth stand,' just as the baker thinks that all the solar system revolves around his morning delivery of rolls, as the postmaster-general believes that he alone is the preserver of society—and surely, surely, these delusions are necessary to keep us going—so did I and, as I believed, Leonora, imagine that the whole world ought to be arranged so as to ensure the keeping alive of heart patients. You have no idea how engrossing such a profession may become—how imbecile, in view of that engrossment, appear the ways of princes, of republics, of municipalities. A rough bit of road beneath the motor tyres, a couple of succeeding 'thank'ee-marms' with their quick jolts would be enough to set me grumbling to Leonora against the Prince or the Grand Duke or the Free City through whose territory we might be passing. I would grumble like a stockbroker whose conversations over the telephone are incommoded by the ringing of bells from a city church. I would talk about mediaeval survivals, about the taxes being surely high enough. The point, by the way, about the missing of the connections of the Calais boat trains at Brussels was that the shortest possible sea journey is frequently of great importance to sufferers from the heart. Now, on the Continent, there are two special heart cure places, Nauheim and Spa, and to reach both of these baths from England if in order to ensure a short sea passage, you come by Calais—you have to make the connection at Brussels. And the Belgian train never waits by so much of the shade of a second for the one coming from Calais or from Paris. And even if the French trains are just on time, you have to run—imagine a heart patient running!—along the unfamiliar ways of the Brussels station and to scramble up the high steps of the moving train. Or, if you miss the connection, you have to wait five or six hours. . . . I used to keep awake whole nights cursing that abuse.

My wife used to run—she never, in whatever else she may have misled me, tried to give me the impression that she was not a gallant soul. But, once in the German

Express, she would lean back, with one hand to her side and her eyes closed. Well, she was a good actress. And I would be in hell. In hell, I tell you. For in Florence I had at once a wife and an unattained mistress—that is what it comes to—and in the retaining of her in this world I had my occupation, my career, my ambition. It is not often that these things are united in one body. Leonora was a good actress too. By Jove she was good! I tell you, she would listen to me by the hour, evolving my plans for a shock-proof world. It is true that, at times, I used to notice about her face an air of inattention as if she were listening, a mother, to the child at her knee, or as if, precisely, I were myself the patient.

You understand that there was nothing the matter with Edward Ashburnham's heart—that he had thrown up his commission and had left India and come half the world over in order to follow a woman who had really had a 'heart' to Nauheim. That was the sort of sentimental ass he was. For, you understand, too, that they really needed to live in India, to economize, to let the house at Branshaw Teleragh.

Of course, at that date, I had never heard of the Kilsyte case. Ashburnham had, you know, kissed a servant girl in a railway train, and it was only the grace of God, the prompt functioning of the communication cord and the ready sympathy of what I believe you call the Hampshire Bench, that kept the poor devil out of Winchester Gaol for years and years. I never heard of that case until the final stages of Leonora's revelations . . .

But just think of that poor wretch . . . I, who have surely the right, beg you to think of that poor wretch. Is it possible that such a luckless devil should be so tormented by blind and inscrutable destiny? For there is no other way to think of it. None. I have the right to say it, since for years he was my wife's lover, since he killed her, since he broke up all the pleasantnesses that there were in my life. There is no priest that has the right to tell me that I must not ask pity for him, from you, silent listener beyond the hearthstone,

from the world, or from the God who created in him those
desires, those madnesses . . .

Of course, I should not hear of the Kilsyte case. I knew
none of their friends; they were for me just good people—
fortunate people with broad and sunny acres in a southern
county. Just good people! By Heavens, I sometimes think
that it would have been better for him, poor dear, if the
case had been such a one that I must needs have heard of
it—such a one as maids and couriers and other Kur guests
whisper about for years after, until gradually it dies away
in the pity that there is knocking about here and there in
the world. Supposing he had spent his seven years in
Winchester Gaol or whatever it is that inscrutable and
blind justice allots to you for following your natural but
ill-timed inclinations—there would have arrived a stage
when nodding gossips on the Kursaal terrace would have
said, 'Poor fellow,' thinking of his ruined career. He would
have been the fine soldier with his back now bent . . .
Better for him, poor devil, if his back had been prematurely
bent.

Why, it would have been a thousand times better. . . .
For, of course, the Kilsyte case, which came at the very
beginning of his finding Leonora cold and unsympathetic,
gave him a nasty jar. He left servants alone after that.

It turned him, naturally, all the more loose amongst
women of his own class. Why, Leonora told me that Mrs
Maidan—the woman he followed from Burma to Nauheim
—assured her he awakened her attention by swearing that
when he kissed the servant in the train he was driven to it.
I daresay he was driven to it, by the mad passion to find
an ultimately satisfying woman. I daresay he was sincere
enough. Heaven help me, I daresay he was sincere enough
in his love for Mrs Maidan. She was a nice little thing, a
dear little dark woman with long lashes, of whom Florence
grew quite fond. She had a lisp and a happy smile. We saw
plenty of her for the first month of our acquaintance, then
she died, quite quietly—of heart trouble.

But you know, poor little Mrs Maidan—she was so

gentle, so young. She cannot have been more than twenty-three and she had a boy husband out in Chitral not more than twenty-four, I believe. Such young things ought to have been left alone. Of course Ashburnham could not leave her alone. I do not believe that he could. Why, even I, at this distance of time am aware that I am a little in love with her memory. I can't help smiling when I think suddenly of her—as you might at the thought of something wrapped carefully away in lavender, in some drawer, in some old house that you have long left. She was so—so submissive. Why, even to me she had the air of being submissive—to me that not the youngest child will ever pay heed to. Yes, this is the saddest story . . .

No, I cannot help wishing that Florence had left her alone—with her playing with adultery. I suppose it was; though she was such a child that one has the impression that she would hardly have known how to spell such a word. No, it was just submissiveness—to the importunities, to the tempestuous forces that pushed that miserable fellow on to ruin. And I do not suppose that Florence really made much difference. If it had not been for her that Ashburnham left his allegiance for Mrs Maidan, then it would have been some other woman. But still, I do not know. Perhaps the poor young thing would have died—she was bound to die, anyhow, quite soon—but she would have died without having to soak her noonday pillow with tears whilst Florence, below the window, talked to Captain Ashburnham about the Constitution of the United States . . . Yes, it would have left a better taste in the mouth if Florence had let her die in peace . . .

Leonora behaved better in a sense. She just boxed Mrs Maidan's ears—yes, she hit her, in an uncontrollable access of rage, a hard blow on the side of the cheek, in the corridor of the hotel, outside Edward's rooms. It was that, you know, that accounted for the sudden, odd intimacy that sprang up between Florence and Mrs Ashburnham.

Because it was, of course, an odd intimacy. If you look at it from the outside nothing could have been more unlikely than that Leonora, who is the proudest creature on God's earth, would have struck up an acquaintanceship with two casual Yankees whom she could not really have regarded as being much more than a carpet beneath her feet. You may ask what she had to be proud of. Well, she was a Powys married to an Ashburnham—I suppose that gave her the right to despise casual Americans as long as she did it unostentatiously. I don't know what anyone has to be proud of. She might have taken pride in her patience, in her keeping her husband out of the bankruptcy court. Perhaps she did.

At any rate that was how Florence got to know her. She came round a screen at the corner of the hotel corridor and found Leonora with the gold key that hung from her wrist caught in Mrs Maidan's hair just before dinner. There was not a single word spoken. Little Mrs Maidan was very pale, with a red mark down her left cheek, and the key would not come out of her black hair. It was Florence who had to disentangle it, for Leonora was in such a state that she could not have brought herself to touch Mrs Maidan without growing sick.

And there was not a word spoken. You see, under those four eyes—her own and Mrs Maidan's—Leonora could just let herself go as far as to box Mrs Maidan's ears. But the moment a stranger came along she pulled herself wonderfully up. She was at first silent and then, the moment the key was disengaged by Florence she was in a state to say: 'So awkward of me ... I was just trying to put the comb straight in Mrs Maidan's hair ...'

Mrs Maidan, however, was not a Powys married to an Ashburnham; she was a poor little O'Flaherty whose husband was a boy of country parsonage origin. So there was no mistaking the sob that she let go as she went desolately away along the corridor. But Leonora was still going to play up. She opened the door of Ashburnham's room quite ostentatiously, so that Florence should hear her address Edward in terms of intimacy and liking. 'Edward,' she called. But there was no Edward there.

You understand that there was no Edward there. It was then, for the only time of her career, that Leonora really compromised herself—She exclaimed . . . 'How frightful! . . . Poor little Maisie! . . .'

She caught herself up at that, but of course it was too late. It was a queer sort of affair . . .

I want to do Leonora every justice. I love her very dearly for one thing and in this matter, which was certainly the ruin of my small household cockle-shell, she certainly tripped up. I do not believe—and Leonora herself does not believe—that poor little Maisie Maidan was ever Edward's mistress. Her heart was really so bad that she would have succumbed to anything like an impassioned embrace. That is the plain English of it, and I suppose plain English is best. She was really what the other two, for reasons of their own, just pretended to be. Queer, isn't it? Like one of those sinister jokes that Providence plays upon one. Add to this that I do not suppose that Leonora would much have minded, at any other moment, if Mrs Maidan had been her husband's mistress. It might have been a relief from Edward's sentimental gurglings over the lady and from the lady's submissive acceptance of those sounds. No, she would not have minded.

But, in boxing Mrs Maidan's ears, Leonora was just striking the face of an intolerable universe. For, that afternoon she had had a frightfully painful scene with Edward.

As far as his letters went, she claimed the right to open them when she chose. She arrogated to herself the right because Edward's affairs were in such a frightful state and he lied so about them that she claimed the privilege of having his secrets at her disposal. There was not, indeed, any other way, for the poor fool was too ashamed of his lapses ever to make a clean breast of anything. She had to drag these things out of him.

It must have been a pretty elevating job for her. But that afternoon, Edward being on his bed for the hour and a half prescribed by the Kur authorities, she had opened a letter that she took to come from a Colonel Hervey. They were going to stay with him in Linlithgowshire for the month of September and she did not know whether the date fixed would be the eleventh or the eighteenth. The address on this letter was, in handwriting, as like Colonel Hervey's as one blade of corn is like another. So she had at the moment no idea of spying on him.

But she certainly was. For she discovered that Edward Ashburnham was paying a blackmailer of whom she had never heard something like three hundred pounds a year ... It was a devil of a blow; it was like death; for she imagined that by that time she had really got to the bottom of her husband's liabilities. You see, they were pretty heavy. What had really smashed them up had been a perfectly common-place affair at Monte Carlo—an affair with a cosmopolitan harpy who passed for the mistress of a Russian Grand Duke. She exacted a twenty thousand pound pearl tiara from him as the price of her favours for a week or so. It would have pipped him a good deal to have found so much, and he was not in the ordinary way a gambler. He might, indeed, just have found the twenty thousand and the not slight charges of a week at an hotel with the fair creature. He must have been worth at that date five hundred thousand dollars and a little over.

Well, he must needs go to the tables and lose forty thousand pounds ... Forty thousand solid pounds, borrowed from sharks! And even after that he must—it was an imperative passion—enjoy the favours of the lady. He got them, of course, when it was a matter of solid bargaining, for far less than twenty thousand, as he might, no doubt, have done from the first. I daresay ten thousand dollars covered the bill.

Anyhow, there was a pretty solid hole in a fortune of a hundred thousand pounds or so. And Leonora had to fix things up; he would have run from money-lender to money-lender. And that was quite in the early days of her discovery of his infidelities—if you like to call them infidelities. And she discovered that one from public sources. God knows what would have happened if she had not discovered it from public sources. I suppose he would have concealed it from her until they were penniless. But she was able, by the grace of God, to get hold of the actual lenders of the money, to learn the exact sums that were needed. And she went off to England.

Yes, she went right off to England to her attorney and his while he was still in the arms of his Circe—at Antibes, to which place they had retired. He got sick of the lady quite quickly, but not before Leonora had had such lessons in the art of business from her attorney that she had her plan as clearly drawn up as was ever that of General Trochu for keeping the Prussians out of Paris in 1870. It was about as effectual at first, or it seemed so.

That would have been, you know, in 1895, about nine years before the date of which I am talking—the date of Florence's getting her hold over Leonora; for that was what it amounted to.... Well, Mrs Ashburnham had simply forced Edward to settle all his property upon her. She could force him to do anything; in his clumsy, good-natured, inarticulate way he was as frightened of her as of the devil. And he admired her enormously, and he was as fond of her as any man could be of any woman. She took advantage of it to treat him as if he had been a person whose estates are being managed by the Court of Bankruptcy. I suppose it was the best thing for him.

Anyhow, she had no end of a job for the first three years or so. Unexpected liabilities kept on cropping up—and that afflicted fool did not make it any easier. You see, along with the passion of the chase went a frame of mind that made him be extraordinarily ashamed of himself. You may not believe it, but he really had such a sort of respect for the chastity of Leonora's imagination that he hated—he was positively revolted at the thought that she should know that the sort of thing that he did existed in the world. So he would stick out in an agitated way against the accusation of ever having done anything. He wanted to preserve the virginity of his wife's thoughts. He told me that himself during the long walks we had at the last—while the girl was on the way to Brindisi.

So, of course, for those three years or so, Leonora had many agitations. And it was then that they really quarrelled.

Yes, they quarrelled bitterly. That seems rather extravagant. You might have thought that Leonora would be just calmly loathing and he lachrymosely contrite. But that was not it a bit... Along with Edward's passions and his shame for them went the violent conviction of the duties of his station—a conviction that was quite unreasonably expensive. I trust I have not, in talking of his liabilities, given the impression that poor Edward was a promiscuous libertine. He was not; he was a sentimentalist. The servant girl in the Kilsyte case had been pretty, but mournful of appearance. I think that, when he had kissed her, he had desired rather to comfort her. And, if she had succumbed to his blandishments I daresay he would have set her up in a little house in Portsmouth or Winchester and would have been faithful to her for four or five years. He was quite capable of that.

No, the only two of his affairs of the heart that cost him money were that of the Grand Duke's mistress and that which was the subject of the blackmailing letter that Leonora opened. That had been a quite passionate affair with quite a nice woman. It had succeeded the one with the Grand Ducal lady. The lady was the wife of a brother officer and Leonora had known all about the passion, which had been quite a real passion and had lasted for several years. You see, poor Edward's passions were quite logical in their progression upwards. They began with a servant, went on to a courtesan and then to a quite nice woman, very unsuitably mated. For she had a quite nasty husband who, by means of letters and things, went on blackmailing poor Edward to the tune of three or four hundred a year— with threats of the Divorce Court. And after this lady came Maisie Maidan, and after poor Maisie only one more affair and then—the real passion of his life. His marriage with Leonora had been arranged by his parents and, though he always admired her immensely, he had hardly ever pretended to be much more than tender to her, though he desperately needed her moral support, too. . . .

But his really trying liabilities were mostly in the nature of generosities proper to his station. He was, according to Leonora, always remitting his tenants' rents and giving the tenants to understand that the reduction would be permanent; he was always redeeming drunkards who came before his magisterial bench; he was always trying to put prostitutes into respectable places—and he was a perfect maniac about children. I don't know how many ill-used people he did not pick up and provide with careers—Leonora has told me, but I daresay she exaggerated and the figure seems so preposterous that I will not put it down. All these things, and the continuance of them seemed to him to be his duty—along with impossible subscriptions to hospitals and Boy Scouts and to provide prizes at cattle shows and anti-vivisection societies. . . .

Well, Leonora saw to it that most of these things were not continued. They could not possibly keep up Branshaw Manor at that rate after the money had gone to the Grand Duke's mistress. She put the rents back at their old figures; discharged the drunkards from their homes, and sent all the societies notice that they were to expect no more subscriptions. To the children, she was more tender; nearly all of them she supported till the age of apprenticeship or domestic service. You see, she was childless herself.

She was childless herself, and she considered herself to be to blame. She had come of a penniless branch of the Powys family, and they had forced her upon poor dear Edward without making the stipulation that the children should be brought up as Catholics. And that, of course, was spiritual death to Leonora. I have given you a wrong impression if I have not made you see that Leonora was a woman of a strong, cold conscience, like all English Catholics. (I cannot, myself, help disliking this religion; there is always, at the bottom of my mind, in spite of Leonora, the feeling of shuddering at the Scarlet Woman, that filtered in upon me in the tranquillity of the little old Friends' Meeting House in Arch Street, Philadelphia.) So I do set down a good deal of Leonora's mismanagement of poor dear Edward's case to the peculiarly English form of her religion. Because, of course, the only thing to have done for Edward would have been to let him sink down until he became a tramp of gentlemanly address, having, maybe, chance love affairs upon the highways. He would have done so much less harm; he would have been much less agonized too. At any rate, he would have had fewer chances of ruining and of remorse. For Edward was great at remorse.

But Leonora's English Catholic conscience, her rigid principles, her coldness, even her very patience, were, I cannot help thinking, all wrong in this special case. She quite seriously and naïvely imagined that the Church of Rome disapproves of divorce; she quite seriously and naïvely believed that her church could be such a monstrous and imbecile institution as to expect her to take on the impossible job of making Edward Ashburnham a faithful husband. She had, as the English would say, the Nonconformist temperament. In the United States of North America we call it the New England conscience. For, of course, that frame of mind has been driven in on the English Catholics. The centuries that they have gone through—centuries of blind and malignant oppression, of ostracism from public employment, of being, as it were, a small beleaguered garrison in a hostile country, and therefore having to act with great formality—all these things have combined to perform that conjuring trick. And I suppose that Papists in England are even technically Nonconformists.

Continental Papists are a dirty, jovial, and unscrupulous crew. But that, at least, lets them be opportunists. They would have fixed poor dear Edward up all right. (Forgive my writing of these monstrous things in this frivolous manner. If I did not I should break down and cry.) In Milan, say, or in Paris, Leonora would have had her marriage dissolved in six months for two hundred dollars paid in the right quarter. And Edward would have drifted about until he became a tramp of the kind I have suggested. Or he would have married a barmaid who would have made him such frightful scenes in public places and would so have torn out his moustache and left visible signs upon his face that he would have been faithful to her for the rest of his days. That was what he wanted to redeem him. . . .

For, along with his passions and his shames there went the dread of scenes in public places, of outcry, of excited physical violence; of publicity, in short. Yes, the barmaid would have cured him. And it would have been all the better if she drank; he would have been kept busy looking after her.

I know that I am right in this. I know it because of the Kilsyte case. You see, the servant girl that he then kissed was nurse in the family of the Nonconformist head of the county—whatever that post may be called. And that gentleman was so determined to ruin Edward, who was the chairman of the Tory caucus, or whatever it is—that the poor dear sufferer had the very devil of a time. They asked questions about it in the House of Commons; they tried to get the Hampshire magistrates degraded; they suggested to the War Ministry that Edward was not the proper person to hold the King's commission. Yes, he got it hot and strong.

The result you have heard. He was completely cured of philandering amongst the lower classes. And that seemed a real blessing to Leonora. It did not revolt her so much to be connected—it is a sort of connection—with people like Mrs Maidan, instead of with a little kitchenmaid.

In a dim sort of way, Leonora was almost contented when she arrived at Nauheim, that evening. . . .

She had got things nearly straight by the long years of scraping in little stations in Chitral and Burma—stations where living is cheap in comparison with the life of a county magnate, and where, moreover, liaisons of one sort or another are normal and inexpensive, too. So that, when Mrs Maidan came along—and the Maidan affair might have caused trouble out there because of the youth of the husband—Leonora had just resigned herself to coming home. With pushing and scraping and with letting Branshaw Teleragh, and with selling a picture and a relic of Charles I or so, she had got—and, poor dear, she had never had a really decent dress to her back in all those years and years—she had got, as she imagined, her poor dear husband back into much the same financial position as had been his before the mistress of the Grand Duke had happened along. And, of course, Edward himself had helped her a little on the financial side. He was a fellow that many men liked. He was so presentable and quite ready to lend you his cigar puncher—that sort of thing. So, every now and then some financier whom he met about would give him a good, sound, profitable tip. And Leonora was never afraid of a bit of a gamble—English Papists seldom are, I do not know why.

So nearly all her investments turned up trumps, and Edward was really in fit case to reopen Branshaw Manor and once more to assume his position in the county. Thus Leonora had accepted Maisie Maidan almost with resignation—almost with a sigh of relief. She really liked the poor child—she had to like somebody. And, at any rate, she felt she could trust Maisie—she could trust her not to rook Edward for several thousands a week, for Maisie had refused to accept so much as a trinket ring from him. It is true that Edward gurgled and raved about the girl in a way that she had never yet experienced. But that, too, was almost a relief. I think she would really have welcomed it if he could have come across the love of his life. It would have given her a rest.

And there could not have been anyone better than poor little Mrs Maidan; she was so ill she could not want to be taken on expensive jaunts. . . . It was Leonora herself who paid Maisie's expenses to Nauheim. She handed over the money to the boy husband, for Maisie would never have allowed it; but the husband was in agonies of fear. Poor devil!

I fancy that, on the voyage from India, Leonora was as happy as ever she had been in her life. Edward was wrapped up, completely, in his girl—he was almost like a father with a child, trotting about with rugs and physic and things, from deck to deck. He behaved, however, with great circumspection, so that nothing leaked through to the other passengers. And Leonora had almost attained to the attitude of a mother towards Mrs Maidan. So it had looked very well—the benevolent, wealthy couple of good people, acting as saviours to the poor, dark-eyed, dying young thing. And that attitude of Leonora's towards Mrs Maidan no doubt partly accounted for the smack in the face. She was hitting a naughty child who had been stealing chocolates at an inopportune moment.

It was certainly an inopportune moment. For, with the opening of that blackmailing letter from that injured brother officer, all the old terrors had redescended upon Leonora. Her road had again seemed to stretch out endless; she imagined that there might be hundreds and hundreds of such things that Edward was concealing from her—that they might necessitate more mortgagings, more pawnings of bracelets, more and always more horrors. She had spent an excruciating afternoon. The matter was one of a divorce case, of course, and she wanted to avoid publicity as much as Edward did, so that she saw the necessity of continuing the payments. And she did not so much mind that. They could find three hundred a year. But it was the horror of there being more such obligations.

She had had no conversation with Edward for many years—none that went beyond the mere arrangements for taking trains or engaging servants. But that afternoon she had to let him have it. And he had been just the same as ever. It was like opening a book after a decade to find the words the same. He had the same motives. He had not wished to tell her about the case because he had not wished her to sully her mind with the idea that there was such a

'thing as a brother officer who could be a blackmailer—
and he had wanted to protect the credit of his old light of
love. That lady was certainly not concerned with her husband. And he swore, and swore, and swore, that there was
nothing else in the world against him. She did not believe
him.

He had done it once too often—and she was wrong for
the first time, so that he acted a rather creditable part in
the matter. For he went right straight out to the post-office
and spent several hours in coding a telegram to his solicitor,
bidding that hard-headed man to threaten to take out at
once a warrant against the fellow who was on his track.
He said afterwards that it was a bit too thick on poor old
Leonora to be ballyragged any more. That was really the
last of his outstanding accounts, and he was ready to take
his personal chance of the Divorce Court if the blackmailer
turned nasty. He would face it out—the publicity, the
papers, the whole bally show. Those were his simple
words. . . .

He had made, however, the mistake of not telling
Leonora where he was going, so that, having seen him go
to his room to fetch the code for the telegram, and seeing,
two hours later, Maisie Maidan come out of his room,
Leonora imagined that the two hours she had spent in
silent agony Edward had spent with Maisie Maidan in his
arms. That seemed to her to be too much.

As a matter of fact, Maisie's being in Edward's room
had been the result, partly of poverty, partly of pride,
partly of sheer innocence. She could not, in the first place,
afford a maid; she refrained as much as possible from
sending the hotel servants on errands, since every penny
was of importance to her, and she feared to have to pay
high tips at the end of her stay. Edward had lent her one
of his fascinating cases containing fifteen different sizes
of scissors, and, having seen, from her window, his departure for the post-office, she had taken the opportunity
of returning the case. She could not see why she should
not, though she felt a certain remorse at the thought that

she had kissed the pillows of his bed. That was the way it took her.

But Leonora could see that, without the shadow of a doubt, the incident gave Florence a hold over her. It let Florence into things and Florence was the only created being who had any idea that the Ashburnhams were not just good people with nothing to their tails. She determined at once, not so much to give Florence the privilege of her intimacy—which would have been the payment of a kind of blackmail—as to keep Florence under observation until she could have demonstrated to Florence that she was not in the least jealous of poor Maisie. So that was why she had entered the dining-room arm in arm with my wife, and why she had so markedly planted herself at our table. She never left us, indeed, for a minute that night, except just to run up to Mrs Maidan's room to beg her pardon and to beg her also to let Edward take her very markedly out into the gardens that night. She said herself, when Mrs Maidan came rather wistfully down into the lounge where we were all sitting: 'Now, Edward, get up and take Maisie to the Casino. I want Mrs Dowell to tell me all about the families in Connecticut who came from Fordingbridge.' For it had been discovered that Florence came of a line that had actually owned Branshaw Teleragh for two centuries before the Ashburnhams came there. And there she sat with me in that hall, long after Florence had gone to bed, so that I might witness her gay reception of that pair. She could play up.

And that enables me to fix exactly the day of our going to the town of M——. For it was the very day poor Mrs Maidan died. We found her dead when we got back— pretty awful, that, when you come to figure out what it all means. . . .

At any rate the measure of my relief when Leonora said that she was an Irish Catholic gives you the measure of my affection for that couple. It was an affection so intense that even to this day I cannot think of Edward without sighing. I do not believe that I could have gone on any more without them. I was getting too tired. And I verily believe, too, that if my suspicion that Leonora was jealous of Florence had been the reason she gave for her outburst I should have turned upon Florence with the maddest kind of rage. Jealousy would have been incurable. But Florence's mere silly gibes at the Irish and at the Catholics could be apologized out of existence. And that I appeared to fix up in two minutes or so.

She looked at me for a long time rather fixedly and queerly while I was doing it. And at last I worked myself up to saying:

'Do accept the situation. I confess that I do not like your religion. But I like you so intensely. I don't mind saying that I have never had anyone to be really fond of, and I do not believe that anyone has ever been fond of me, as I believe you really to be.'

'Oh, I'm fond enough of you,' she said. 'Fond enough to say that I wish every man was like you. But there are others to be considered.' She was thinking, as a matter of fact, of poor Maisie. She picked a little piece of pellitory out of the breast-high wall in front of us. She chafed it for a long minute between her finger and thumb, then she threw it over the coping.

'Oh, I accept the situation,' she said at last, 'if you can.'

VI

I remember laughing at the phrase, 'accept the situation,' which she seemed to repeat with a gravity too intense. I said to her something like:

'It's hardly as much as that. I mean, that I must claim the liberty of a free American citizen to think what I please about your co-religionists. And I suppose that Florence must have liberty to think what she pleases and to say what politeness allows her to say.'

'She had better,' Leonora answered, 'not say one single word against my people or my faith.'

It struck me at the time, that there was an unusual, an almost threatening, hardness in her voice. It was almost as if she were trying to convey to Florence, through me, that she would seriously harm my wife if Florence went to something that was an extreme. Yes, I remember thinking at the time that it was almost as if Leonora were saying, through me to Florence:

'You may outrage me as you will; you may take all that I personally possess, but do not you dare to say one single thing in view of the situation that that will set up—against the faith that makes me become the doormat for your feet.'

But obviously, as I saw it, that could not be her meaning. Good people, be they ever so diverse in creed, do not threaten each other. So that I read Leonora's words to mean just no more than:

'It would be better if Florence said nothing at all against my co-religionists, because it is a point that I am touchy about.'

That was the hint that, accordingly, I conveyed to Florence when, shortly afterwards, she and Edward came down from the tower. And I want you to understand that, from that moment until after Edward and the girl and Florence were all dead together, I had never the remotest glimpse, not the shadow of a suspicion, that there was anything wrong, as the saying is. For five minutes, then, I entertained the possibility that Leonora might be jealous; but there was never another flicker in that flame-like personality. How in the world should I get it?

For, all that time, I was just a male sick nurse. And what chance had I against those three hardened gamblers, who were all in league to conceal their hands from me? What earthly chance? They were three to one—and they made me happy. Oh God, they made me so happy that I doubt if even paradise, that shall smooth out all temporal wrongs, shall ever give me the like. And what could they have done better, or what could they have done that could have been worse? I don't know. . . .

I suppose that, during all that time I was a deceived

husband and that Leonora was pimping for Edward. That was the cross that she had to take up during her long Calvary of a life. . . .

You ask how it feels to be a deceived husband. Just Heavens, I do not know. It feels just nothing at all. It is not Hell, certainly it is not necessarily Heaven. So I suppose it is the intermediate stage. What do they call it? Limbo. No, I feel nothing at all about that. They are dead; they have gone before their Judge who, I hope, will open to them the springs of His compassion. It is not my business to think about it. It is simply my business to say, as Leonora's people say: 'Requiem aeternam dona eis, Domine, et lux perpetua luceat eis. In memoria aeterna erit. . . .' But what were they? The just? The unjust? God knows! I think that the pair of them were only poor wretches, creeping over this earth in the shadow of an eternal wrath. It is very terrible. . . .

It is almost too terrible, the picture of that judgment, as it appears to me sometimes, at nights. It is probably the suggestion of some picture that I have seen somewhere. But upon an immense plain, suspended in mid-air, I seem to see three figures, two of them clasped close in an intense embrace, and one intolerably solitary. It is in black and white, my picture of that judgment, an etching, perhaps; only I cannot tell an etching from a photographic reproduction. And the immense plain is the hand of God, stretching out for miles and miles, with great spaces above it and below it. And they are in the sight of God, and it is Florence that is alone. . . .

And, do you know, at the thought of that intense solitude I feel an overwhelming desire to rush forward and comfort her. You cannot, you see, have acted as nurse to a person for twelve years without wishing to go on nursing them, even though you hate them with the hatred of the adder, and even in the palm of God. But, in the nights, with that vision of judgment before me, I know that I hold myself back. For I hate Florence. I hate Florence with such a hatred that I would not spare her an eternity of loneliness.

She need not have done what she did. She was an American, a New Englander. She had not the hot passions of these Europeans. She cut out that poor imbecile of an Edward—and I pray God that he is really at peace, clasped close in the arms of that poor, poor girl! And, no doubt, Maisie Maidan will find her young husband again, and Leonora will burn, clear and serene, a northern light and one of the archangels of God. And me. . . . Well, perhaps, they will find me an elevator to run. . . . But Florence. . . .

She should not have done it. She should not have done it. It was playing it too low down. She cut out poor dear Edward from sheer vanity; she meddled between him and Leonora from a sheer, imbecile spirit of district visiting. Do you understand that, whilst she was Edward's mistress, she was perpetually trying to reunite him to his wife? She would gabble on to Leonora about forgiveness—treating the subject from the bright, American point of view. And Leonora would treat her like the whore she was. Once she said to Florence in the early morning:

'You come to me straight out of his bed to tell me that that is my proper place. I know it, thank you.'

But even that could not stop Florence. She went on saying that it was her ambition to leave this world a little brighter by the passage of her brief life, and how thankfully she would leave Edward, whom she thought she had brought to a right frame of mind, if Leonora would only give him a chance. He needed, she said, tenderness beyond anything.

And Leonora would answer—for she put up with this outrage for years—Leonora, as I understand, would answer something like:

'Yes, you would give him up. And you would go on writing to each other in secret, and committing adultery in hired rooms. I know the pair of you, you know. No. I prefer the situation as it is.'

Half the time Florence would ignore Leonora's remarks. She would think they were not quite ladylike. The other half of the time she would try to persuade Leonora that her love for Edward was quite spiritual—on account of her heart. Once she said:

'If you can believe that of Maisie Maidan, as you say you do, why cannot you believe it of me?'

Leonora was, I understand, doing her hair at that time in front of the mirror in her bedroom. And she looked round at Florence, to whom she did not usually vouchsafe a glance,—she looked round coolly and calmly, and said: 'Never do you dare to mention Mrs Maidan's name again. You murdered her. You and I murdered her between us. I am as much a scoundrel as you. I don't like to be reminded of it.'

Florence went off at once into a babble of how could she have hurt a person whom she hardly knew, a person whom, with the best intentions, in pursuance of her efforts to leave the world a little brighter, she had tried to save from Edward. That was how she figured it out to herself. She really thought that.... So Leonora said patiently:

'Very well, just put it that I killed her and that it's a painful subject. One does not like to think that one had killed some one. Naturally not. I ought never to have brought her from India.'

And that, indeed, is exactly how Leonora looked at it. It is stated a little baldly, but Leonora was always a great one for bald statements.

What had happened on the day of our jaunt to the ancient city of M—— had been this:

Leonora, who had been even then filled with pity and contrition for the poor child, on returning to our hotel had gone straight to Mrs Maidan's room. She had wanted just to pet her. And she had perceived at first only, on the clear, round table covered with velvet, a letter addressed to her. It ran something like:

'Oh, Mrs Ashburnham, how could you have done it? I trusted you so. You never talked to me about me and Edward, but I trusted you. How could you buy me from my husband? I have just heard how you have—in the hall they were talking about it, Edward and the American lady.

You paid the money for me to come here. Oh, how could you? How could you? I am going straight back to Bunny. . . .'

Bunny was Mrs Maidan's husband.

And Leonora said that, as she went on reading the letter, she had, without looking round her, a sense that that hotel room was cleared, that there were no papers on the table, that there were no clothes on the hooks, and that there was a strained silence—a silence, she said, as if there were something in the room that drank up such sounds as there were. She had to fight against that feeling, whilst she read the postscript of the letter.

'I did not know you wanted me for an adulteress,' the postscript began. The poor child was hardly literate. 'It was surely not right of you and I never wanted to be one. And I heard Edward call me a poor little rat to the American lady. He always called me a little rat in private, and I did not mind. But, if he called me it to her, I think he does not love me any more. Oh, Mrs Ashburnham, you knew the world and I knew nothing. I thought it would be all right if you thought it could, and I thought you would not have brought me if you did not, too. You should not have done it, and we out of the same convent. . . .'

Leonora said that she screamed when she read that.

And then she saw that Maisie's boxes were all packed, and she began a search for Mrs Maidan herself—all over the hotel. The manager said that Mrs Maidan had paid her bill, and had gone up to the station to ask the Reisever-kehrsbureau to make her out a plan for her immediate return to Chitral. He imagined that he had seen her come back, but he was not quite certain. No one in the large hotel had bothered his head about the child. And she, wandering solitarily in the hall, had no doubt sat down beside a screen that had Edward and Florence on the other side. I never heard then or after what had passed between that precious couple. I fancy Florence was just about beginning her cutting out of poor dear Edward by addressing to him some words of friendly warning as to the ravages he might be making in the girl's heart. That would be the sort of way she would begin. And Edward would have sentimentally assured her that there was nothing in it; that Maisie was just a poor little rat whose passage to Nauheim his wife had paid out of her own pocket. That would have been enough to do the trick.

For the trick was pretty efficiently done. Leonora, with panic growing and with contrition very large in her heart, visited every one of the public rooms of the hotel—the dining-room, the lounge, the *schreibzimmer*, the winter garden. God knows what they wanted with a winter garden in an hotel that is only open from May till October. But there it was. And then Leonora ran—yes, she ran up the stairs—to see if Maisie had not returned to her rooms. She had determined to take that child right away from that hideous place. It seemed to her to be all unspeakable. I do not mean to say that she was not quite cool about it. Leonora was always Leonora. But the cold justice of the thing demanded that she should play the part of mother to this child who had come from the same convent. She figured it out to amount to that. She would leave Edward to Florence—and to me—and she would devote all her time to providing that child with an atmosphere of love until she could be returned to her poor young husband. It was naturally too late.

She had not cared to look round Maisie's rooms at first. Now, as soon as she came in, she perceived, sticking out beyond the bed, a small pair of feet in high-heeled shoes. Maisie had died in the effort to strap up a great portmanteau. She had died so grotesquely that her little body had fallen forward into the trunk, and it had closed upon her, like the jaws of a gigantic alligator. The key was in her hand. Her dark hair, like the hair of a Japanese, had come down and covered her body and her face.

Leonora lifted her up—she was the merest feather-weight—and laid her on the bed with her hair about her. She was smiling, as if she had just scored a goal in a hockey match. You understand she had not committed

3*

suicide. Her heart had just stopped. I saw her, with the long lashes on the cheeks, with the smile about the lips, with the flowers all about her. The stem of a white lily rested in her hand so that the spike of flowers was upon her shoulder. She looked like a bride in the sunlight of the mortuary candles that were all about her, and the white coifs of the two nuns that knelt at her feet with their faces hidden might have been two swans that were to bear her away to kissing-kindness land, or wherever it is. Leonora showed her to me. She would not let either of the others see her. She wanted, you know, to spare poor dear Edward's feelings. He never could bear the sight of a corpse. And, since she never gave him an idea that Maisie had written to her, he imagined that the death had been the most natural thing in the world. He soon got over it. Indeed, it was the one affair of his life about which he never felt much remorse.

PART TWO

I

THE death of Mrs Maidan occurred on the 4th of August, 1904. And then nothing happened until the 4th of August, 1913. There is the curious coincidence of dates, but I do not know whether that is one of those sinister, as if half-jocular and altogether merciless proceedings on the part of a cruel Providence that we call a coincidence. Because it may just as well have been the superstitious mind of Florence that forced her to certain acts, as if she had been hypnotized. It is, however, certain that the 4th of August always proved a significant date for her. To begin with, she was born on the 4th of August. Then, on that date, in the year 1899, she set out with her uncle for the tour round the world in company with a young man called Jimmy. But that was not merely a coincidence. Her kindly old uncle, with the supposedly damaged heart, was, in his delicate way, offering her, in this trip, a birthday present to celebrate her coming of age. Then, on the 4th of August, 1900, she yielded to an action that certainly coloured her whole life—as well as mine. She had no luck. She was probably offering herself a birthday present that morning. . . .

On the 4th of August, 1901, she married me, and set sail for Europe in a great gale of wind—the gale that affected her heart. And no doubt there, again, she was offering herself a birthday gift—the birthday gift of my miserable life. It occurs to me that I have never told you anything about my marriage. That was like this: I have told you, as I think, that I first met Florence at the Stuyvesants', in Fourteenth Street. And, from that moment,

I determined with all the obstinacy of a possibly weak nature, if not to make her mine, at least to marry her. I had no occupation—I had no business affairs. I simply camped down there in Stamford, in a vile hotel, and just passed my days in the house, or on the verandah of the Misses Hurlbird. The Misses Hurlbird, in an odd, obstinate way, did not like my presence. But they were hampered by the national manners of these occasions. Florence had her own sitting-room. She could ask to it whom she liked, and I simply walked into that apartment. I was as timid as you will, but in that matter I was like a chicken that is determined to get across the road in front of an automobile. I would walk into Florence's pretty, little, old-fashioned room, take off my hat, and sit down.

Florence had, of course, several other fellows, too— strapping young New Englanders, who worked during the day in New York and spent only the evenings in the village of their birth. And, in the evenings, they would march in on Florence with almost as much determination as I myself showed. And I am bound to say that they were received with as much disfavour as was my portion—from the Misses Hurlbird. . . .

They were curious old creatures, those two. It was almost as if they were members of an ancient family under some curse—they were so gentlewomanly, so proper, and they sighed so. Sometimes I would see tears in their eyes. I do not know that my courtship of Florence made much progress at first. Perhaps that was because it took place almost entirely during the daytime, on hot afternoons, when the clouds of dust hung like fog, right up as high as the tops of the thin-leaved elms. The night, I believe, is the proper season for the gentle feats of love, not a Connecticut July afternoon, when any sort of proximity is an almost appalling thought. But, if I never so much as kissed Florence, she let me discover very easily, in the course of a fortnight, her simple wants. And I could supply those wants. . . .

She wanted to marry a gentleman of leisure; she wanted

a European establishment. She wanted her husband to have an English accent, an income of fifty thousand dollars a year from real estate and no ambitions to increase that income. And—she faintly hinted—she did not want much physical passion in the affair. Americans, you know, can envisage such unions without blinking.

She gave out this information in floods of bright talk— she would pop a little bit of it into comments over a view of the Rialto, Venice, and, whilst she was brightly describing Balmoral Castle, she would say that her ideal husband would be one who could get her received at the British Court. She had spent, it seemed, two months in Great Britain—seven weeks in touring from Stratford to Strathpeffer, and one as paying guest in an old English family near Ledbury, an impoverished, but still stately family, called Bagshawe. They were to have spent two months more in that tranquil bosom, but inopportune events, apparently in her uncle's business, had caused their rather hurried return to Stamford. The young man called Jimmy had remained in Europe to perfect his knowledge of that continent. He certainly did: he was most useful to us afterwards.

But the point that came out—that there was no mistaking—was that Florence was coldly and calmly determined to take no look at any man who could not give her a European settlement. Her glimpse of English home life had effected this. She meant, on her marriage, to have a year in Paris, and then to have her husband buy some real estate in the neighbourhood of Fordingbridge, from which place the Hurlbirds had come in the year 1688. On the strength of that she was going to take her place in the ranks of English county society. That was fixed.

I used to feel mightily elevated when I considered these details, for I could not figure out that amongst her acquaintance in Stamford there was any fellow that would fill the bill. The most of them were not as wealthy as I, and those that were were not the type to give up the fascinations of Wall Street even for the protracted companionship of Florence. But nothing really happened during the month of July. On the 1st of August Florence apparently told her aunts that she intended to marry me.

She had not told me so, but there was no doubt about the aunts, for, on that afternoon, Miss Florence Hurlbird, Senior, stopped me on my way to Florence's sitting-room and took me, agitatedly, into the parlour. It was a singular interview, in that old-fashioned colonial room, with the spindle-legged furniture, the silhouettes, the miniatures, the portrait of General Braddock, and the smell of lavender. You see, the two poor maiden ladies were in agonies—and they could not say one single thing direct. They would almost wring their hands and ask if I had considered such a thing as different temperaments. I assure you they were almost affectionate, concerned for me even, as if Florence were too bright for my solid and serious virtues.

For they had discovered in me solid and serious virtues. That might have been because I had once dropped the remark that I preferred General Braddock to General Washington. For the Hurlbirds had backed the losing side in the War of Independence, and had been seriously impoverished and quite efficiently oppressed for that reason. The Misses Hurlbird could never forget it.

Nevertheless they shuddered at the thought of a European career for myself and Florence. Each of them really wailed when they heard that that was what I hoped to give their niece. That may have been partly because they regarded Europe as a sink of iniquity, where strange laxities prevailed. They thought the Mother Country as Erastian as any other. And they carried their protests to extraordinary lengths, for them. . . .

They even, almost, said that marriage was a sacrament; but neither Miss Florence nor Miss Emily could quite bring herself to utter the word. And they almost brought themselves to say that Florence's early life had been characterized by flirtations—something of that sort.

I know I ended the interview by saying:

'I don't care. If Florence has robbed a bank I am going to marry her and take her to Europe.'

And at that Miss Emily wailed and fainted. But Miss Florence, in spite of the state of her sister, threw herself on my neck and cried out:

'Don't do it, John. Don't do it. You're a good young man,' and she added, whilst I was getting out of the room to send Florence to her aunt's rescue:

'We ought to tell you more. But she's our dear sister's child.'

Florence, I remember, received me with a chalk-pale face and the exclamation:

'Have those old cats been saying anything against me?' But I assured her that they had not and hurried her into the room of her strangely afflicted relatives. I had really forgotten all about that exclamation of Florence's until this moment. She treated me so very well—with such tact —that, if I ever thought of it afterwards I put it down to her deep affection for me.

And that evening, when I went to fetch her for a buggy-ride, she had disappeared. I did not lose any time. I went into New York and engaged berths on the 'Pocahontas,' that was to sail on the evening of the fourth of the month, and then, returning to Stamford, I tracked out, in the course of the day, that Florence had been driven to Rye Station. And there I found that she had taken the cars to Waterbury. She had, of course, gone to her uncle's. The old man received me with a stony, husky face. I was not to see Florence; she was ill; she was keeping her room. And, from something that he let drop—an odd Biblical phrase that I have forgotten—I gathered that all that family simply did not intend her to marry ever in her life.

I procured at once the name of the nearest minister and a rope ladder—you have no idea how primitively these matters were arranged in those days in the United States. I daresay that may be so still. And at one o'clock in the morning of the 4th of August I was standing in Florence's bedroom. I was so one-minded in my purpose that it never struck me there was anything improper in being, at one o'clock in the morning, in Florence's bedroom. I just wanted to wake her up. She was not, however, asleep. She expected me, and her relatives had only just left her. She received me with an embrace of a warmth. . . . Well, it was the first time I had ever been embraced by a woman—and it was the last when a woman's embrace has had in it any warmth for me. . . .

I suppose it was my own fault, what followed. At any rate, I was in such a hurry to get the wedding over, and was so afraid of her relatives finding me there, that I must have received her advances with a certain amount of absence of mind. I was out of that room and down the ladder in under half a minute. She kept me waiting at the foot an unconscionable time—it was certainly three in the morning before we knocked up that minister. And I think that that wait was the only sign Florence ever showed of having a conscience as far as I was concerned, unless her lying for some moments in my arms was also a sign of conscience. I fancy that, if I had shown warmth then, she would have acted the proper wife to me, or would have put me back again. But, because I acted like a Philadelphia gentleman, she made me, I suppose, go through with the part of a male nurse. Perhaps she thought that I should not mind.

After that, as I gather, she had not any more remorse. She was only anxious to carry out her plans. For, just before she came down the ladder, she called me to the top of that grotesque implement that I went up and down like a tranquil jumping-jack. I was perfectly collected. She said to me with a certain fierceness:

'It is determined that we sail at four this afternoon? You are not lying about having taken berths?'

I understood that she would naturally be anxious to get away from the neighbourhood of her apparently insane relatives, so that I readily excused her for thinking that I should be capable of lying about such a thing. I made it, therefore, plain to her that it was my fixed determination to sail by the 'Pocahontas.' She said then—it was a moon-lit morning, and she was whispering in my ear whilst I stood on the ladder. The hills that surround Waterbury showed, extraordinarily tranquil, around the villa. She said, almost coldly:

'I wanted to know, so as to pack my trunks.' And she added: 'I may be ill, you know. I guess my heart is a little like Uncle Hurlbird's. It runs in families.'

I whispered that the 'Pocahontas' was an extraordinarily steady boat. . . .

Now I wonder what had passed through Florence's mind during the two hours that she had kept me waiting at the foot of the ladder. I would give not a little to know. Till then, I fancy she had had no settled plan in her mind. She certainly never mentioned her heart till that time. Perhaps the renewed sight of her Uncle Hurlbird had given her the idea. Certainly her Aunt Emily, who had come over with her to Waterbury, would have rubbed into her, for hours and hours, the idea that any accentuated discussions would kill the old gentleman. That would recall to her mind all the safeguards against excitement with which the poor silly old gentleman had been hedged in during their trip round the world. That, perhaps, put it into her head. Still, I believe there was some remorse on my account, too. Leonora told me that Florence said there was—for Leonora knew all about it, and once went so far as to ask her how she could do a thing so infamous. She excused herself on the score of an overmastering passion. Well, I always say that an overmastering passion is a good excuse for feelings. You cannot help them. And it is a good excuse for straight actions—she might have bolted with the fellow, before or after she married me. And, if they had not enough money to get along with, they might have cut their throats, or sponged on her family, though, of course, Florence wanted such a lot that it would have suited her very badly to have for a husband a clerk in a dry-goods store, which was what old Hurlbird would have made of that fellow. He hated him. No, I do not think that there is much excuse for Florence.

God knows. She was a frightened fool, and she was fantastic, and I suppose that, at that time, she really cared for that imbecile. He certainly didn't care for her. Poor thing. . . . At any rate, after I had assured her that the 'Pocahontas' was a steady ship, she just said:

'You'll have to look after me in certain ways—like Uncle Hurlbird is looked after. I will tell you how to do it.' And then she stepped over the sill, as if she were stepping on board a boat. I suppose she had burnt hers!

I had, no doubt, eye-openers enough. When we re-entered the Hurlbird mansion at eight o'clock the Hurl-birds were just exhausted. Florence had a hard, triumphant air. We had got married about four in the morning and had sat about in the woods above the town till then, listening to a mocking-bird imitate an old tom-cat. So I guess Florence had not found getting married to me a very stimulating process. I had not found anything much more inspiring to say than how glad I was, with variations. I think I was too dazed. Well, the Hurlbirds were too dazed to say much. We had breakfast together, and then Florence went to pack her grips and things. Old Hurlbird took the opportunity to read me a full-blooded lecture, in the style of an American oration, as to the perils for young American girlhood lurking in the European jungle. He said that Paris was full of snakes in the grass, of which he had had bitter experience. He concluded, as they always do, poor, dear old things, with the aspiration that all American women should one day be sexless—though that is not the way they put it. . . .

Well, we made the ship all right by one-thirty—and there was a tempest blowing. That helped Florence a good deal. For we were not ten minutes out from Sandy Hook before Florence went down into her cabin and her heart took her. An agitated stewardess came running up to me, and I went running down. I got my directions how to be-have to my wife. Most of them came from her, though it was the ship doctor who discreetly suggested to me that I had better refrain from manifestations of affection. I was ready enough.

I was, of course, full of remorse. It occurred to me that her heart was the reason for the Hurlbirds' mysterious desire to keep their youngest and dearest unmarried. Of course, they would be too refined to put the motive into words. They were old stock New Englanders. They would not want to have to suggest that a husband must not kiss the back of his wife's neck. They would not like to suggest that he might, for the matter of that. I wonder, though, how Florence got the doctor to enter the conspiracy—the several doctors.

Of course her heart squeaked a bit—she had the same configuration of the lungs as her Uncle Hurlbird. And, in his company, she must have heard a great deal of heart talk from specialists. Anyhow, she and they tied me pretty well down—and Jimmy, of course, that dreary boy—what in the world did she see in him? He was lugubrious, silent, morose. He had no talent as a painter. He was very sallow and dark, and he never shaved sufficiently. He met us at Havre, and he proceeded to make himself useful for the next two years, during which he lived in our flat in Paris, whether we were there or not. He studied painting at Julien's, or some such place. . . .

That fellow had his hands always in the pockets of his odious, square-shouldered, broad-hipped, American coats, and his dark eyes were always full of ominous appearances. He was, besides, too fat. Why, I was much the better man. . . .

And I daresay Florence would have given me the better. She showed signs of it. I think, perhaps, the enigmatic smile with which she used to look back at me over her shoulder when she went into the bathing place was a sort of invitation. I have mentioned that. It was as if she were saying: 'I am going in here. I am going to stand so stripped and white and straight—and you are a man. . . .' Perhaps it was that . . .

No, she cannot have liked that fellow long. He looked like sallow putty. I understand that he had been slim and dark and very graceful at the time of her first disgrace. But, loafing about in Paris, on her pocket-money and on the allowance that old Hurlbird made him to keep out of the United States, had given him a stomach like a man of forty, and dyspeptic irritation on top of it.

God, how they worked me! It was those two between them who really elaborated the rules. I have told you something about them—how I had to head conversations, for all those eleven years, off such topics as love, poverty, crime, and so on. But, looking over what I have written, I see that I have unintentionally misled you when I said that Florence was never out of my sight. Yet that was the impression that I really had until just now. When I come to think of it she was out of my sight most of the time.

You see, that fellow impressed upon me that what Florence needed most of all were sleep and privacy. I must never enter her room without knocking, or her poor little heart might flutter away to its doom. He said these things with his lugubrious croak, and his black eyes like a crow's, so that I seemed to see poor Florence die ten times a day—a little, pale, frail corpse. Why, I would as soon have thought of entering her room without her permission as of burgling a church. I would sooner have committed that crime. I would certainly have done it if I had thought the state of her heart demanded the sacrilege. So at ten o'clock at night the door closed upon Florence, who had gently, and, as if reluctantly, backed up that fellow's recommendations; and she would wish me good night as if she were a *cinquecento* Italian lady saying good-bye to her lover. And at ten o'clock of the next morning there she would come out of the door of her room as fresh as Venus rising from any of the couches that are mentioned in Greek legends.

Her room door was locked because she was nervous about thieves; but an electric contrivance on a cord was understood to be attached to her little wrist. She had only to press a bulb to raise the house. And I was provided with an axe—an axe!—great gods, with which to break down her door in case she ever failed to answer my knock, after I knocked really loud several times. It was pretty well thought out, you see.

What wasn't so well thought out were the ultimate consequences—our being tied to Europe. For that young man rubbed it so well into me that Florence would die if she crossed the Channel—he impressed it so fully on my mind that, when later Florence wanted to go to Fording-bridge, I cut the proposal short—absolutely short, with a curt no. It fixed her and it frightened her. I was even backed up by all the doctors. I seemed to have had endless interviews with doctor after doctor, cool, quiet men, who would ask, in reasonable tones, whether there was any reason for our going to England—any special reason. And since I could not see any special reason, they would give the verdict: 'Better not, then.' I daresay they were honest enough, as things go. They probably imagined that the mere associations of the steamer might have effects on Florence's nerves. That would be enough, that and a conscientious desire to keep our money on the Continent.

It must have rattled poor Florence pretty considerably, for you see, the main idea—the only main idea of her heart, that was otherwise cold—was to get to Fording-bridge and be a county lady in the home of her ancestors. But Jimmy got her, there: he shut on her the door of the Channel; even on the fairest day of blue sky, with the cliffs of England shining like mother of pearl in full view of Calais, I would not have let her cross the steamer gangway to save her life. I tell you it fixed her.

It fixed her beautifully, because she could not announce herself as cured, since that would have put an end to the locked bedroom arrangements. And, by the time she was sick of Jimmy—which happened in the year 1903—she had taken on Edward Ashburnham. Yes, it was a bad fix for her, because Edward could have taken her to Fording-bridge, and, though he could not give her Branshaw Manor, that home of her ancestors being settled on his wife, she could at least have pretty considerably queened it there or thereabouts, what with our money and the support of the Ashburnhams. Her uncle, as soon as he considered that she had really settled down with me—and I sent him only the most glowing accounts of her virtue and constancy—made over to her a very considerable part of his fortune for which he had no use. I suppose that we had, between us, fifteen thousand a year in English money, though I never quite knew how much of hers went to Jimmy. At any rate, we could have shone in Fordingbridge.

I never quite knew, either, how she and Edward got rid of Jimmy. I fancy that fat and disreputable raven must have had his six golden front teeth knocked down his throat by Edward one morning whilst I had gone out to buy some flowers in the Rue de la Paix, leaving Florence and the flat in charge of those two. And serve him very right, is all that I can say. He was a bad sort of blackmailer; I hope Florence does not have his company in the next world.

As God is my Judge, I do not believe that I would have separated those two if I had known that they really and passionately loved each other. I do not know where the public morality of the case comes in, and, of course, no man really knows what he would have done in any given case. But I truly believe that I would have united them, observing ways and means as decent as I could. I believe that I should have given them money to live upon and that I should have consoled myself somehow. At that date I might have found some young thing, like Maisie Maidan, or the poor girl, and I might have had some peace. For peace I never had with Florence, and I hardly believe that I cared for her in the way of love after a year or two of it. She became for me a rare and fragile object, something burdensome, but very frail. Why it was as if I had been given a thin-shelled pullet's egg to carry on my palm from Equatorial Africa to Hoboken. Yes, she became for me, as it were, the subject of a bet—the trophy of an athlete's achievement, a parsley crown that is the symbol of his chastity, his soberness, his abstentions, and of his inflexible will. Of intrinsic value as a wife, I think she had none at all for me. I fancy I was not even proud of the way she dressed.

But her passion for Jimmy was not even a passion, and, mad as the suggestion may appear, she was frightened for her life. Yes, she was afraid of me. I will tell you how that happened.

I had, in the old days, a darky servant, called Julius, who valeted me, and waited on me, and loved me, like the crown of his head. Now, when we left Waterbury to go to the 'Pocahontas,' Florence entrusted to me one very special and very precious leather grip. She told me that her life might depend on that grip, which contained her drugs against heart attacks. And, since I was never much of a hand at carrying things, I entrusted this, in turn, to Julius, who was a grey-haired chap of sixty or so, and very picturesque at that. He made so much impression on Florence that she regarded him as a sort of father, and absolutely refused to let me take him to Paris. He would have inconvenienced her.

Well, Julius was so overcome with grief at being left behind that he must needs go and drop the precious grip. I saw red, I saw purple. I flew at Julius. On the ferry, it was, I filled up one of his eyes; I threatened to strangle him. And, since an unresisting negro can make a deplorable noise and a deplorable spectacle, and, since that was Florence's first adventure in the married state, she got a pretty idea of my character. It affirmed in her the desperate resolve to conceal from me the fact that she was not what she would have called 'a pure woman.' For that was really the mainspring of her fantastic actions. She was afraid that I should murder her....

So she got up the heart attack, at the earliest possible opportunity, on board the liner. Perhaps she was not so very much to be blamed. You must remember that she was a New Englander, and that New England had not yet come to loathe darkies as it does now. Whereas, if she had come from even so little south as Philadelphia, and had been of an oldish family, she would have seen that for me to kick Julius was not so outrageous an act as for her cousin, Reggie Hurlbird, to say—as I have heard him say to his English butler—that for two cents he would bat him on the pants. Besides, the medicine-grip did not bulk as largely in her eyes as it did in mine, where it was the symbol of the existence of an adored wife of a day. To her it was just a useful lie. . . .

Well, there you have the position, as clear as I can make it—the husband an ignorant fool, the wife a cold sensualist with imbecile fears—for I was such a fool that I should never have known what she was or was not—and the black-mailing lover. And then the other lover came along. . . .

Well, Edward Ashburnham was worth having. Have I conveyed to you the splendid fellow that he was—the fine soldier, the excellent landlord, the extraordinarily kind, careful, and industrious magistrate, the upright, honest, fair-dealing, fair-thinking, public character? I suppose I have not conveyed it to you. The truth is, that I never knew it until the poor girl came along—the poor girl who was just as straight, as splendid and as upright as he. I swear she was. I suppose I ought to have known. I suppose that was, really, why I liked him so much—so infinitely much. Come to think of it, I can remember a thousand little acts of kindliness, of thoughtfulness for his inferiors, even on the Continent. Look here, I know of two families of dirty, unpicturesque, Hessian paupers that that fellow, with an infinite patience, rooted up, got their police re-ports, set on their feet, or exported to my patient land. And he would do it quite inarticulately, set in motion by seeing a child crying in the street. He would wrestle with dic-tionaries, in that unfamiliar tongue. . . . Well, he could not bear to see a child cry. Perhaps he could not bear to see a woman and not give her the comfort of his physical attractions.

But, although I liked him so intensely, I was rather apt to take these things for granted. They made me feel comfortable with him, good towards him; they made me trust him. But I guess I thought it was part of the character of any English gentleman. Why, one day he got it into his head that the head waiter at the Excelsior had been crying —the fellow with the grey face and grey whiskers. And then he spent the best part of a week, in correspondence and up at the British consul's, in getting the fellow's wife to come back from London and bring back his girl baby. She had bolted with a Swiss scullion. If she had not come inside the week he would have gone to London himself to fetch her. He was like that.

Edward Ashburnham was like that, and I thought it was only the duty of his rank and station. Perhaps that was all that it was—but I pray God to make me discharge mine as well. And, but for the poor girl, I daresay that I should never have seen it, however much the feeling might have been over me. She had for him such enthusiasm that, although even now I do not understand the technicalities of English life, I can gather enough. She was with them during the whole of our last stay at Nauheim.

Nancy Rufford was her name; she was Leonora's only friend's only child, and Leonora was her guardian, if that is the correct term. She had lived with the Ashburnhams ever since she had been of the age of thirteen, when her mother was said to have committed suicide owing to the brutalities of her father. Yes, it is a cheerful story. . . .

Edward always called her 'the girl,' and it was very pretty, the evident affection he had for her and she for him. And Leonora's feet she would have kissed—those two were for her the best man and the best woman on earth—and in heaven. I think that she had not a thought of evil in her head—the poor girl.

Well, anyhow, she chanted Edward's praises to me for the hour together, but, as I have said, I could not make much of it. It appeared that he had the D.S.O., and that his troop loved him beyond the love of men. You never saw such a troop as his. And he had the Royal Humane Society's medal with a clasp. That meant, apparently, that

he had twice jumped off the deck of a troopship to rescue
what the girl called 'Tommies,' who had fallen overboard
in the Red Sea and such places. He had been twice recommended for the v.c., whatever that might mean, and,
although owing to some technicalities he had never received that apparently coveted order, he had some special
place about his sovereign at the coronation. Or perhaps it
was some post in the Beefeaters'. She made him out like a
cross between Lohengrin and the Chevalier Bayard. Perhaps he was. . . . But he was too silent a fellow to make that
side of him really decorative. I remember going to him at
about that time and asking him what the D.S.O. was, and
he grunted out:

'It's a sort of thing they give grocers who've honourably
supplied the troops with adulterated coffee in war-time'—
something of that sort. He did not quite carry conviction
to me, so, in the end, I put it directly to Leonora. I asked
her fully and squarely—prefacing the question with some
remarks, such as those that I have already given you, as to
the difficulty one has in really getting to know people when
one's intimacy is conducted as an English acquaintanceship—I asked her whether her husband was not really a
splendid fellow—along at least the lines of his public
functions. She looked at me with a slightly awakened air—
with an air that would have been almost startled if Leonora
could ever have been startled.

'Didn't you know?' she asked. 'If I come to think of it
there is not a more splendid fellow in any three counties,
pick them where you will—along those lines.' And she
added, after she had looked at me reflectively for what
seemed a long time:

'To do my husband justice there could not be a better
man on the earth. There would not be room for it—along
those lines.'

'Well,' I said, 'then he must really be Lohengrin and the
Cid in one body. For there are not any other lines that
count.'

Again she looked at me for a long time.

'It's your opinion that there are no other lines that count?' she asked slowly.

'Well,' I answered gaily, 'you're not going to accuse him of not being a good husband, or of not being a good guardian to your ward?'

She spoke then, slowly, like a person who is listening to the sounds in a sea-shell held to her ear—and, would you believe it?—she told me afterwards that, at that speech of mine, for the first time she had a vague inkling of the tragedy that was to follow so soon—although the girl had lived with them for eight years or so:

'Oh, I'm not thinking of saying that he is not the best of husbands, or that he is not very fond of the girl.'

And then I said something like:

'Well, Leonora, a man sees more of these things than even a wife. And, let me tell you, that in all the years I've known Edward he has never, in your absence, paid a moment's attention to any other woman—not by the quivering of an eyelash. I should have noticed. And he talks of you as if you were one of the angels of God.'

'Oh,' she came up to the scratch, as you could be sure Leonora would always come up to the scratch, 'I am perfectly sure that he always speaks nicely of me.'

I daresay she had practice in that sort of scene—people must have been always complimenting her on her husband's fidelity and adoration. For half the world—the whole of the world that knew Edward and Leonora believed that his conviction in the Kilsyte affair had been a miscarriage of justice—a conspiracy of false evidence, got together by Nonconformist adversaries. But think of the fool that I was. . . .

II

Let me think where we were. Oh, yes . . . that conversation took place on the 4th of August, 1913. I remember saying to her that, on that day, exactly nine years before, I had made their acquaintance, so that it had seemed quite appropriate and like a birthday speech to utter my little testimonial to my friend Edward. I could quite confidently say that, though we four had been about together in all sorts of places, for all that length of time, I had not, for my part, one single complaint to make of either of them. And I added, that that was an unusual record for people who had been so much together. You are not to imagine that it was only at Nauheim that we met. That would not have suited Florence.

I find, on looking at my diaries, that on the 4th of September, 1904, Edward accompanied Florence and my-self to Paris, where we put him up till the twenty-first of that month. He made another short visit to us in December of that year—the first year of our acquaintance. It must have been during this visit that he knocked Mr Jimmy's teeth down his throat. I daresay Florence had asked him to come over for that purpose. In 1905 he was in Paris three times—once with Leonora, who wanted some frocks. In 1906 we spent the best part of six weeks together at Mentone, and Edward stayed with us in Paris on his way back to London. That was how it went.

The fact was that in Florence the poor wretch had got hold of a Tartar, compared with whom Leonora was a sucking kid. He must have had a hell of a time. Leonora wanted to keep him for—what shall I say—for the good of her church, as it were, to show that Catholic women do not lose their men. Let it go at that, for the moment. I will write more about her motives later, perhaps. But Florence was sticking on to the proprietor of the home of her ancestors. No doubt he was also a very passionate lover. But I am convinced that he was sick of Florence within three years of even interrupted companionship and the life that she led him. . . .

If ever Leonora so much as mentioned in a letter that they had had a woman staying with them—or, if she so much as mentioned a woman's name in a letter to me—off would go a desperate cable in cipher to that poor wretch at Branshaw, commanding him on pain of an instant and horrible disclosure to come over and assure her of his fidelity. I daresay he would have faced it out; I daresay he would have thrown over Florence and taken the risk of exposure. But there he had Leonora to deal with. And Leonora assured him that, if the minutest fragment of the real situation ever got through to my senses, she would wreak upon him the most terrible vengeance that she could think of. And he did not have a very easy job. Florence called for more and more attentions from him as the time went on. She would make him kiss her at any moment of the day; and it was only by his making it plain that a divorced lady could never assume a position in the county of Hampshire that he could prevent her from making a bolt of it with him in her train. Oh, yes, it was a difficult job for him.

For Florence, if you please, gaining in time a more composed view of nature, and overcome by her habits of garrulity, arrived at a frame of mind in which she found it almost necessary to tell me all about it—nothing less than that. She said that her situation was too unbearable with regard to me.

She proposed to tell me all, secure a divorce from me, and go with Edward and settle in California. . . . I do not suppose that she was really serious in this. It would have meant the extinction of all hopes of Branshaw Manor for her. Besides she had got it into her head that Leonora, who was as sound as a roach, was consumptive. She was always begging Leonora, before me, to go and see a doctor. But, none the less, poor Edward seems to have believed in her determination to carry him off. He would not have gone; he cared for his wife too much. But, if Florence had put him at it, that would have meant my getting to know of it, and his incurring Leonora's vengeance. And she could have made it pretty hot for him in ten or a dozen different ways. And she assured me that she would have used every one of them. She was determined to spare my feelings. And she was quite aware that, at that date, the hottest she could have made it for him would have been to refuse, herself, ever to see him again. . . .

Well, I think I have made it pretty clear. Let me come to the 4th of August, 1913, the last day of my absolute ignorance—and, I assure you, of my perfect happiness. For the coming of that dear girl only added to it all.

On that 4th of August I was sitting in the lounge with a rather odious Englishman called Bagshawe, who had arrived that night, too late for dinner. Leonora had just gone to bed and I was waiting for Florence and Edward and the girl to come back from a concert at the Casino. They had not gone there all together. Florence, I remember, had said at first that she would remain with Leonora and me, and Edward and the girl had gone off alone. And then Leonora had said to Florence with perfect calmness:

'I wish you would go with those two. I think the girl ought to have the appearance of being chaperoned with Edward in these places. I think the time has come.' So Florence, with her light step, had slipped out after them. She was all in black for some cousin or other. Americans are particular in those matters.

We had gone on sitting in the lounge till towards ten, when Leonora had gone up to bed. It had been a very hot day, but there it was cool. The man called Bagshawe had been reading *The Times* on the other side of the room, but then he moved over to me with some trifling question as a prelude to suggesting an acquaintance. I fancy he asked me something about the poll-tax on Kur-guests, and whether it could not be sneaked out of. He was that sort of person.

Well, he was an unmistakable man, with a military figure, rather exaggerated, with bulbous eyes that avoided your own, and a pallid complexion that suggested vices practised in secret, along with an uneasy desire for making acquaintance at whatever cost. . . . The filthy toad. . . .

He began by telling me that he came from Ludlow Manor, near Ledbury. The name had a slightly familiar sound, though I could not fix it in my mind. Then he began to talk about a duty on hops, about Californian hops, about Los Angeles, where he had been. He was fencing for a topic with which he might gain my affection.

And then, quite suddenly, in the bright light of the street, I saw Florence running. It was like that—Florence running with a face whiter than paper and her hand on the black stuff over her heart. I tell you, my own heart stood still; I tell you I could not move. She rushed in at the swing doors. She looked round that place of rush chairs, cane tables, and newspapers. She saw me and opened her lips. She saw the man who was talking to me. She stuck her hands over her face as if she wished to push her eyes out. And she was not there any more.

I could not move; I could not stir a finger. And then that man said:

'By Jove: Florry Hurlbird.' He turned upon me with an oily and uneasy sound meant for a laugh. He was really going to ingratiate himself with me.

'Do you know who that is?' he asked. 'The last time I saw that girl she was coming out of the bedroom of a young man called Jimmy at five o'clock in the morning. In my house at Ledbury. You saw her recognize me.' He was standing on his feet, looking down at me. I don't know what I looked like. At any rate, he gave a sort of gurgle and then stuttered:

'Oh, I say . . .' Those were the last words I ever heard of Mr Bagshawe's. A long time afterwards I pulled myself out of the lounge and went up to Florence's room. She had not locked the door—for the first time of our married life. She was lying, quite respectably arranged, unlike Mrs Maidan, on her bed. She had a little phial that rightly should have contained nitrate of amyl, in her right hand. That was on the 4th of August, 1913.

PART THREE

I

THE odd thing is that what sticks out in my recollection of the rest of that evening was Leonora's saying:

'Of course you might marry her,' and, when I asked whom, she answered:

'The girl.'

Now that is to me a very amazing thing—amazing for the light of possibilities that it casts into the human heart. For I had never had the slightest conscious idea of marrying the girl; I never had the slightest idea even of caring for her. I must have talked in an odd way, as people do who are recovering from an anaesthetic. It is as if one had a dual personality, the one I being entirely unconscious of the other. I had thought nothing; I had said such an extraordinary thing.

I don't know that analysis of my own psychology matters at all to this story. I should say that it didn't or, at any rate, that I had given enough of it. But that odd remark of mine had a strong influence upon what came after. I mean, that Leonora would probably never have spoken to me at all about Florence's relations with Edward if I hadn't said, two hours after my wife's death:

'Now I can marry the girl.'

She had, then, taken it for granted that I had been suffering all that she had been suffering, or, at least, that I had permitted all that she had permitted. So that, a month ago, about a week after the funeral of poor Edward, she could say to me in the most natural way in the world—I had been talking about the duration of my stay at Branshaw—she said with her clear, reflective intonation:

'Oh, stop here for ever and ever if you can.' And then she added, 'You couldn't be more of a brother to me, or more of a counsellor, or more of a support. You are all the consolation I have in the world. And isn't it odd to think that if your wife hadn't been my husband's mistress, you would probably never have been here at all?'

That was how I got the news—full in the face, like that. I didn't say anything and I don't suppose I felt anything, unless maybe it was with that mysterious and unconscious self that underlies most people. Perhaps one day when I am unconscious or walking in my sleep I may go and spit upon poor Edward's grave. It seems about the most unlikely thing I could do; but there it is.

No, I remember no emotion of any sort, but just the clear feeling that one has from time to time when one hears that some Mrs So-and-So is *au mieux* with a certain gentleman. It made things plainer, suddenly, to my curiosity. It was as if I thought, at that moment, of a windy November evening, that, when I came to think it over afterwards, a dozen unexplained things would fit themselves into place. But I wasn't thinking things over then. I remember that distinctly. I was just sitting back, rather stiffly, in a deep arm-chair. That is what I remember. It was twilight.

Branshaw Manor lies in a little hollow with lawns across it and pine-woods on the fringe of the dip. The immense wind, coming from across the forest, roared overhead. But the view from the window was perfectly quiet and grey. Not a thing stirred, except a couple of rabbits on the extreme edge of the lawn. It was Leonora's own little study that we were in and we were waiting for the tea to be brought. I, as I have said, was sitting in the deep chair, Leonora was standing in the window twirling the wooden acorn at the end of the window-blind cord desultorily round and round. She looked across the lawn and said, as far as I can remember:

'Edward has been dead only ten days and yet there are rabbits on the lawn.'

I understand that rabbits do a great deal of harm to the

short grass in England. And then she turned round to me and said without any adornment at all, for I remember her exact words:

'I think it was stupid of Florence to commit suicide.'

I cannot tell you the extraordinary sense of leisure that we two seemed to have at that moment. It wasn't as if we were waiting for a train, it wasn't as if we were waiting for a meal—it was just that there was nothing to wait for. Nothing.

There was an extreme stillness with the remote and intermittent sound of the wind. There was the grey light in that brown, small room. And there appeared to be nothing else in the world.

I know then that Leonora was about to let me into her full confidence. It was as if—or no, it was the actual fact that—Leonora with an odd English sense of decency had determined to wait until Edward had been in his grave for a full week before she spoke. And with some vague motive of giving her an idea of the extent to which she must permit herself to make confidences, I said slowly—and these words too I remember with exactitude—

'Did Florence commit suicide? I didn't know.'

I was just, you understand, trying to let her know that, if she were going to speak she would have to talk about a much wider range of things than she had before thought necessary.

So that that was the first knowledge I had that Florence had committed suicide. It had never entered my head. You may think that I had been singularly lacking in suspiciousness; you may consider me even to have been an imbecile. But consider exactly the position.

In such circumstances of clamour, of outcry, of the crash of many people running together, of the professional reticence of such people as hotel-keepers, the traditional reticence of such 'good people' as the Ashburnhams—in such circumstances it is some little material object, always, that catches the eye and that appeals to the imagination. I had no possible guide to the idea of suicide and the sight of the little flask of nitrate of amyl in Florence's hand suggested instantly to my mind the idea of the failure of her heart. Nitrate of amyl, you understand, is the drug that is given to relieve sufferers from angina pectoris.

Seeing Florence, as I had seen her, running with a white face and with one hand held over her heart, and seeing her, as I immediately afterwards saw her, lying upon her bed with the so familiar little brown flask clenched in her fingers, it was natural enough for my mind to frame the idea. As happened now and again, I thought, she had gone out without her remedy and, having felt an attack coming on whilst she was in the gardens, she had run in to get the nitrate in order, as quickly as possible, to obtain relief. And it was equally inevitable my mind should frame the thought that her heart, unable to stand the strain of the running, should have broken in her side. How could I have known that, during all the years of our married life, that little brown flask had contained, not nitrate of amyl, but prussic acid? It was inconceivable.

Why, not even Edward Ashburnham, who was, after all, more intimate with her than I was, had an inkling of the truth. He just thought that she had dropped dead of heart disease. Indeed, I fancy that the only people who ever knew that Florence had committed suicide were Leonora, the Grand Duke, the head of the police, and the hotel-keeper. I mention these last three because my recollection of that night is only the sort of pinkish effulgence from the electric-lamps in the hotel lounge. There seemed to bob into my consciousness, like floating globes, the faces of those three. Now it would be the bearded, monarchical, benevolent head of the Grand Duke; then the sharp-featured, brown, cavalry-moustached features of the chief of police; then the globular, polished, and high-collared vacuousness that represented Monsieur Schontz, the pro-prietor of the hotel. At times one head would be there alone, at another the spiked helmet of the official would be close to the healthy baldness of the prince; then M. Schontz's oiled locks would push in between the two. The sovereign's soft, exquisitely trained voice would say, 'Ja, ja, ja!' each word dropping out like so many soft pellets of suet; the subdued rasp of the official would come: 'Zum Befehl Durchlaucht,' like five revolver-shots; the voice of M. Schontz would go on and on under its breath like that of an unclean priest reciting from his breviary in the corner of a railway-carriage. That was how it presented itself to me.

They seemed to take no notice of me; I don't suppose that I was even addressed by one of them. But, as long as one or the other, or all three of them were there, they stood between me as if, I being the titular possessor of the corpse, had a right to be present at their conferences. Then they all went away and I was left alone for a long time.

And I thought nothing; absolutely nothing. I had no ideas; I had no strength. I felt no sorrow, no desire for action, no inclination to go upstairs and fall upon the body of my wife. I just saw the pink effulgence, the cane tables, the palms, the globular match-holders, the indented ash-trays. And then Leonora came to me and it appears that I addressed to her that singular remark:

'Now I can marry the girl.'

But I have given you absolutely the whole of my recollection of that evening, as it is the whole of my recollection of the succeeding three or four days. I was in a state just simply cataleptic. They put me to bed and I stayed there; they brought me my clothes and I dressed; they led me to an open grave and I stood beside it. If they had taken me to the edge of a river, or if they had flung me beneath a railway train, I should have been drowned or mangled in the same spirit. I was the walking dead.

Well, those are my impressions.

What had actually happened had been this. I pieced it together afterwards. You will remember I said that Edward Ashburnham and the girl had gone off, that night, to a concert at the Casino and that Leonora had asked Florence, almost immediately after their departure, to follow them and to perform the office of chaperone. Florence, you may also remember, was all in black, being the mourning that she wore for a deceased cousin, Jean Hurlbird. It was a very black night and the girl was dressed in cream-coloured muslin, that must have glimmered under the tall trees of the dark park like a phosphorescent fish in a cupboard. You couldn't have had a better beacon.

And it appears that Edward Ashburnham led the girl not up the straight allée that leads to the Casino, but in under the dark trees of the park. Edward Ashburnham told me all this in his final outburst. I have told you that, upon that occasion, he became deucedly vocal. I didn't pump him. I hadn't any motive. At that time I didn't in the least connect him with my wife. But the fellow talked like a cheap novelist.—Or like a very good novelist for the matter of that, if it's the business of a novelist to make you see things clearly. And I tell you I see that thing as clearly as if it were a dream that never left me. It appears that, not very far from the Casino, he and the girl sat down in the darkness upon a public bench. The lights from that place of entertainment must have reached them through the tree-trunks, since, Edward said, he could quite plainly see the girl's face—that beloved face with the high forehead, the queer mouth, the tortured eyebrows, and the direct eyes. And to Florence, creeping up behind them, they must have presented the appearance of silhouettes. For I take it that Florence came creeping up behind them over the short grass to a tree that, I quite well remember, was immediately behind that public seat. It was a not very difficult feat for a woman instinct with jealousy. The Casino orchestra was, as Edward remembered to tell me, playing the Rakocsy march, and although it was not loud enough, at that distance, to drown the voice of Edward Ashburnham it was certainly sufficiently audible to efface, amongst the noises of the night, the slight brushings and rustlings that might have been made by the feet of Florence or by her gown in coming over the short grass. And that miserable woman must have got it in the face, good and strong. It must have been horrible for her. Horrible! Well, I suppose she deserved all that she got.

Anyhow, there you have the picture, the immensely tall trees, elms most of them, towering and feathering away up into the black mistiness that trees seem to gather about them at night; the silhouettes of those two upon the seat; the beams of light coming from the Casino, the woman all in black peeping with fear behind the tree-trunk. It is melodrama; but I can't help it.

And then, it appears, something happened to Edward Ashburnham. He assured me—and I see no reason for disbelieving him—that until that moment he had had no idea whatever of caring for the girl. He said that he had regarded her exactly as he would have regarded a daughter. He certainly loved her, but with a very deep, very tender and very tranquil love. He had missed her when she went away to her convent-school; he had been glad when she had returned. But of more than that he had been totally unconscious. Had he been conscious of it, he assured me, he would have fled from it as from a thing accursed. He realized that it was the last outrage upon Leonora. But the real point was his entire unconsciousness. He had gone with her into that dark park with no quickening of the pulse, with no desire for the intimacy of solitude. He had gone, intending to talk about polo-ponies and tennis-racquets; about the temperament of the reverend Mother at the convent she had left and about whether her frock for a party when they got home should be white or blue. It hadn't come into his head that they would talk about a single thing that they hadn't always talked about; it had not even come into his head that the tabu which extended around her was not inviolable. And then, suddenly, that—

He was very careful to assure me that at that time there was no physical motive about his declaration. It did not appear to him to be a matter of a dark night and a propinquity and so on. No, it was simply of her effect on the moral side of his life that he appears to have talked. He said that he never had the slightest notion to enfold her in

his arms or so much as to touch her hand. He swore that
he did not touch her hand. He said that they sat, she at one
end of the bench, he at the other; he leaning slightly towards her and she looking straight towards the light of the
Casino, her face illuminated by the lamps. The expression
upon her face he could only describe as 'queer.'

At another time, indeed, he made it appear that he
thought she was glad. It is easy to imagine that she was
glad, since at that time she could have had no idea of what
was really happening. Frankly, she adored Edward Ashburnham. He was for her, in everything that she said at
that time, the model of humanity, the hero, the athlete, the
father of his country, the law-giver. So that for her, to be
suddenly, intimately and overwhelmingly praised must
have been a matter for mere gladness, however overwhelming it were. It must have been as if a god had approved
her handiwork or a king her loyalty. She just sat still and
listened, smiling.

And it seemed to her that all the bitterness of her childhood, the terrors of her tempestuous father, the bewailings
of her cruel-tongued mother were suddenly atoned for.
She had her recompense at last. Because, of course, if you
come to figure it out, a sudden pouring forth of passion
by a man whom you regard as a cross between a pastor and
a father might, to a woman, have the aspect of mere praise
for good conduct. It wouldn't, I mean, appear at all in the
light of an attempt to gain possession. The girl, at least,
regarded him as firmly anchored to his Leonora. She had
not the slightest inkling of any infidelities. He had always
spoken to her of his wife in terms of reverence and deep
affection. He had given her the idea that he regarded
Leonora as absolutely impeccable and as absolutely satisfying. Their union had appeared to her to be one of those
blessed things that are spoken of and contemplated with
reverence by her church.

So that, when he spoke of her as being the person he
cared most for in the world, she naturally thought that he
meant to except Leonora and she was just glad. It was

like a father saying that he approved of a marriageable daughter . . . And Edward, when he realized what he was doing, curbed his tongue at once. She was just glad and she went on being just glad.

I suppose that that was the most monstrously wicked thing that Edward Ashburnham ever did in his life. And yet I am so near to all these people that I cannot think any of them wicked. It is impossible of me to think of Edward Ashburnham as anything but straight, upright, and honourable. That, I mean, is, in spite of everything, my permanent view of him. I try at times by dwelling on some of the things that he did to push that image of him away, as you might try to push aside a large pendulum. But it always comes back—the memory of his innumerable acts of kindness, of his efficiency, of his unspiteful tongue. He was such a fine fellow.

So I feel myself forced to attempt to excuse him in this as in so many other things. It is, I have no doubt, a most monstrous thing to attempt to corrupt a young girl just out of a convent. But I think Edward had no idea at all of corrupting her. I believe that he simply loved her. He said that that was the way of it and I, at least, believe him and I believe too that she was the only woman he ever really loved. He said that that was so; and he did enough to prove it. And Leonora said that it was so and Leonora knew him to the bottom of his heart.

I have come to be very much of a cynic in these matters; I mean that it is impossible to believe in the permanence of man's or woman's love. Or, at any rate, it is impossible to believe in the permanence of any early passion. As I see it, at least, with regard to man, a love affair, a love for any definite woman—is something in the nature of a widening of the experience. With each new woman that a man is attracted to there appears to come a broadening of the outlook, or, if you like, an acquiring of new territory. A turn of the eyebrow, a tone of the voice, a queer characteristic gesture—all these things, and it is these things that cause to arise the passion of love—all these things are like so many objects on the horizon of the landscape that tempt a man to walk beyond the horizon, to explore. He wants to get, as it were, behind those eyebrows with the peculiar turn, as if he desired to see the world with the eyes that they overshadow. He wants to hear that voice applying itself to every possible proposition, to every possible topic; he wants to see those characteristic gestures against every possible background. Of the question of the sex-instinct I know very little and I do not think that it counts for very much in a really great passion. It can be aroused by such nothings—by an untied shoe-lace, by a glance of the eye in passing—that I think it might be left out of the calculation. I don't mean to say that any great passion can exist without a desire for consummation. That seems to me to be a commonplace and to be therefore a matter needing no comment at all. It is a thing, with all its accidents, that must be taken for granted, as, in a novel, or a biography, you take it for granted that the characters have their meals with some regularity. But the real fierceness of desire, the real heat of a passion long continued and withering up the soul of a man is the craving for identity with the woman that he loves. He desires to see with the same eyes, to touch with the same sense of touch, to hear with the same ears, to lose his identity, to be enveloped, to be supported. For, whatever may be said of the relation of the sexes, there is no man who loves a woman that does not desire to come to her for the renewal of his courage, for the cutting asunder of his difficulties. And that will be the mainspring of his desire for her. We are all so afraid, we are all so alone, we all so need from the outside the assurance of our own worthiness to exist.

So, for a time, if such a passion come to fruition, the man will get what he wants. He will get the moral support, the encouragement, the relief from the sense of loneliness, the assurance of his own worth. But these things pass away; inevitably they pass away as the shadows pass across sun-dials. It is sad, but it is so. The pages of the book will become familiar; the beautiful corner of the road will have been turned too many times. Well, this is the saddest story.

And yet I do believe that for every man there comes at last a woman—or, no, that is the wrong way of formulating it. For every man there comes at last a time of life when the woman who then sets her seal upon his imagination has set her seal for good. He will travel over no more horizons; he will never again set the knapsack over his shoulders; he will retire from those scenes. He will have gone out of the business.

That at any rate was the case with Edward and the poor girl. It was quite literally the case. It was quite literally the case that his passions—for the mistress of the Grand Duke, for Mrs Basil, for little Mrs Maidan, for Florence, for whom you will—these passions were merely preliminary canters compared to his final race with death for her. I am certain of that. I am not going to be so American as to say that all true love demands some sacrifice. It doesn't. But I think that love will be truer and more permanent in which self-sacrifice has been exacted. And, in the case of the other women, Edward just cut in and cut them out as he did with the polo-ball from under the nose of Count Baron von Lelöffel. I don't mean to say that he didn't wear himself as thin as a lath in the endeavour to capture the other women; but over her he wore himself to rags and tatters and death—in the effort to leave her alone.

And, in speaking to her on that night, he wasn't, I am convinced, committing a baseness. It was as if his passion for her hadn't existed; as if the very words that he spoke, without knowing that he spoke them, created the passion as they went along. Before he spoke, there was nothing; afterwards, it was the integral fact of his life. Well, I must get back to my story.

And my story was concerning itself with Florence—with Florence, who heard those words from behind the tree. That of course is only conjecture, but I think the conjecture is pretty well justified. You have the fact that those two went out, that she followed them almost immediately

afterwards through the darkness and, a little later, she
came running back to the hotel with that pallid face and
the hand clutching her dress over her heart. It can't have
been only Bagshawe. Her face was contorted with agony
before ever her eyes fell upon me or upon him beside me.
But I dare say Bagshawe may have been the determining
influence in her suicide. Leonora says that she had that
flask, apparently of nitrate of amyl, but actually of prussic
acid, for many years and that she was determined to use it
if ever I discovered the nature of her relationship with that
fellow Jimmy. You see, the mainspring of her nature must
have been vanity. There is no reason why it shouldn't have
been; I guess it is vanity that makes most of us keep
straight, if we do keep straight, in this world.

If it had been merely a matter of Edward's relations with
the girl I dare say Florence would have faced it out. She
would no doubt have made him scenes, have threatened
him, have appealed to his sense of honour, to his promises.
But Mr Bagshawe and the fact that the date was the 4th
of August must have been too much for her superstitious
mind. You see, she had two things that she wanted. She
wanted to be a great lady, installed in Branshaw Teleragh.
She wanted also to retain my respect.

She wanted, that is to say, to retain my respect for as
long as she lived with me. I suppose, if she had persuaded
Edward Ashburnham to bolt with her she would have let
the whole thing go with a run. Or perhaps she would have
tried to exact from me a new respect for the greatness of
her passion on the lines of all for love and the world well
lost. That would be just like Florence.

In all matrimonial associations there is, I believe, one
constant factor—a desire to deceive the person with whom
one lives as to some weak spot in one's character or in one's
career. For it is intolerable to live constantly with one
human being who perceives one's small meannesses. It is
really death to do so—that is why so many marriages turn
out unhappily.

I, for instance, am a rather greedy man; I have a taste

for good cookery and a watering tooth at the mere sound of the names of certain comestibles. If Florence had discovered this secret of mine I should have found her knowledge of it so unbearable that I never could have supported all the other privations of the régime that she extracted from me. I am bound to say that Florence never discovered this secret.

Certainly she never alluded to it; I dare say she never took sufficient interest in me.

And the secret weakness of Florence—the weakness that she could not bear to have me discover, was just that early escapade with the fellow called Jimmy. Let me, as this is in all probability the last time I shall mention Florence's name, dwell a little upon the change that had taken place in her psychology. She would not, I mean, have minded if I had discovered that she was the mistress of Edward Ashburnham. She would rather have liked it. Indeed, the chief trouble of poor Leonora in those days was to keep Florence from making, before me, theatrical displays, on one line or another, of that very fact. She wanted, in one mood, to come rushing to me, to cast herself on her knees at my feet and to declaim a carefully arranged, frightfully emotional, outpouring as to her passion. That was to show that she was like one of the great erotic women of whom history tells us. In another mood she would desire to come to me disdainfully and to tell me that I was considerably less than a man and that what had happened was what must happen when a real male came along. She wanted to say that in cool, balanced, and sarcastic sentences. That was when she wished to appear like the heroine of a French comedy. Because of course she was always play acting.

But what she didn't want me to know was the fact of her first escapade with the fellow called Jimmy. She had arrived at figuring out the sort of low-down Bowery tough that that fellow was. Do you know what it is to shudder, in later life, for some small, stupid action—usually for some small, quite genuine piece of emotionalism—of your early life? Well, it was that sort of shuddering that came over

Florence at the thought that she had surrendered to such
a low fellow. I don't know that she need have shuddered.
It was her footling old uncle's work; he ought never to
have taken those two round the world together and shut
himself up in his cabin for the greater part of the time.
Anyhow, I am convinced that the sight of Mr Bagshawe
and the thought that Mr Bagshawe—for she knew that
unpleasant and toad-like personality—the thought that
Mr Bagshawe would almost certainly reveal to me that he
had caught her coming out of Jimmy's bedroom at five
o'clock in the morning on the 4th of August, 1900—that
was the determining influence in her suicide. And no doubt
the effect of the date was too much for her superstitious
personality. She had been born on the 4th of August; she
had started to go round the world on the 4th of August;
she had become a low fellow's mistress on the 4th of
August. On the same day of the year she had married me;
on that 4th she had lost Edward's love, and Bagshawe had
appeared like a sinister omen—like a grin on the face of
Fate. It was the last straw. She ran upstairs, arranged herself decoratively upon her bed—she was a sweetly pretty
woman with smooth pink and white cheeks, long hair, the
eyelashes falling like a tiny curtain on her cheeks. She
drank the little phial of prussic acid and there she lay.—
Oh, extremely charming and clear-cut—looking with a
puzzled expression at the electric-light bulb that hung
from the ceiling, or perhaps through it, to the stars above.
Who knows? Anyhow, there was an end of Florence.

You have no idea how quite extraordinarily for me that
was the end of Florence. From that day to this I have never
given her another thought; I have not bestowed upon her
so much as a sigh. Of course, when it has been necessary
to talk about her to Leonora, or when for the purpose of
these writings I have tried to figure her out, I have thought
about her as I might do about a problem in algebra. But
it has always been as a matter for study, not for remembrance. She just went completely out of existence, like
yesterday's paper.

I was so deadly tired. And I dare say that my week or ten days of affaissement—of what was practically catalepsy —was just the repose that my exhausted nature claimed after twelve years of the repression of my instincts, after twelve years of playing the trained poodle. For that was all that I had been. I suppose that it was the shock that did it—the several shocks. But I am unwilling to attribute my feelings at that time to anything so concrete as a shock. It was a feeling so tranquil. It was as if an immensely heavy —an unbearably heavy knapsack, supported upon my shoulders by straps, had fallen off and left my shoulders themselves that the straps had cut into, numb and without sensation of life. I tell you, I had no regret. What had I to regret? I suppose that my inner soul—my dual personality —had realized long before that Florence was a personality of paper—that she represented a real human being with a heart, with feelings, with sympathies and with emotions only as a bank-note represents a certain quantity of gold. I know that sort of feeling came to the surface in me the moment the man Bagshawe told me that he had seen her coming out of that fellow's bedroom. I thought suddenly that she wasn't real; she was just a mass of talk out of guide-books, of drawings out of fashion-plates. It is even possible that, if that feeling had not possessed me, I should have run up sooner to her room and might have prevented her drinking the prussic acid. But I just couldn't do it; it would have been like chasing a scrap of paper—an occupation ignoble for a grown man.

And, as it began, so that matter has remained. I didn't care whether she had come out of that bedroom or whether she hadn't. It simply didn't interest me. Florence didn't matter.

I suppose you will retort that I was in love with Nancy Rufford and that my indifference was therefore discreditable. Well, I am not seeking to avoid discredit. I was in love with Nancy Rufford as I am in love with the poor child's memory, quietly and quite tenderly in my American sort of way. I had never thought about it until I heard Leonora state that I might now marry her. But, from that moment until her worse than death, I do not suppose that I much thought about anything else. I don't mean to say that I sighed about her or groaned; I just wanted to marry her as some people want to go to Carcassonne.

Do you understand the feeling—the sort of feeling that you must get certain matters out of the way, smooth out certain fairly negligible complications before you can go to a place that has, during all your life, been a sort of dream city? I didn't attach much importance to my superior years. I was forty-five, and she, poor thing, was only just rising twenty-two. But she was older than her years and quieter. She seemed to have an odd quality of sainthood, as if she must inevitably end in a convent with a white coif framing her face. But she had frequently told me that she had no vocation; it just simply wasn't there— the desire to become a nun. Well, I guess that I was a sort of convent myself; it seemed fairly proper that she should make her vows to me.

No, I didn't see any impediment on the score of age. I dare say no man does and I was pretty confident that with a little preparation, I could make a young girl happy. I could spoil her as few young girls have ever been spoiled; and I couldn't regard myself as personally repulsive. No man can, or if he ever comes to do so, that is the end of him. But, as soon as I came out of my catalepsy, I seemed to perceive that my problem—that what I had to do to prepare myself for getting into contact with her, was just to get back into contact with life. I had been kept for twelve years in a rarefied atmosphere; what I then had to do was a little fighting with real life, some wrestling with men of business, some travelling amongst larger cities, something harsh, something masculine. I didn't want to present myself to Nancy Rufford as a sort of an old maid. That was why, just a fortnight after Florence's suicide, I set off for the United States.

II

Immediately after Florence's death Leonora began to put the leash upon Nancy Rufford and Edward. She had guessed what had happened under the trees near the Casino. They stayed at Nauheim some three weeks after I went, and Leonora has told me that that was the most deadly time of her existence. It seemed like a long, silent duel with invisible weapons, so she said. And it was rendered all the more difficult by the girl's entire innocence. For Nancy was always trying to go off alone with Edward—as she had been doing all her life, whenever she was home for holidays. She just wanted him to say nice things to her again.

You see, the position was extremely complicated. It was as complicated as it well could be, along delicate lines. There was the complication caused by the fact that Edward and Leonora never spoke to each other except when other people were present. Then, as I have said, their demeanours were quite perfect. There was the complication caused by the girl's entire innocence; there was the further complication that both Edward and Leonora really regarded the girl as their daughter. Or it might be more precise to say that they regarded her as being Leonora's daughter. And Nancy was a queer girl; it is very difficult to describe her to you.

She was tall and strikingly thin; she had a tortured mouth, agonized eyes, and a quite extraordinary sense of fun. You might put it that at times she was exceedingly grotesque and at times extraordinarily beautiful. Why, she had the heaviest head of black hair that I have ever come across; I used to wonder how she could bear the weight of it. She was just over twenty-one and at times she seemed as old as the hills, at times not much more than sixteen. At one moment she would be talking of the lives of the saints and at the next she would be tumbling all over the lawn with the St Bernard puppy. She could ride to hounds like a Maenad and she could sit for hours perfectly still,

steeping handkerchief after handkerchief in vinegar when
Leonora had one of her headaches. She was, in short, a
miracle of patience who could be almost miraculously impatient. It was, no doubt, the convent training that effected
that. I remember that one of her letters to me, when she
was about sixteen, ran something like:

'On Corpus Christi'—or it may have been some other
saint's day, I cannot keep these things in my head—'our
school played Roehampton at Hockey. And, seeing that
our side was losing, being three goals to one against us at
half-time, we retired into the chapel and prayed for victory. We won by five goals to three.' And I remember that
she seemed to describe afterwards a sort of saturnalia.
Apparently, when the victorious fifteen or eleven came into
the refectory for supper, the whole school jumped upon
the tables and cheered and broke the chairs on the floor
and smashed the crockery—for a given time, until the
Reverend Mother rang a hand-bell. That is of course the
Catholic tradition—saturnalia that can end in a moment,
like the crack of a whip. I don't, of course, like the tradition, but I am bound to say that it gave Nancy—or at any
rate Nancy had—a sense of rectitude that I have never seen
surpassed. It was a thing like a knife that looked out of her
eyes and that spoke with her voice, just now and then. It
positively frightened me. I suppose that I was almost afraid
to be in a world where there could be so fine a standard.
I remember when she was about fifteen or sixteen on going
back to the convent I once gave her a couple of English
sovereigns as a tip. She thanked me in a peculiarly heart-
felt way, saying that it would come in extremely handy.
I asked her why and she explained. There was a rule at the
school that the pupils were not to speak when they walked
through the garden from the chapel to the refectory. And,
since this rule appeared to be idiotic and arbitrary, she
broke it on purpose day after day. In the evening the
children were all asked if they had committed any faults
during the day, and every evening Nancy confessed that
she had broken this particular rule. It cost her sixpence a

time, that being the fine attached to the offence. Just for the information I asked her why she always confessed, and she answered in these exact words:

'Oh, well, the girls of the Holy Child have always been noted for their truthfulness. It's a beastly bore, but I've got to do it.'

I dare say that the miserable nature of her childhood, coming before the mixture of saturnalia and discipline that was her convent life, added something to her queernesses. Her father was a violent madman of a fellow, a major of one of what I believe are called the Highland regiments. He didn't drink, but he had an ungovernable temper, and the first thing that Nancy could remember was seeing her father strike her mother with his clenched fist so that her mother fell over sideways from the breakfast-table and lay motionless. The mother was no doubt an irritating woman and the privates of that regiment appeared to have been irritating, too, so that the house was a place of outcries and perpetual disturbances. Mrs Rufford was Leonora's dearest friend and Leonora could be cutting enough at times. But I fancy she was as nothing to Mrs Rufford. The Major would come in to lunch harassed and already spitting out oaths after an unsatisfactory morning's drilling of his stubborn men beneath a hot sun. And then Mrs Rufford would make some cutting remark and pandemonium would break loose. Once, when she had been about twelve, Nancy had tried to intervene between the pair of them. Her father had struck her full upon the forehead a blow so terrible that she had lain unconscious for three days. Nevertheless, Nancy seemed to prefer her father to her mother. She remembered rough kindnesses from him. Once or twice when she had been quite small he had dressed her in a clumsy, impatient, but very tender way. It was nearly always impossible to get a servant to stay in the family and, for days at a time, apparently, Mrs Rufford would be incapable. I fancy she drank. At any rate, she had so cutting a tongue that even Nancy was afraid of her—she so made fun of any tenderness, she so sneered at all emotional displays. Nancy must have been a very emotional child.

Then one day, quite suddenly, on her return from a ride at Fort William, Nancy had been sent, with her governess, who had a white face, right down South to that convent school. She had been expecting to go there in two months' time. Her mother disappeared from her life at that time. A fortnight later Leonora came to the convent and told her that her mother was dead. Perhaps she was. At any rate, I never heard until the very end what became of Mrs Rufford. Leonora never spoke of her.

And then Major Rufford went to India, from which he returned very seldom and only for very short visits; and Nancy lived herself gradually into the life at Branshaw Teleragh. I think that, from that time onwards, she led a very happy life, till the end. There were dogs and horses and old servants and the Forest. And there were Edward and Leonora, who loved her.

I had known her all the time—I mean, that she always came to the Ashburnhams' at Nauheim for the last fortnight of their stay—and I watched her gradually growing. She was very cheerful with me. She always even kissed me, night and morning, until she was about eighteen. And she would skip about and fetch me things and laugh at my tales of life in Philadelphia. But, beneath her gaiety, I fancy that there lurked some terrors. I remember one day, when she was just eighteen, during one of her father's rare visits to Europe, we were sitting in the gardens, near the iron-stained fountain. Leonora had one of her headaches and we were waiting for Florence and Edward to come from their baths. You have no idea how beautiful Nancy looked that morning.

We were talking about the desirability of taking tickets in lotteries—of the moral side of it, I mean. She was all in white, and so tall and fragile; and she had only just put her hair up, so that the carriage of her neck had that charming touch of youth and of unfamiliarity. Over her throat there played the reflection from a little pool of water, left by a thunderstorm of the night before, and all the rest of her features were in the diffused and luminous shade of her white parasol. Her dark hair just showed beneath her broad, white hat of pierced, chip straw; her throat was very long and leaned forward, and her eyebrows, arching a little as she laughed at some old-fashionedness in my phraseology, had abandoned their tense line. And there was a little colour in her cheeks and light in her deep blue eyes. And to think that that vivid white thing, that saintly and swan-like being—to think that ... Why, she was like the sail of a ship, so white and so definite in her movements. And to think that she will never ... Why, she will never do anything again. I can't believe it ...

Anyhow, we were chattering away about the morality of lotteries. And then, suddenly, there came from the arcades behind us the overtones of her father's unmistakable voice; it was as if a modified foghorn had boomed with a reed inside it. I looked round to catch sight of him. A tall, fair, stiffly upright man of fifty, he was walking away with an Italian baron who had had much to do with the Belgian Congo. They must have been talking about the proper treatment of natives, for I heard him say:

'Oh, hang humanity!'

When I looked again at Nancy her eyes were closed and her face was more pallid than her dress, which had at least some pinkish reflections from the gravel. It was dreadful to see her with her eyes closed like that.

'Oh!' she exclaimed, and her hand that had appeared to be groping, settled for a moment on my arm. 'Never speak of it. Promise never to tell my father of it. It brings back those dreadful dreams ...' And, when she opened her eyes she looked straight into mine. 'The blessed saints,' she said, 'you would think they would spare you such things. I don't believe all the sinning in the world could make one deserve them.'

They say the poor thing was always allowed a light at night, even in her bedroom. ... And yet, no young girl could more archly and lovingly have played with an adored father. She was always holding him by both coat lapels; cross-questioning him as to how he spent his time; kissing the top of his head. Ah, she was well-bred, if ever anyone was.

The poor, wretched man cringed before her—but she could not have done more to put him at his ease. Perhaps she had had lessons in it at her convent. It was only that peculiar note of his voice, used when he was overbearing or dogmatic, that could unman her—and that was only visible when it came unexpectedly. That was because the bad dreams that the blessed saints allowed her to have for her sins always seemed to her to herald themselves by the booming sound of her father's voice. It was that sound that had always preceded his entrance for the terrible lunches of her childhood . . .

I have reported, earlier in this chapter, that Leonora said, during that remainder of their stay at Nauheim, after I had left, it had seemed to her that she was fighting a long duel with unseen weapons against silent adversaries. Nancy, as I have also said, was always trying to go off with Edward alone. That had been her habit for years. And Leonora found it to be her duty to stop that. It was very difficult. Nancy was used to having her own way, and for years she had been used to going off with Edward, ratting, rabbiting, catching salmon down at Fordingbridge, district-visiting of the sort that Edward indulged in, or calling on the tenants. And at Nauheim she and Edward had always gone up to the Casino alone in the evenings—at any rate, when-ever Florence did not call for his attendance. It shows the obviously innocent nature of the regard of those two that even Florence had never had any idea of jealousy. Leonora had cultivated the habit of going to bed at ten o'clock.

I don't know how she managed it, but, for all the time they were at Nauheim, she contrived never to let those two be alone together, except in broad daylight, in very crowded places. If a Protestant had done that it would no doubt have awakened a self-consciousness in the girl. But Catholics, who have always reservations and queer spots of secrecy, can manage these things better. And I dare say that two things made this easier—the death of Florence and the fact that Edward was obviously sickening. He appeared, indeed, to be very ill; his shoulders began to be bowed; there were pockets under his eyes; he had extraordinary moments of inattention.

And Leonora describes herself as watching him as a fierce cat watches an unconscious pigeon in a roadway. In that silent watching, again, I think she was a Catholic—of a people that can think thoughts alien to ours and keep them to themselves. And the thoughts passed through her mind; some of them even got through to Edward with never a word spoken. At first she thought that it might be remorse, or grief, for the death of Florence that was oppressing him. But she watched and watched, and uttered apparently random sentences about Florence before the girl, and she perceived that he had no grief and no remorse. He had not any idea that Florence could have committed suicide without writing at least a tirade to him. The absence of that made him certain that it had been heart disease. For Florence had never undeceived him on that point. She thought it made her seem more romantic.

No, Edward had no remorse. He was able to say to himself that he had treated Florence with gallant attentiveness of the kind that she desired until two hours before her death. Leonora gathered that from the look in his eyes, and from the way he straightened his shoulders over her as she lay in her coffin—from that and a thousand other little things. She would speak suddenly about Florence to the girl and he would not start in the least; he would not even pay attention, but would sit with bloodshot eyes gazing at the tablecloth. He drank a good deal, at that time—a steady soaking of drink every evening till long after they had gone to bed.

For Florence made the girl go to bed at ten, unreasonable though that seemed to Nancy. She would understand that, whilst they were in a sort of half mourning for Florence, she ought not to be seen at public places, like the Casino; but she could not see why she should not accompany her uncle upon his evening strolls through the park. I don't know what Leonora put up as an excuse— something, I fancy, in the nature of a nightly orison that she made the girl and herself perform for the soul of Florence. And then, one evening, about a fortnight later, when the girl, growing restive at even devotional exercises, clamoured once more to be allowed to go for a walk with Edward, and when Leonora was really at her wits' end, Edward gave himself into her hands. He was just standing up from dinner and had his face averted.

But he turned his heavy head and his bloodshot eyes upon his wife and looked full at her.

'Doctor von Hauptmann,' he said, 'has ordered me to go to bed immediately after dinner. My heart's much worse.'

He continued to look at Leonora for a long minute— with a sort of heavy contempt. And Leonora understood that, with his speech, he was giving her the excuse that she needed for separating him from the girl, and with his eyes he was reproaching her for thinking that he would try to corrupt Nancy.

He went silently up to his room and sat there for a long time—until the girl was well in bed—reading in the Anglican prayer-book. And about half-past ten she heard his footsteps pass her door, going outwards. Two and a half hours later they came back, stumbling heavily.

She remained, reflecting upon this position until the last night of their stay at Nauheim. Then she suddenly acted. For, just in the same way, suddenly after dinner, she looked at him and said:

'Teddy, don't you think you could take a night off from your doctor's orders and go with Nancy to the Casino. The poor child has had her visit so spoiled.'

He looked at her in turn for a long, balancing minute.

'Why, yes,' he said at last.

Nancy jumped out of her chair and kissed him.

Those two words, Leonora said, gave her the greatest relief of any two syllables she had ever heard in her life. For she realized that Edward was breaking up, not under the desire for possession, but from the dogged determination to hold his hand. She could relax some of her vigilance.

Nevertheless, she sat in the darkness behind her half-closed jalousies, looking over the street and the night and the trees until, very late, she could hear Nancy's clear voice coming closer and saying:

'You did look an old guy with that false nose.'

There had been some sort of celebration of a local holiday up in the Kursaal. And Edward replied with his sort of sulky good nature:

'As for you, you looked like old Mother Sideacher.'

The girl came swinging along, a silhouette beneath a gas-lamp; Edward, another, slouched at her side. They were talking just as they had talked any time since the girl had been seventeen; with the same tones, the same joke about an old beggar woman who always amused them at Branshaw. The girl, a little later, opened Leonora's door whilst she was still kissing Edward on the forehead as she had done every night.

'We've had a most glorious time,' she said. 'He's ever so much better. He raced me for twenty yards home. Why are you all in the dark?'

Leonora could hear Edward going about in his room, but, owing to the girl's chatter, she could not tell whether he went out again or not. And then, very much later, because she thought that if he were drinking again something must be done to stop it, she opened for the first time, and very softly, the never-opened door between their rooms. She wanted to see if he had gone out again. Edward was kneeling beside his bed with his head hidden in the counterpane. His arms, outstretched, held out before him a little image of the Blessed Virgin—a tawdry, scarlet and Prussian blue affair that the girl had given him on her first return from the convent. His shoulders heaved convulsively three times, and heavy sobs came from him before she

could close the door. He was not a Catholic; but that was
the way it took him.

Leonora slept for the first time that night with a sleep
from which she never once started.

III

And then Leonora completely broke down—on the day
that they returned to Branshaw Teleragh. It is the inflic-
tion of our miserable minds—it is the scourge of atrocious
but probably just destiny that no grief comes by itself. No,
any great grief, though the grief itself may have gone,
leaves in its place a train of horrors, of misery, and despair.
For Leonora was, in herself, relieved. She felt that she
could trust Edward with the girl and she knew that Nancy
could be absolutely trusted. And then, with the slackening
of her vigilance, came the slackening of her entire mind.
This is perhaps the most miserable part of the entire story.
For it is miserable to see a clear intelligence waver; and
Leonora wavered.

You are to understand that Leonora loved Edward with
a passion that was yet like an agony of hatred. And she had
lived with him for years and years without addressing to
him one word of tenderness. I don't know how she could
do it. At the beginning of that relationship she had been
just married off to him. She had been one of seven
daughters in a bare, untidy Irish manor-house to which
she had returned from the convent I have so often spoken
of. She had left it just a year and she was just nineteen. It
is impossible to imagine such inexperience as was hers. You
might almost say that she had never spoken to a man except
a priest. Coming straight from the convent, she had gone
in behind the high walls of the manor-house that was
almost more cloistral than any convent could have been.
There were the seven girls, there was the strained mother,
there was the worried father at whom, three times in the
course of that year, the tenants took pot-shots from behind

a hedge. The women-folk, upon the whole, the tenants respected. Once a week each of the girls, since there were seven of them, took a drive with the mother in the old basketwork chaise drawn by a very fat, very lumbering pony. They paid occasionally a call, but even these were so rare that, Leonora has assured me, only three times in the year that succeeded her coming home from the convent did she enter another person's house. For the rest of the time the seven sisters ran about in the neglected gardens between the unpruned espaliers. Or they played lawn-tennis or fives in an angle of a great wall that surrounded the garden—an angle from which the fruit trees had long died away. They painted in water-colour; they embroidered; they copied verses into albums. Once a week they went to Mass; once a week to the confessional, accompanied by an old nurse. They were happy since they had known no other life.

It appeared to them a singular extravagance when, one day, a photographer was brought over from the county town and photographed them standing, all seven, in the shadow of an old apple tree with the grey lichen on the raddled trunk.

But it wasn't an extravagance.

Three weeks before Colonel Powys had written to Colonel Ashburnham:

'I say, Harry, couldn't your Edward marry one of my girls? It would be a god-send to me, for I'm at the end of my tether and, once one girl begins to go off, the rest of them will follow.'

He went on to say that all his daughters were tall, up-standing, clean-limbed and absolutely pure, and he reminded Colonel Ashburnham that, they having been married on the same day, though in different churches, since the one was a Catholic and the other an Anglican—they had said to each other, the night before, that, when the time came, one of their sons should marry one of their daughters. Mrs Ashburnham had been a Powys and remained Mrs Powys' dearest fried. They had drifted about

the world as English soldiers do, seldom meeting, but their
women always in correspondence one with another. They
wrote about minute things such as the teething of Edward
and of the earlier daughters or the best way to repair a
Jacob's ladder in a stocking. And, if they met seldom, yet
it was often enough to keep each other's personalities fresh
in their minds, gradually growing greyer, gradually growing a little stiff in the joints, but always with enough to talk
about and with a store of reminiscences. Then, as his girls
began to come of age when they must leave the convent in
which they were regularly interned during his years of
active service, Colonel Powys retired from the army with
the necessity of making a home for them. It happened that
the Ashburnhams had never seen any of the Powys girls,
though, whenever the four parents met in London, Edward
Ashburnham was always of the party. He was at that time
twenty-two and, I believe, almost as pure in mind as
Leonora herself. It is odd how a boy can have his virgin
intelligence untouched in this world.

That was partly due to the careful handling of his
mother, partly to the fact that the house to which he went
at Winchester had a particularly pure tone and partly to
Edward's own peculiar aversion from anything like coarse
language or gross stories. At Sandhurst he had just kept
out of the way of that sort of thing. He was keen on soldiering, keen on mathematics, on land-surveying, on politics
and, by a queer warp of his mind, on literature. Even when
he was twenty-two he would pass hours reading one of
Scott's novels or the Chronicles of Froissart.

Mrs Ashburnham considered that she was to be congratulated, and almost every week she wrote to Mrs Powys,
dilating upon her satisfaction.

Then, one day, taking a walk down Bond Street with her
son, after having been at Lord's, she noticed Edward suddenly turn his head round to take a second look at a well-
dressed girl who had passed them. She wrote about that,
too, to Mrs Powys, and expressed some alarm. It had been,
on Edward's part, the merest reflex action. He was so very

abstracted at that time owing to the pressure his crammer was putting upon him that he certainly hadn't known what he was doing.

It was this letter of Mrs Ashburnham's to Mrs Powys that had caused the letter from Colonel Powys to Colonel Ashburnham—a letter that was half humorous, half longing. Mrs Ashburnham caused her husband to reply, with a letter a little more jocular—something to the effect that Colonel Powys ought to give them some idea of the goods that he was marketing. That was the cause of the photograph. I have seen it, the seven girls, all in white dresses, all very much alike in feature—all, except Leonora, a little heavy about the chins and a little stupid about the eyes. I dare say it would have made Leonora, too, look a little heavy and a little stupid, for it was not a good photograph. But the black shadow from one of the branches of the apple tree cut right across her face, which is all but invisible.

There followed an extremely harassing time for Colonel and Mrs Powys. Mrs Ashburnham had written to say that, quite sincerely, nothing would give greater ease to her maternal anxieties than to have her son marry one of Mrs Powys' daughters if only he showed some inclination to do so. For, she added, nothing but a love-match was to be thought of in her Edward's case. But the poor Powys couple had to run things so very fine that even the bringing together of the young people was a desperate hazard.

The mere expenditure upon sending one of the girls over from Ireland to Branshaw was terrifying to them; and whichever girl they selected might not be the one to ring Edward's bell. On the other hand, the expenditure upon mere food and extra sheets for a visit from the Ashburnhams to them was terrifying, too. It would mean, mathematically, going short in so many meals themselves, afterwards. Nevertheless, they chanced it, and all the three Ashburnhams came on a visit to the lonely manor-house. They could give Edward some rough shooting, some rough fishing and a whirl of femininity; but I should

say the girls made really more impression upon Mrs Ashburnham than upon Edward himself. They appeared to
her to be so clean run and so safe. They were indeed so
clean run that, in a faint sort of way, Edward seems to have
regarded them rather as boys than as girls. And then, one
evening, Mrs Ashburnham had with her boy one of those
conversations that English mothers have with English sons.
It seems to have been a criminal sort of proceeding, though
I don't know what took place at it. Anyhow, next morning
Colonel Ashburnham asked on behalf of his son for the
hand of Leonora. This caused some consternation to the
Powys couple, since Leonora was the third daughter and
Edward ought to have married the eldest. Mrs Powys, with
her rigid sense of the proprieties, almost wished to reject
the proposal. But the Colonel, her husband, pointed out
that the visit would have cost them sixty pounds, what with
the hire of an extra servant, of a horse and car, and with
the purchase of beds and bedding and extra tablecloths.
There was nothing else for it but the marriage. In that way
Edward and Leonora became man and wife.

I don't know that a very minute study of their progress
towards complete disunion is necessary. Perhaps it is. But
there are many things that I cannot well make out, about
which I cannot well question Leonora, or about which
Edward did not tell me. I do not know that there was ever
any question of love from Edward to her. He regarded her,
certainly, as desirable amongst her sisters. He was obstinate
to the extent of saying that if he could not have her he
would not have any of them. And, no doubt, before the
marriage, he made her pretty speeches out of books that
he had read. But, as far as he could describe his feelings at
all, later, it seems that, calmly and without any quickening
of the pulse, he just carried the girl off, there being no
opposition. It had, however, been all so long ago that it
seemed to him, at the end of his poor life, a dim and misty
affair. He had the greatest admiration for Leonora.

He had the very greatest admiration. He admired her
for her truthfulness, for her cleanness of mind, and the

clean-run-ness of her limbs, for her efficiency, for the fairness of her skin, for the gold of her hair, for her religion,
for her sense of duty. It was a satisfaction to take her about
with him.

But she had not for him a touch of magnetism. I suppose, really, he did not love her because she was never
mournful; what really made him feel good in life was to
comfort somebody who would be darkly and mysteriously
mournful. That he had never had to do for Leonora. Perhaps, also, she was at first too obedient. I do not mean to
say that she was submissive—that she deferred, in her
judgments, to his. She did not. But she had been handed
over to him, like some patient mediaeval virgin; she had
been taught all her life that the first duty of a woman is
to obey. And there she was.

In her, at least, admiration for his qualities very soon
became love of the deepest description. If his pulses never
quickened she, so I have been told, became what is called
an altered being when he approached her from the other
side of a dancing-floor. Her eyes followed him about full
of trustfulness, of admiration, of gratitude, and of love. He
was also, in a great sense, her pastor and guide—and he
guided her into what, for a girl straight out of a convent,
was almost heaven. I have not the least idea of what an
English officer's wife's existence may be like. At any rate,
there were feasts, and chatterings, and nice men who gave
her the right sort of admiration, and nice women who
treated her as if she had been a baby. And her confessor
approved of her life, and Edward let her give little treats
to the girls of the convent she had left, and the Reverend
Mother approved of him. There could not have been a
happier girl for five or six years.

For it was only at the end of that time that clouds began,
as the saying is, to arise. She was then about twenty-three,
and her purposeful efficiency made her perhaps have a
desire for mastery. She began to perceive that Edward was
extravagant in his largesses. His parents died just about
that time, and Edward, though they both decided that he

should continue his soldiering, gave a great deal of attention to the management of Branshaw through a steward.
Aldershot was not very far away, and they spent all his
leaves there.

And, suddenly, she seemed to begin to perceive that his
generosities were almost fantastic. He subscribed much too
much to things connected with his mess, he pensioned off
his father's servants, old or new, much too generously.
They had a large income, but every now and then they
would find themselves hard up. He began to talk of mort-
gaging a farm or two, though it never actually came to that.

She made tentative efforts at remonstrating with him.
Her father, whom she saw now and then, said that Edward
was much too generous to his tenants; the wives of his
brother officers remonstrated with her in private; his large
subscriptions made it difficult for their husbands to keep
up with them. Ironically enough, the first real trouble
between them came from his desire to build a Roman
Catholic chapel at Branshaw. He wanted to do it to honour
Leonora, and he proposed to do it very expensively.
Leonora did not want it; she could perfectly well drive
from Branshaw to the nearest Catholic Church as often as
she liked. There were no Roman Catholic tenants and no
Roman Catholic servants except her old nurse who could
always drive with her. She had as many priests to stay with
her as could be needed—and even the priests did not want
a gorgeous chapel in that place where it would have merely
seemed an invidious instance of ostentation. They were
perfectly ready to celebrate Mass for Leonora and her
nurse, when they stayed at Branshaw, in a cleaned-up out-
house. But Edward was as obstinate as a hog about it.

He was truly grieved at his wife's want of sentiment—
at her refusal to receive that amount of public homage
from him. She appeared to him to be wanting in imagination—to be cold and hard. I don't exactly know what part
her priests played in the tragedy that it all became; I dare
say they behaved quite creditably but mistakenly. But then,
who would not have been mistaken with Edward? I believe

he was even hurt that Leonora's confessor did not make strenuous efforts to convert him. There was a period when he was quite ready to become an emotional Catholic.

I don't know why they did not take him on the hop; but they have queer sorts of wisdoms, those people, and queer sorts of tact. Perhaps they thought that Edward's too early conversion would frighten off other Protestant desirables from marrying Catholic girls. Perhaps they saw deeper into Edward than he saw himself and thought that he would make a not very creditable convert. At any rate they—and Leonora—left him very much alone. It mortified him very considerably. He has told me that if Leonora had then taken his aspirations seriously everything would have been different. But I dare say that was nonsense.

At any rate, it was over the question of the chapel that they had their first and really disastrous quarrel. Edward at that time was not well; he supposed himself to be over-worked with his regimental affairs—he was managing the mess at the time. And Leonora was not well—she was beginning to fear that their union might be sterile. And then her father came over from Glasmoyle to stay with them.

Those were troublesome times in Ireland, I understand. At any rate, Colonel Powys had tenants on the brain—his own tenants having shot at him with shot-guns. And, in conversation with Edward's land-steward, he got it into his head that Edward managed his estates with a mad generosity towards his tenants. I understand, also, that those years—the 'nineties—were very bad for farming. Wheat was fetching only a few shillings the hundred; the price of meat was so low that cattle hardly paid for raising; whole English counties were ruined. And Edward allowed his tenants very high rebates.

To do both justice Leonora has since acknowledged that she was in the wrong at that time and that Edward was following out a more far-seeing policy in nursing his really very good tenants over a bad period. It was not as if the whole of his money came from the land; a good deal of it was in rails. But old Colonel Powys had that bee in his

bonnet and, if he never directly approached Edward himself on the subject, he preached unceasingly, whenever he
had the opportunity, to Leonora. His pet idea was that
Edward ought to sack all his own tenants and import a set
of farmers from Scotland. That was what they were doing
in Essex. He was of opinion that Edward was riding hot-
foot to ruin.

That worried Leonora very much—it worried her dreadfully; she lay awake nights; she had an anxious line round
her mouth. And that, again, worried Edward. I do not
mean to say that Leonora actually spoke to Edward about
his tenants—but he got to know that some one, probably
her father, had been talking to her about the matter. He
got to know it because it was the habit of his steward to
look in on them every morning about breakfast-time to
report any little happenings. And there was a farmer called
Mumford who had only paid half his rent for the last three
years. One morning the land-steward reported that Mumford would be unable to pay his rent at all that year.
Edward reflected for a moment and then he said something
like:

'Oh well, he's an old fellow and his family have been our
tenants for over two hundred years. Let him off altogether.'

And then Leonora—you must remember that she had
reason for being very nervous and unhappy at that time—
let out a sound that was very like a groan. It startled
Edward, who more than suspected what was passing in
her mind—it startled him into a state of anger. He said
sharply:

'You wouldn't have me turn out people who've been
earning money for us for centuries—people to whom we
have responsibilities—and let in a pack of Scotch farmers?'

He looked at her, Leonora said, with what was
practically a glance of hatred and then, precipitately, he
left the breakfast-table. Leonora knew that it probably
made it all the worse that he had been betrayed into a
manifestation of anger before a third party. It was the first
and last time that he ever was betrayed into such a mani-

festation of anger. The land-steward, a moderate and well-balanced man whose family also had been with the Ashburnhams for over a century, took it upon himself to explain that he considered Edward was pursuing a perfectly proper course with his tenants. He erred perhaps a little on the side of generosity, but hard times were hard times, and every one had to feel the pinch, landlord as well as tenants. The great thing was not to let the land get into a poor state of cultivation. Scotch farmers just skinned your fields and let them go down and down. But Edward had a very good set of tenants who did their best for him and for themselves. These arguments at that time carried very little conviction to Leonora. She was, nevertheless, much concerned by Edward's outburst of anger.

The fact is that Leonora had been practising economies in her department. Two of the under-housemaids had gone and she had not replaced them; she had spent much less that year upon dress. The fare she had provided at the dinners they gave had been much less bountiful and not nearly so costly as had been the case in preceding years, and Edward began to perceive a hardness and determination in his wife's character. He seemed to see a net closing round him—a net in which they would be forced to live like one of the comparatively poor county families of the neighbourhood. And, in the mysterious way in which two people, living together, get to know each other's thoughts without a word spoken, he had known, even before his outbreak, that Leonora was worrying about his managing of the estates. This appeared to him to be intolerable. He had, too, a great feeling of self-contempt because he had been betrayed into speaking harshly to Leonora before that land-steward. She imagined that his nerve must be deserting him, and there can have been few men more miserable than Edward was at that period.

You see, he was really a very simple soul—very simple. He imagined that no man can satisfactorily accomplish his life's work without loyal and whole-hearted co-operation of the woman he lives with. And he was beginning to perceive dimly that, whereas his own traditions were entirely collective, his wife was a sheer individualist. His own theory—the feudal theory of an over-lord doing his best by his dependents, the dependents meanwhile doing their best for the over-lord—this theory was entirely foreign to Leonora's nature. She came of a family of small Irish landlords—that hostile garrison in a plundered country. And she was thinking unceasingly of the children she wished to have.

I don't know why they never had any children—not that I really believe that children would have made any difference. The dissimilarity of Edward and Leonora was too profound. It will give you some idea of the extraordinary naïveté of Edward Ashburnham that, at the time of his marriage and for perhaps a couple of years after, he did not really know how children are produced. Neither did Leonora. I don't mean to say that this state of things continued, but there it was. I dare say it had a good deal of influence on their mentalities. At any rate, they never had a child. It was the Will of God.

It certainly presented itself to Leonora as being the Will of God—as being a mysterious and awful chastisement of the Almighty. For she had discovered shortly before this period that her parents had not exacted from Edward's family the promise that any children she should bear should be brought up as Catholics. She herself had never talked of the matter with either her father, her mother, or her husband. When at last her father had let drop some words leading her to believe that that was the fact, she tried desperately to extort the promise from Edward. She encountered an unexpected obstinacy. Edward was perfectly willing that the girls should be Catholic; the boys must be Anglican. I don't understand the bearing of these things in English society. Indeed, Englishmen seem to me to be a little mad in matters of politics or of religion. In Edward it was particularly queer because he himself was perfectly ready to become a Romanist. He seemed, however, to contemplate going over to Rome himself and yet

letting his boys be educated in the religion of their immediate ancestors. This may appear illogical, but I dare say
it is not so illogical as it looks. Edward, that is to say,
regarded himself as having his own body and soul at his
own disposal. But his loyalty to the traditions of his family
would not permit him to bind any future inheritors of his
name or beneficiaries by the death of his ancestors. About
the girls it did not so much matter. They would know
other homes and other circumstances. Besides, it was the
usual thing. But the boys must be given the opportunity
of choosing—and they must have first of all the Anglican
teaching. He was perfectly unshakable about this.

Leonora was in an agony during all this time. You will
have to remember she seriously believed that children who
might be born to her went in danger, if not absolutely of
damnation, at any rate of receiving false doctrine. It was
an agony more terrible than she could describe. She didn't
indeed attempt to describe it, but I could tell from her
voice when she said, almost negligently, 'I used to lie awake
whole nights. It was no good my spiritual advisers trying
to console me.' I knew from her voice how terrible and
how long those nights must have seemed and of how little
avail were the consolations of her spiritual advisers. Her
spiritual advisers seemed to have taken the matter a little
more calmly. They certainly told her that she must not
consider herself in any way to have sinned. Nay, they seem
even to have exhorted, to have threatened her, with a view
to getting her out of what they considered to be a morbid
frame of mind. She would just have to make the best of
things, to influence the children when they came, not by
propaganda, but by personality. And they warned her that
she would be committing a sin if she continued to think
that she had sinned. Nevertheless, she continued to think
that she had sinned.

Leonora could not but be aware that the man whom she
loved passionately and whom, nevertheless, she was beginning to try to rule with a rod of iron—that this man
was becoming more and more estranged from her. He

seemed to regard her as being not only physically and mentally cold, but even as being actually wicked and mean. There were times when he would almost shudder if she spoke to him. And she could not understand how he could consider her wicked or mean. It only seemed to her a sort of madness in him that he should try to take upon his own shoulders the burden of his troop, of his regiment, of his estate and of half of his county. She could not see that in trying to curb what she regarded as megalomania she was doing anything wicked. She was just trying to keep things together for the sake of the children who did not come. And, little by little, the whole of their intercourse became simply one of agonized discussion as to whether Edward should subscribe to this or that institution or should try to reclaim this or that drunkard. She simply could not see it.

Into this really terrible position of strain, from which there appeared to be no issue, the Kilsyte case came almost as a relief. It is part of the peculiar irony of things that Edward would certainly never have kissed that nursemaid if he had not been trying to please Leonora. Nursemaids do not travel first-class, and, that day, Edward travelled in a third-class carriage in order to prove to Leonora that he was capable of economies. I have said that the Kilsyte case came almost as a relief to the strained situation that then existed between them. It gave Leonora an opportunity of backing him up in a whole-hearted and absolutely loyal manner. It gave her the opportunity of behaving to him as he considered a wife should behave to her husband.

You see, Edward found himself in a railway carriage with a quite pretty girl of about nineteen. And the quite pretty girl of about nineteen, with dark hair and red cheeks and blue eyes, was quietly weeping. Edward had been sitting in his corner thinking about nothing at all. He had chanced to look at the nursemaid; two large, pretty tears came out of her eyes and dropped into her lap. He immediately felt that he had got to do something to comfort her. That was his job in life. He was desperately unhappy himself and it seemed to him the most natural thing in the world that they should pool their sorrows. He was quite democratic; the idea of the difference in their station never seems to have occurred to him. He began to talk to her. He discovered that her young man had been seen walking out with Annie of Number 54. He moved over to her side of the carriage. He told her that the report probably wasn't true; that, after all, a young man might take a walk with Annie from Number 54 without its denoting anything very serious. And he assured me that he felt at least quite half-fatherly when he put his arm around her waist and kissed her. The girl, however, had not forgotten the difference of her station.

All her life, by her mother, by other girls, by school-teachers, by the whole tradition of her class she had been warned against gentlemen. She was being kissed by a gentleman. She screamed, tore herself away; sprang up and pulled a communication cord.

Edward came fairly well out of the affair in the public estimation; but it did him, mentally, a good deal of harm.

IV

It is very difficult to give an all-round impression of any man. I wonder how far I have succeeded with Edward Ashburnham. I dare say I haven't succeeded at all. It is even very difficult to see how such things matter. Was it the important point about poor Edward that he was very well built, carried himself well, was moderate at the table and led a regular life—that he had, in fact, all the virtues that are usually accounted English? Or have I in the least succeeded in conveying that he was all those things and had all those virtues? He certainly was them and had them up to the last months of his life. They were the things that one would set upon his tombstone. They will, indeed, be set upon his tombstone by his widow.

And have I, I wonder, given the due impression of how his life was portioned and his time laid out? Because, until the very last, the amount of time taken up by his various passions was relatively small. I have been forced to write very much about his passions, but you have to consider— I should like to be able to make you consider—that he rose every morning at seven, took a cold bath, breakfasted at eight, was occupied with his regiment from nine until one; played polo or cricket with the men when it was the season for cricket, till tea-time. Afterwards he would occupy himself with the letters from his land-steward or with the affairs of his mess, till dinner-time. He would dine and pass the evening playing cards, or playing billiards with Leonora or at social functions of one kind or another. And the greater part of his life was taken up by that—by far the greater part of his life. His love-affairs, until the very end, were sandwiched in at odd moments or took place during the social evenings, the dances, and dinners. But I guess I have made it hard for you, O silent listener, to get that impression. Anyhow, I hope I have not given you the idea that Edward Ashburnham was a pathological case. He wasn't. He was just a normal man and very much of a sentimentalist. I dare say the quality of his youth, the nature of his mother's influence, his ignorances, the crammings that he received at the hands of army coaches —I dare say that all these excellent influences upon his adolescence were very bad for him. But we all have to put up with that sort of thing and no doubt it is very bad for all of us. Nevertheless, the outline of Edward's life was an outline perfectly normal of the life of a hard-working, sentimental, and efficient professional man.

That question of first impressions has always bothered me a good deal—but quite academically. I mean that, from time to time I have wondered whether it were or were not best to trust to one's first impressions in dealing with people. But I never had anybody to deal with except waiters and chambermaids and the Ashburnhams, with whom I didn't know that I was having any dealings. And, as far as waiters and chambermaids were concerned, I have generally found that my first impressions were correct enough. If my first idea of a man was that he was civil, obliging, and attentive, he generally seemed to go on being all those things. Once, however, at our Paris flat we had a maid who appeared to be charming and transparently honest. She stole, nevertheless, one of Florence's diamond rings. She did it, however, to save her young man from going to prison. So here, as somebody says somewhere, was a special case.

And, even in my short incursion into American business life—an incursion that lasted during part of August and nearly the whole of September—I found that to rely upon first impressions was the best thing I could do. I found myself automatically docketing and labelling each man as he was introduced to me, by the run of his features and by the first words that he spoke. I can't, however, be regarded as really doing business during the time that I spent in the United States. I was just winding things up. If it hadn't been for my idea of marrying the girl I might possibly have looked for something to do in my own country. For my experiences there were vivid and amusing. It was exactly as if I had come out of a museum into a riotous fancy-dress ball. During my life with Florence I had almost come to forget that there were such things as fashions or occupations or the greed of gain. I had, in fact, forgotten that there was such a thing as a dollar and that a dollar can be extremely desirable if you don't happen to possess one. And I had forgotten, too, that there was such a thing as gossip that mattered. In that particular, Philadelphia was the most amazing place I have ever been in in my life. I was not in that city for more than a week or ten days and I didn't there transact anything much in the way of business; nevertheless, the number of times that I was warned by everybody against everybody else was simply amazing. A man I didn't know would come up behind my lounge chair in the hotel, and, whispering cautiously beside my ear, would warn me against some other man that I equally didn't know but who would be standing by the bar. I don't know what they thought I was there to do—perhaps

5*

to buy out the city's debt or get a controlling hold of some railway interest. Or, perhaps, they imagined that I wanted to buy a newspaper, for they were either politicians or reporters, which, of course, comes to the same thing. As a matter of fact, my property in Philadelphia was mostly real estate in the old-fashioned part of the city and all I wanted to do there was just to satisfy myself that the houses were in good repair and the doors kept properly painted. I wanted also to see my relations, of whom I had a few. These were mostly professional people and they were mostly rather hard up because of the big bank failure in 1907 or thereabouts. Still, they were very nice. They would have been nicer still if they hadn't, all of them, had what appeared to me to be the mania that what they called influences were working against them. At any rate, the impression of that city was one of old-fashioned rooms, rather English than American in type, in which handsome but careworn ladies, cousins of my own, talked principally about mysterious movements that were going on against them. I never got to know what it was all about; perhaps they thought I knew or perhaps there weren't any movements at all. It was all very secret and subtle and subterranean. But there was a nice young fellow called Carter who was a sort of second-nephew of mine, twice removed. He was handsome and dark and gentle and tall and modest. I understand also that he was a good cricketer. He was employed by the real-estate agents who collected my rents. It was he, therefore, who took me over my own property and I saw a good deal of him and of a nice girl called Mary, to whom he was engaged. At that time I did, what I certainly shouldn't do now—I made some careful inquiries as to his character. I discovered from his employers that he was just all that he appeared, honest, industrious, high-spirited, friendly, and ready to do anyone a good turn. His relatives, however, as they were mine, too—seemed to have something darkly mysterious against him. I imagined that he must have been mixed up in some case of graft or that he had at least betrayed several innocent and trusting maidens. I pushed, however, that particular mystery home and discovered it was only that he was a Democrat. My own people were mostly Republicans. It seemed to make it worse and more darkly mysterious to them that young Carter was what they called a sort of Vermont Democrat which was the whole ticket and no mistake. But I don't know what it means. Anyhow, I suppose that my money will go to him when I die—I like the recollection of his friendly image and of the nice girl he was engaged to. May Fate deal very kindly with them.

I have said just now that, in my present frame of mind, nothing would ever make me make inquiries as to the character of any man that I liked at first sight. (The little digression as to my Philadelphia experiences was really meant to lead around to this.) For who in this world can give anyone a character? Who in this world knows anything of any other heart—or of his own? I don't mean to say that one cannot form an average estimate of the way a person will behave. But one cannot be certain of the way any man will behave in every case—and until one can do that a 'character' is of no use to anyone. That, for instance, was the way with Florence's maid in Paris. We used to trust that girl with blank cheques for the payment of the tradesmen. For quite a time she was so trusted by us. Then, suddenly, she stole a ring. We should not have believed her capable of it; she would not have believed herself capable of it. It was nothing in her character. So, perhaps, it was with Edward Ashburnham.

Or, perhaps, it wasn't. No, I rather think it wasn't. It is difficult to figure out. I have said that the Kilsyte case eased the immediate tension for him and Leonora. It let him see that she was capable of loyalty to him; it gave her her chance to show that she believed in him. She accepted without question his statement that, in kissing the girl, he wasn't trying to do more than administer fatherly comfort to a weeping child. And, indeed, his own world—including the magistrates—took that view of the case. Whatever people say, one's world can be perfectly charitable at times . . . But, again, as I have said, it did Edward a great deal of harm.

That, at least, was his view of it. He assured me that, before that case came on and was wrangled about by counsel with all the sorts of dirty-mindedness that counsel in that sort of case can impute, he had not had the least idea that he was capable of being unfaithful to Leonora. But, in the midst of that tumult—he says that it came suddenly into his head whilst he was in the witness-box— in the midst of those august ceremonies of the law there came suddenly into his mind the recollection of the soft- ness of the girl's body as he had pressed her to him. And, from that moment, that girl appeared desirable to him— and Leonora completely unattractive.

He began to indulge in day-dreams in which he approached the nursemaid more tactfully and carried the matter much further. Occasionally he thought of other women in terms of wary courtship—or, perhaps, it would be more exact to say that he thought of them in terms of tactful comforting, ending in absorption. That was his own view of the case. He saw himself as the victim of the law. I don't mean to say that he saw himself as a kind of Dreyfus. The law, practically, was quite kind to him. It stated that in its view Captain Ashburnham had been misled by an ill-placed desire to comfort a member of the opposite sex, and it fined him five shillings for his want of tact, or of knowledge of the world. But Edward maintained that it had put ideas into his head.

I don't believe it, though he certainly did. He was twenty-seven then, and his wife was out of sympathy with him—some crash was inevitable. There was between them a momentary rapprochement; but it could not last. It made it, probably, all the worse that, in that particular matter, Leonora had come so very well up to the scratch. For, whilst Edward respected her more and was grateful to her, it made her seem by so much the more cold in other matters that were near his heart—his responsibilities, his career, his tradition. It brought his despair of her up to a point of exasperation—and it riveted on him the idea that he might find some other woman who would give him the moral support that he needed. He wanted to be looked upon as a sort of Lohengrin.

At that time, he says, he went about deliberately looking for some woman who could help him. He found several— for there were quite a number of ladies in his set who were capable of agreeing with this handsome and fine fellow that the duties of a feudal gentleman were feudal. He would have liked to pass his days talking to one or other of these ladies. But there was always an obstacle—if the lady were married there would be a husband who claimed the greater part of her time and attention. If, on the other hand, it were an unmarried girl, he could not see very much of her for fear of compromising her. At that date, you understand, he had not the least idea of seducing any one of these ladies. He wanted only moral support at the hands of some female, because he found men difficult to talk to about ideals. Indeed, I do not believe that he had, at any time, any idea of making any one his mistress. That sounds queer; but I believe it is quite true as a statement of character.

It was, I believe, one of Leonora's priests—a man of the world—who suggested that she should take him to Monte Carlo. He had the idea that what Edward needed, in order to fit him for the society of Leonora, was a touch of irresponsibility. For Edward, at that date, had much the aspect of a prig. I mean that, if he played polo and was an excellent dancer he did the one for the sake of keeping himself fit and the other because it was a social duty to show himself at dances, and, when there, to dance well. He did nothing for fun except what he considered to be his work in life. As the priest saw it, this must for ever estrange him from Leonora—not because Leonora set much store by the joy of life, but because she was out of sympathy with Edward's work. On the other hand, Leonora did like to have a good time, now and then, and, as the priest saw it, if Edward could be got to like having a good time now and then, too, there would be a bond of sympathy between them. It was a good idea, but it worked out wrongly.

It worked out, in fact, in the mistress of the Grand Duke. In anyone less sentimental than Edward that would not have mattered. With Edward it was fatal. For, such was his honourable nature, that for him to enjoy a woman's favours made him feel that she had a bond on him for life. That was the way it worked out in practice. Psychologically it meant that he could not have a mistress without falling violently in love with her. He was a serious person—and in this particular case it was very expensive. The mistress of the Grand Duke—a Spanish dancer of passionate appearance—singled out Edward for her glances at a ball that was held in their common hotel. Edward was tall, handsome, blond, and very wealthy as she understood— and Leonora went up to bed early. She did not care for public dances, but she was relieved to see that Edward appeared to be having a good time with several amiable girls. And that was the end of Edward—for the Spanish dancer of passionate appearance wanted one night of him for his beaux yeux. He took her into the dark gardens and, remembering suddenly the girl of the Kilsyte case, he kissed her. He kissed her passionately, violently, with a sudden explosion of the passion that had been bridled all his life—for Leonora was cold, or at any rate, well behaved. La Dolciquita liked this reversion, and he passed the night in her bed.

When the palpitating creature was at last asleep in his arms he discovered that he was madly, was passionately, was overwhelmingly in love with her. It was a passion that had arisen like fire in dry corn. He could think of nothing else; he could live for nothing else. But La Dolciquita was a reasonable creature without an ounce of passion in her. She wanted a certain satisfaction of her appetites and Edward had appealed to her the night before. Now that was done with, and, quite coldly, she said that she wanted money if he was to have any more of her. It was a perfectly reasonable commercial transaction. She did not care two buttons for Edward or for any man and he was asking her to risk a very good situation with the Grand Duke. If Edward could put up sufficient money to serve as a kind of insurance against accident she was ready to like Edward for a time that would be covered, as it were, by the policy. She was getting fifty thousand dollars a year from her Grand Duke; Edward would have to pay a premium of two years' hire for a month of her society. There would not be much risk of the Grand Duke's finding it out and it was not certain that he would give her the keys of the street if he did find out. But there was the risk—a twenty per cent. risk, as she figured it out. She talked to Edward as if she had been a solicitor with an estate to sell—perfectly quietly and perfectly coldly without any inflections in her voice. She did not want to be unkind to him; but she could see no reason for being kind to him. She was a virtuous business woman with a mother and two sisters and her own old age to be provided comfortably for. She did not expect more than a five years' further run. She was twenty-four and, as she said: 'We Spanish women are horrors at thirty.' Edward swore that he would provide for her for life if she would come to him and leave off talking so horribly; but she only shrugged one shoulder slowly and contemptuously. He tried to convince this woman, who, as he saw it, had surrendered to him her virtue, that he regarded it as in any case his duty to provide for her, and to cherish her and even to love her—for life. In return for her sacrifice he would do that. In return, again, for his honourable love she would listen for ever to the accounts of his estate. That was how he figured it out.

She shrugged the same shoulder with the same gesture and held out her left hand with the elbow at her side:

'Enfin, mon ami,' she said, 'put in this hand the price of that tiara at Forli's or . . .' And she turned her back on him.

Edward went mad; his world stood on its head; the palms in front of the blue sea danced grotesque dances. You see, he believed in the virtue, tenderness, and moral support of women. He wanted more than anything to argue

with La Dolciquita; to retire with her to an island and
point out to her the damnation of her point of view and
how salvation can only be found in true love and the feudal
system. She had once been his mistress, he reflected, and
by all the moral laws she ought to have gone on being his
mistress or at the very least his sympathetic confidante.
But her rooms were closed to him; she did not appear
in the hotel. Nothing: blank silence. To break that down
he had to have twenty thousand pounds. You have heard
what happened.

He spent a week of madness; he hungered; his eyes
sank in; he shuddered at Leonora's touch. I dare say that
nine-tenths of what he took to be his passion for La
Dolciquita was really discomfort at the thought that he
had been unfaithful to Leonora. He felt uncommonly bad,
that is to say—oh, unbearably bad, and he took it all to be
love. Poor devil, he was incredibly naïve. He drank like a
fish after Leonora was in bed and he spread himself over
the tables, and this went on for about a fortnight. Heaven
knows what would have happened; he would have thrown
away every penny that he possessed.

On the night after he had lost about forty thousand
pounds and whilst the whole hotel was whispering about
it, La Dolciquita walked composedly into his bedroom. He
was too drunk to recognize her, and she sat in his arm-
chair, knitting and holding smelling salts to her nose—for
he was pretty far gone with alcoholic poisoning—and, as
soon as he was able to understand her, she said:

'Look here, mon ami, do not go to the tables again. Take
a good sleep now and come and see me this afternoon.'

He slept till the lunch-hour. By that time Leonora had
heard the news. A Mrs Colonel Whelen had told her.
Mrs Colonel Whelen seems to have been the only sensible
person who was ever connected with the Ashburnhams.
She had argued it out that there must be a woman of the
harpy variety connected with Edward's incredible behaviour and mien; and she advised Leonora to go straight
off to Town—which might have the effect of bringing

Edward to his senses—and to consult her solicitor and her spiritual adviser. She had better go that very morning; it was no good arguing with a man in Edward's condition.

Edward, indeed, did not know that she had gone. As soon as he woke he went straight to La Dolciquita's room and she stood him his lunch in her own apartments. He fell on her neck and wept, and she put up with it for a time. She was quite a good-natured woman. And, when she had calmed him down with Eau de Mélisse, she said:

'Look here, my friend, how much money have you left? Five thousand dollars? Ten?' For the rumour went that Edward had lost two kings' ransoms a night for fourteen nights and she imagined that he must be near the end of his resources.

The Eau de Mélisse had calmed Edward to such an extent that, for the moment, he really had a head on his shoulders. He did nothing more than grunt:

'And then?'

'Why,' she answered, 'I may just as well have the ten thousand dollars as the tables. I will go with you to Antibes for a week for that sum.'

Edward grunted: 'Five.' She tried to get seven thousand five hundred; but he stuck to his five thousand and the hotel expenses at Antibes. The sedative carried him just as far as that and then he collapsed again. He had to leave for Antibes at three; he could not do without it. He left a note for Leonora saying that he had gone off for a week with the Clinton Morleys, yachting.

He did not enjoy himself very much at Antibes. La Dolciquita could talk of nothing with any enthusiasm except money, and she tired him unceasingly, during every waking hour, for presents of the most expensive description. And, at the end of a week, she just quietly kicked him out. He hung about in Antibes for three days. He was cured of the idea that he had any duties towards La Dolciquita—feudal or otherwise. But his sentimentalism required of him an attitude of Byronic gloom—as if his court had gone into half-mourning. Then his appetite suddenly returned, and he remembered Leonora. He found at his hotel at Monte Carlo a telegram from Leonora, dispatched from London, saying: 'Please return as soon as convenient.' He could not understand why Leonora should have abandoned him so precipitately when she only thought that he had gone yachting with the Clinton Morleys. Then he discovered that she had left the hotel before he had written the note. He had a pretty rocky journey back to town; he was frightened out of his life—and Leonora had never seemed so desirable to him.

V

I call this the Saddest Story, rather than 'The Ashburnham Tragedy,' just because it is so sad, just because there was no current to draw things along to a swift and inevitable end. There is about it none of the elevation that accompanies tragedy; there is about it no nemesis, no destiny. Here were two noble people—for I am convinced that both Edward and Leonora had noble natures—here, then, were two noble natures, drifting down life, like fireships afloat on a lagoon and causing miseries, heartaches, agony of the mind, and death. And they themselves steadily deteriorated. And why? For what purpose? To point what lesson? It is all a darkness.

There is not even any villain in the story—for even Major Basil, the husband of the lady who next, and really, comforted the unfortunate Edward—even Major Basil was not a villain in this piece. He was a slack, loose, shiftless sort of fellow—but he did not do anything to Edward. Whilst they were in the same station in Burma he borrowed a good deal of money—though, really, since Major Basil had no particular vices, it was difficult to know why he wanted it. He collected—different types of horses' bits from the earliest times to the present day—but, since he did not prosecute even this occupation with any vigour, he cannot have needed much money for the acquirement, say, of the bit of Genghis Khan's charger—if Genghis Khan had a charger. And when I say that he borrowed a good deal of money from Edward I do not mean to say that he had more than a thousand pounds from him during the five years that the connection lasted. Edward, of course, did not have a great deal of money; Leonora was seeing to that. Still, he may have had five hundred pounds a year English, for his *menus plaisirs*—for his regimental subscriptions and for keeping his men smart. Leonora hated that; she would have preferred to buy dresses for herself or to have devoted the money to paying off a mortgage. Still, with her sense of justice, she saw that, since she was managing a property bringing in three thousand a year with a view to re-establishing it as a property of five thousand a year, and since the property really, if not legally, belonged to Edward, it was reasonable and just that Edward should get a slice of his own. Of course she had the devil of a job.

I don't know that I have got the financial details exactly right. I am a pretty good head at figures, but my mind, still, sometimes mixes up pounds with dollars and I get a figure wrong. Anyhow, the proposition was something like this: Properly worked and without rebates to the tenants and keeping up schools and things, the Branshaw estate should have brought in about five thousand a year when Edward had it. It brought in actually about four. (I am talking in pounds, not dollars.) Edward's excesses with the Spanish Lady had reduced its value to about three—as the maximum figure, without reductions. Leonora wanted to get it back to five.

She was, of course, very young to be faced with such a proposition—twenty-four is not a very advanced age. So she did things with a youthful vigour that she would, very likely, have made more merciful, if she had known more about life. She got Edward remarkably on the hop. He had to face her in a London hotel, when he crept back from Monte Carlo with his poor tail between his poor legs. As far as I can make out she cut short his first mumblings and his first attempts at affectionate speech with words something like:

'We're on the verge of ruin. Do you intend to let me pull things together? If not I shall retire to Hendon on my jointure.' (Hendon represented a convent to which she occasionally went for what is called a 'retreat' in Catholic circles.)

And poor dear Edward knew nothing—absolutely nothing. He did not know how much money he had, as he put it, 'blued' at the tables. It might have been a quarter of a million for all he remembered. He did not know whether she knew about La Dolciquita or whether she imagined that he had gone off yachting or had stayed at Monte Carlo. He was just dumb and he just wanted to get into a hole and not have to talk. Leonora did not make him talk and she said nothing herself.

I do not know much about English legal procedure—I cannot, I mean, give technical details of how they tied him up. But I know that, two days later, without her having said more than I have reported to you, Leonora and her attorney had become the trustees, as I believe it is called, of all Edward's property, and there was an end of Edward as the good landlord and father of his people. He went out.

Leonora then had three thousand a year at her disposal. She occupied Edward with getting himself transferred to a part of his regiment that was in Burma—if that is the right way to put it. She herself had an interview, lasting a week or so—with Edward's land-steward. She made him understand that the estate would have to yield up to its last penny. Before they left for India she had let Branshaw for seven years at a thousand a year. She sold two Vandykes and a little silver for eleven thousand pounds and she raised, on mortgage, twenty-nine thousand. That went to Edward's money-lending friends in Monte Carlo. So she had to get the twenty-nine thousand back, for she did not regard the Vandykes and the silver as things she would have to replace. They were just frills to the Ashburnham vanity. Edward cried for two days over the disappearance of his ancestors and then she wished she had not done it; but it did not teach her anything and it lessened such esteem as she had for him. She did not also understand that to let Branshaw affected him with a feeling of physical soiling—that it was almost as bad for him as if a woman belonging to him had become a prostitute. That was how it did affect him; but I dare say she felt just as bad about the Spanish dancer.

So she went at it. They were eight years in India, and during the whole of that time she insisted that they must be self-supporting—they had to live on his Captain's pay, plus the extra allowance for being at the front. She gave him the five hundred a year for Ashburnham frills, as she called it to herself—and she considered she was doing him very well.

Indeed, in a way, she did him very well—but it was not his way. She was always buying him expensive things which, as it were, she took off her own back. I have, for instance, spoken of Edward's leather cases. Well, they were not Edward's at all; they were Leonora's manifestations. He liked to be clean, but he preferred, as it were, to be threadbare. She never understood that, and all that pigskin was her idea of a reward to him for putting her up to a little speculation by which she made eleven hundred pounds. She did, herself, the threadbare business. When they went up to a place called Simla, where, as I understand, it is cool in the summer and very social—when they went up to Simla for their healths it was she who had him prancing around, as we should say in the United States, on a thousand-dollar horse with the gladdest of glad rags all over him. She herself used to go into 'retreat.' I believe that was very good for her health and it was also very inexpensive.

It was probably also very good for Edward's health, because he pranced about mostly with Mrs Basil, who was a nice woman and very, very kind to him. I suppose she was his mistress, but I never heard it from Edward, of course. I seem to gather that they carried it on in a high romantic fashion, very proper to both of them—or, at any rate, for Edward; she seems to have been a tender and gentle soul who did what he wanted. I do not mean to say that she was without character; that was her job, to do what Edward wanted. So I figured it out, that for those five years, Edward wanted long passages of deep affection kept up in long, long talks and that every now and then they 'fell,' which would give Edward an opportunity for remorse and an excuse to lend the Major another fifty. I don't think that Mrs Basil considered it to be 'falling'; she just pitied him and loved him.

You see, Leonora and Edward had to talk about something during all these years. You cannot be absolutely dumb when you live with a person unless you are an inhabitant of the North of England or the State of Maine. So Leonora imagined the cheerful device of letting him see the accounts of his estate and discussing them with him. He did not discuss them much; he was trying to behave prettily. But it was old Mr Mumford—the farmer who did not pay his rent—that threw Edward into Mrs Basil's arms. Mrs Basil came upon Edward in the dusk, in the Burmese garden, with all sorts of flowers and things. And he was cutting up that crop—with his sword, not a walking-stick. He was also carrying on and cursing in a way you would not believe.

She ascertained that an old gentleman called Mumford had been ejected from his farm and had been given a little cottage rent-free, where he lived on ten shillings a week from a farmers' benevolent society, supplemented by seven that was being allowed him by the Ashburnham trustees. Edward had just discovered that fact from the estate accounts. Leonora had left them in his dressing-room and he had begun to read them before taking off his marching-kit. That was how he came to have a sword. Leonora considered that she had been unusually generous to old Mr Mumford in allowing him to inhabit a cottage, rent-free, and in giving him seven shillings a week. Anyhow, Mrs Basil had never seen a man in such a state as Edward was.

She had been passionately in love with him for quite a time, and he had been longing for her sympathy and admiration with a passion as deep. That was how they came to speak about it, in the Burmese garden, under the pale sky, with sheaves of severed vegetation, misty and odorous, in the night around their feet. I think they behaved themselves with decorum for quite a time after that, though Mrs Basil spent so many hours over the accounts of the Ashburnham estate that she got the name of every field by heart. Edward had a huge map of his lands in his harness-room and Major Basil did not seem to mind. I believe that people do not mind much in lonely stations.

It might have lasted for ever if the Major had not been made what is called a brevet-colonel during the shuffling of troops that went on just before the South African War. He was sent off somewhere else and, of course, Mrs Basil could not stay with Edward. Edward ought, I suppose, to have gone to the Transvaal. It would have done him a great deal of good to get killed. But Leonora would not let him; she had heard awful stories of the extravagance of the hussar regiment in war-time—how they left hundred-bottle cases of champagne, at five guineas a bottle, on the veldt and so on. Besides, she preferred to see how Edward was spending his five hundred a year. I don't mean to say that Edward had any grievance in that. He was never a man of the deeds of heroism sort and it was just as good for him to be sniped at up in the hills of the North Western frontier, as to be shot at by an old gentleman in a top-hat at the bottom of some spruit. Those are more or less his words about it. I believe he quite distinguished himself over there. At any rate, he had his D.S.O. and was made a brevet-major.

Leonora, however, was not in the least keen on his soldiering. She hated also his deeds of heroism. One of their bitterest quarrels came after he had, for the second time, in the Red Sea, jumped overboard from the troopship and rescued a private soldier. She stood it the first time and even complimented him. But the Red Sea was awful, that trip, and the private soldiers seemed to develop a suicidal craze. It got on Leonora's nerves; she figured Edward, for the rest of that trip, jumping overboard every ten minutes. And the mere cry of 'Man overboard' is a disagreeable, alarming, and disturbing thing. The ship gets stopped and there are all sorts of shouts. And Edward would not promise not to do it again, though, fortunately, they struck a streak of cooler weather when they were in the Persian Gulf. Leonora had got it into her head that Edward was trying to commit suicide, so I guess it was pretty awful for her when he would not give the promise. Leonora ought never to have been on that troopship; but she got there somehow, as an economy.

Major Basil discovered his wife's relation with Edward just before he was sent to his other station. I don't know whether that was a blackmailer's adroitness or just a trick of destiny. He may have known of it all the time or he may not. At any rate, he got hold of, just about then, some letters and things. It cost Edward three hundred pounds immediately. I do not know how it was arranged; I cannot imagine how even a blackmailer can make his demands. I suppose there is some sort of way of saving your face. I figure the Major as disclosing the letters to Edward with furious oaths, then accepting his explanations that the letters were perfectly innocent if the wrong construction were not put upon them. Then the Major would say: 'I say, old chap, I'm deuced hard up. Couldn't you lend me three hundred or so?' I fancy that was how it was. And, year by year, after that there would come a letter from the Major, saying that he was deuced hard up and couldn't Edward lend him three hundred or so?

Edward was pretty hard hit when Mrs Basil had to go away. He really had been very fond of her, and he remained faithful to her memory for quite a long time. And Mrs Basil had loved him very much and continued to cherish a hope of reunion with him. Three days ago there came a quite proper but very lamentable letter from her to Leonora, asking to be given particulars as to Edward's death. She had read the advertisement of it in an Indian paper. I think she must have been a very nice woman. . . .

And then the Ashburnhams were moved somewhere up towards a place or a district called Chitral. I am no good at geography of the Indian Empire. By that time they had settled down into a model couple and they never spoke in private to each other. Leonora had given up even showing the accounts of the Ashburnham estate to Edward. He thought that that was because she had piled up such a lot of money that she did not want him to know how she was getting on any more. But, as a matter of fact, after five or six years it had penetrated to her mind that it was painful to Edward to have to look on at the accounts of his estate and have no hand in the management of it. She was trying to do him a kindness. And, up in Chitral, poor dear little Maisie Maidan came along. . . .

That was the most unsettling to Edward of all his affairs. It made him suspect that he was inconstant. The affair with the Dolciquita he had sized up as a short attack of madness like hydrophobia. His relations with Mrs Basil had not seemed to him to imply moral turpitude of a gross kind. The husband had been complaisant; they had really loved each other; his wife was very cruel to him and had long ceased to be a wife to him. He thought that Mrs Basil had been his soul-mate, separated from him by an unkind fate —something sentimental of that sort.

But he discovered that, whilst he was still writing long weekly letters to Mrs Basil, he was beginning to be furiously impatient if he missed seeing Maisie Maidan during the course of the day. He discovered himself watching the doorways with impatience; he discovered that he disliked her boy husband very much for hours at a time. He discovered that he was getting up at unearthly hours in order to have time, later in the morning, to go for a walk with Maisie Maidan. He discovered himself using little slang words that she used and attaching a sentimental value to those words. These, you understand, were discoveries that came so late that he could do nothing but drift. He was losing weight; his eyes were beginning to fall in; he had touches of bad fever. He was, as he described it, pipped.

And, one ghastly hot day, he suddenly heard himself say to Leonora:

'I say, couldn't we take Mrs Maidan with us to Europe and drop her at Nauheim?'

He hadn't had the least idea of saying that to Leonora. He had merely been standing, looking at an illustrated paper, waiting for dinner. Dinner was twenty minutes late or the Ashburnhams would not have been alone together. No, he hadn't had the least idea of framing that speech. He had just been standing in a silent agony of fear, of longing, of heat, of fever. He was thinking that they were going back to Branshaw in a month and that Maisie Maidan was going to remain behind and die. And then, that had come out.

The punkah swished in the darkened room; Leonora lay exhausted and motionless in her cane lounge; neither of them stirred. They were both at that time very ill in indefinite ways.

And then Leonora said:

'Yes. I promised it to Charlie Maidan this afternoon. I have offered to pay her ex's myself.'

Edward just saved himself from saying: 'Good God!' You see, he had not the least idea of what Leonora knew—about Maisie, about Mrs Basil, even about La Dolciquita. It was a pretty enigmatic situation for him. It struck him that Leonora must be intending to manage his loves as she managed his money affairs and it made her more hateful to him—and more worthy of respect.

Leonora, at any rate, had managed his money to some purpose. She had spoken to him, a week before, for the first time in several years—about money. She had made twenty-two thousand pounds out of the Branshaw land and seven by the letting of Branshaw furnished. By fortunate investments—in which Edward had helped her—she had made another six or seven thousand that might well become more. The mortgages were all paid off, so that, except for the departure of the two Vandykes and the silver, they were as well off as they had been before the Dolciquita had acted the locust. It was Leonora's great achievement. She laid the figures before Edward, who maintained an unbroken silence.

'I propose,' she said, 'that you should resign from the Army and that we should go back to Branshaw. We are both too ill to stay here any longer.'

Edward said nothing at all.

'This,' Leonora continued passionlessly, 'is the great day of my life.'

Edward said:

'You have managed the job amazingly. You are a wonderful woman.' He was thinking that if they went back to Branshaw they would leave Maisie Maidan behind. That thought occupied him exclusively. They must, undoubtedly, return to Branshaw; there could be no doubt that Leonora was too ill to stay in that place. She said:

'You understand that the management of the whole of the expenditure of the income will be in your hands. There will be five thousand a year.'

She thought that he cared very much about the expenditure of an income of five thousand a year and that the fact that she had done so much for him would rouse in him some affection for her. But he was thinking exclusively of Maisie Maidan—of Maisie, thousands of miles away from him. He was seeing the mountains between them—blue mountains and the sea and sunlit plains. He said:

'That is very generous of you.' And she did not know whether that were praise or a sneer. That had been a week before. And all that week he had passed in an increasing agony at the thought that those mountains, that sea, and those sunlit plains would be between him and Maisie Maidan. That thought shook him in the burning nights: the sweat poured from him and he trembled with cold, in the burning noons—at that thought. He had no minute's rest; his bowels turned round and round within him: his tongue was perpetually dry and it seemed to him that the breath between his teeth was like air from a pesthouse.

He gave no thought to Leonora at all; he had sent in his papers. They were to leave in a month. It seemed to him to be his duty to leave that place and to go away, to support Leonora. He did his duty.

It was horrible, in their relationship at that time, that whatever she did caused him to hate her. He hated her when he found that she proposed to set him up as the Lord of Branshaw again—as a sort of dummy lord, in swaddling clothes. He imagined that she had done this in order to separate him from Maisie Maidan. Hatred hung in all the heavy nights and filled the shadowy corners of the room. So when he heard that she had offered to the Maidan boy to take his wife to Europe with him, automatically he hated her since he hated all that she did. It seemed to him, at that time, that she could never be other than cruel even if, by accident, an act of hers were kind. . . . Yes, it was a horrible situation.

But the cool breezes of the ocean seemed to clear up that hatred as if it had been a curtain. They seemed to give him back admiration for her, and respect. The agreeableness of having money lavishly at command, the fact that it had bought for him the companionship of Maisie Maidan—these things began to make him see that his wife might have been right in the starving and scraping upon which she had insisted. He was at ease; he was even radiantly happy when he carried cups of bouillon for Maisie Maidan along the deck. One night, when he was leaning beside Leonora, over the ship's side, he said suddenly:

'By Jove, you're the finest woman in the world. I wish we could be better friends.'

She just turned away without a word and went to her cabin. Still, she was very much better in health.

And now, I suppose, I must give you Leonora's side of the case. . . .

That is very difficult. For Leonora, if she preserved an unchanged front, changed very frequently her point of view. She had been drilled—in her tradition, in her upbringing—to keep her mouth shut. But there were times, she said, when she was so near yielding to the temptation of speaking that afterwards she shuddered to think of those times. You must postulate that what she desired above all things was to keep a shut mouth to the world, to Edward and to the women that he loved. If she spoke she would despise herself.

From the moment of his unfaithfulness with La Dolciquita she never acted the part of wife to Edward. It was not that she intended to keep herself from him as a principle, for ever. Her spiritual advisers, I believe, forbade that. But she stipulated that he must, in some way, perhaps symbolical, come back to her. She was not very clear as to what she meant; probably she did not know herself. Or perhaps she did.

There were moments when he seemed to be coming back to her; there were moments when she was within a hair of yielding to her physical passion for him. In just the same way, at moments, she almost yielded to the temptation to denounce Mrs Basil to her husband or Maisie Maidan to hers. She desired then to cause the horrors and pains of public scandals. For, watching Edward more intently and with more straining of ears than that which a cat bestows upon a bird overhead, she was aware of the progress of his passion for each of these ladies. She was aware of it from the way in which his eyes returned to doors and gateways; she knew from his tranquillities when he had received satisfactions.

At times she imagined herself to see more than was warranted. She imagined that Edward was carrying on intrigues with other women—with two at once; with three. For whole periods she imagined him to be a monster of libertinage and she could not see that he could have anything against her. She left him his liberty; she was starving herself to build up his fortunes; she allowed herself none of the joys of femineity—no dresses, no jewels—hardly even friendships, for fear they should cost money.

And yet, oddly, she could not but be aware that both Mrs Basil and Maisie Maidan were nice women. The curious, discounting eye which one woman can turn on another did not prevent her seeing that Mrs Basil was very good to Edward and Mrs Maidan very good for him. That seemed to her to be a monstrous and incomprehensible working of Fate's. Incomprehensible! Why, she asked herself again and again, did none of the good deeds that she did for her husband ever come through to him, or appear to him as good deeds? By what trick of mania could not he let her be as good to him as Mrs Basil was? Mrs Basil was not so extraordinarily dissimilar to herself. She was, it was true, tall, dark, with soft mournful voice and a great kindness of manner for every created thing, from punkah men to flowers on the trees. But she was not so well read as Leonora, at any rate in learned books. Leonora could not stand novels. But, even with all her differences, Mrs Basil did not appear to Leonora to differ so very much from herself. She was truthful, honest and, for the rest, just a woman. And Leonora had a vague sort of idea that, to a man, all women are the same after three weeks of close intercourse. She thought that the kindness should no longer appeal, the soft and mournful voice no longer thrill, the tall darkness no longer give a man the illusion that he was going into the depths of an unexplored wood. She could not understand how Edward could go on and on maundering over Mrs Basil. She could not see why he should continue to write her long letters after their separation. After that, indeed, she had a very bad time.

She had at that period what I will call the 'moustrous' theory of Edward. She was always imagining him ogling at every woman that he came across. She did not, that year, go into 'retreat' at Simla because she was afraid that he would corrupt her maid in her absence. She imagined him carrying on intrigues with native women or Eurasians. At dances she was in a fever of watchfulness....

She persuaded herself that this was because she had a dread of scandals. Edward might get himself mixed up with a marriageable daughter of some man who would make a row or some husband who would matter. But, really, she acknowledged afterwards to herself, she was hoping that, Mrs Basil being out of the way, the time might have come when Edward should return to her. All that period she passed in an agony of jealousy and fear—the fear that Edward might really become promiscuous in his habits.

So that, in an odd way, she was glad when Maisie Maidan came along—and she realized that she had not, before, been afraid of husbands and of scandals, since, then, she did her best to keep Maisie's husband un-suspicious. She wished to appear so trustful of Edward that Maidan could not possibly have any suspicions. It was an evil position for her. But Edward was very ill and she wanted to see him smile again. She thought that if he could smile again through her agency he might return, through gratitude and satisfied love—to her. At that time she thought that Edward was a person of light and fleeting passions. And she could understand Edward's passion for Maisie, since Maisie was one of those women to whom other women will allow magnetism.

She was very pretty; she was very young; in spite of her heart she was very gay and light on her feet. And Leonora was really very fond of Maisie, who was fond enough of Leonora. Leonora, indeed, imagined that she could manage this affair all right. She had no thought of Maisie's being led into adultery; she imagined that if she could take Maisie and Edward to Nauheim, Edward would see enough of her to get tired of her pretty little chatterings, and of the pretty little motions of her hands and feet. And she thought she could trust Edward. For there was not any doubt of Maisie's passion for Edward. She raved about him to Leonora as Leonora had heard girls rave about drawing masters in schools. She was perpetually asking her boy husband why he could not dress, ride, shoot, play polo, or even recite sentimental poems, like their major. And young Maidan had the greatest admiration for Edward, and he adored, was bewildered by, and entirely trusted his wife. It appeared to him that Edward was devoted to Leonora. And Leonora imagined that when poor Maisie was cured of her heart and Edward had seen enough of her, he would return to her. She had the vague, passionate idea that, when Edward had exhausted a number of other types of women he must turn to her. Why should not her type have its turn in his heart? She imagined that, by now, she understood him better, that she understood better his vanities and that, by making him happier, she could arouse his love.

Florence knocked all that on the head. . . .

PART FOUR

I

I HAVE, I am aware, told this story in a very rambling way so that it may be difficult for anyone to find their path through what may be a sort of maze. I cannot help it. I have stuck to my idea of being in a country cottage with a silent listener, hearing between the gusts of the wind and amidst the noises of the distant sea, the story as it comes. And, when one discusses an affair—a long, sad affair—one goes back, one goes forward. One remembers points that one has forgotten and one explains them all the more minutely since one recognizes that one has forgotten to mention them in their proper places and that one may have given, by omitting them, a false impression. I console myself with thinking that this is a real story and that, after all, real stories are probably told best in the way a person telling a story would tell them. They will then seem most real.

At any rate, I think I have brought my story up to the date of Maisie Maidan's death. I mean that I have explained everything that went before it from the several points of view that were necessary—from Leonora's, from Edward's and, to some extent, from my own. You have the facts for the trouble of finding them; you have the points of view as far as I could ascertain or put them. Let me imagine myself back, then, at the day of Maisie's death—or rather at the moment of Florence's dissertation on the Protest, up in the old Castle of the town of M——. Let us consider Leonora's point of view with regard to Florence; Edward's, of course, I cannot give you, for Edward naturally never spoke of his affair with my wife. (I may, in

what follows, be a little hard on Florence; but you must
remember that I have been writing away at this story now
for six months and reflecting longer and longer upon these
affairs.)

And the longer I think about them the more certain I
become that Florence was a contaminating influence—she
depressed and deteriorated poor Edward; she deteriorated,
hopelessly, the miserable Leonora. There is no doubt that
she caused Leonora's character to deteriorate. If there was
a fine point about Leonora it was that she was proud and
that she was silent. But that pride and that silence broke
when she made that extraordinary outburst, in the
shadowy room that contained the Protest, and in the little
terrace looking over the river. I don't mean to say that she
was doing a wrong thing. She was certainly doing right in
trying to warn me that Florence was making eyes at her
husband. But, if she did the right thing, she was doing it
in the wrong way. Perhaps she should have reflected longer;
she should have spoken, if she wanted to speak, only after
reflection. Or it would have been better if she had acted—
if, for instance, she had so chaperoned Florence that private
communication between her and Edward became impossible. She should have gone eavesdropping; she should
have watched outside bedroom doors. It is odious; but
that is the way the job is done. She should have taken
Edward away the moment Maisie was dead. No, she acted
wrongly. . . .

And yet, poor thing, is it for me to condemn her—and
what did it matter in the end? If it had not been Florence,
it would have been some other . . . Still, it might have been
a better woman than my wife. For Florence was vulgar;
Florence was a common flirt who would not, at the last,
lacher prise; and Florence was an unstoppable talker. You
could not stop her; nothing would stop her. Edward and
Leonora were at least proud and reserved people. Pride
and reserve are not the only things in life; perhaps they
are not even the best things. But if they happen to be your
particular virtues you will go all to pieces if you let them

go. And Leonora let them go. She let them go before poor
Edward did even. Consider her position when she burst
out over the Luther-Protest. . . . Consider her agonies. . . .

You are to remember that the main passion of her life
was to get Edward back; she had never, till that moment,
despaired of getting him back. That may seem ignoble;
but you have also to remember that her getting him back
represented to her not only a victory for herself. It would,
as it appeared to her, have been a victory for all wives and
a victory for her Church. That was how it presented itself
to her. These things are a little inscrutable. I don't know
why the getting back of Edward should have represented
to her a victory for all wives, for Society and for her
Church. Or, maybe, I have a glimmering of it.

She saw life as a perpetual sex-battle between husbands
who desire to be unfaithful to their wives, and wives who
desire to recapture their husbands in the end. That was
her sad and modest view of matrimony. Man, for her, was
a sort of brute who must have his divagations, his moments
of excess, his nights out, his, let us say, rutting seasons.
She had read few novels, so that the idea of a pure and
constant love succeeding the sound of wedding bells had
never been very much presented to her. She went, numbed
and terrified, to the Mother Superior of her childhood's
convent with the tale of Edward's infidelities with the
Spanish dancer, and all that the old nun, who appeared to
her to be infinitely wise, mystic, and reverend, had done
had been to shake her head sadly and to say:

'Men are like that. By the blessing of God it will all
come right in the end.'

That was what was put before her by her spiritual
advisers as her programme in life. Or, at any rate, that was
how their teachings came through to her—that was the
lesson she told me she had learned of them. I don't know
exactly what they taught her. The lot of women was
patience and patience and again patience—*ad majorem
Dei gloriam*—until upon the appointed day, if God saw
fit, she should have her reward. If then, in the end, she

should have succeeded in getting Edward back she would have kept her man within the limits that are all that wife-hood has to expect. She was even taught that such excesses in men are natural, excusable—as if they had been children.

And the great thing was that there should be no scandal before the congregation. So she had clung to the idea of getting Edward back with a fierce passion that was like an agony. She had looked the other way; she had occupied herself solely with one idea. That was the idea of having Edward appear, when she did get him back, wealthy, glorious as it were, on account of his lands, and upright. She would show, in fact, that in an unfaithful world one Catholic woman had succeeded in retaining the fidelity of her husband. And she thought she had come near her desires.

Her plan with regard to Maisie had appeared to be working admirably. Edward had seemed to be cooling off towards the girl. He did not hunger to pass every minute of the time at Nauheim beside the child's recumbent form; he went out to polo matches; he played auction bridge in the evenings; he was cheerful and bright. She was certain that he was not trying to seduce that poor child; she was beginning to think that he had never tried to do so. He seemed in fact to be dropping back into what he had been for Maisie in the beginning—a kind, attentive, superior officer in the regiment, paying gallant attentions to a bride. They were as open in their little flirtations as the dayspring from on high. And Maisie had not appeared to fret when he went off on excursions with us; she had to lie down for so many hours on her bed every afternoon, and she had not appeared to crave for the attentions of Edward at those times.

And Edward was beginning to make little advances to Leonora. Once or twice, in private—for he often did it before people—he had said: 'How nice you look!' or 'What a pretty dress!' She had gone with Florence to Frankfurt, where they dress as well as in Paris, and had got herself a gown or two. She could afford it, and Florence was an excellent adviser as to dress. She seemed to have got hold of the clue to the riddle.

Yes, Leonora seemed to have got hold of the clue to the riddle. She imagined herself to have been in the wrong to some extent in the past. She should not have kept Edward on such a tight rein with regard to money. She thought she was on the right tack in letting him—as she had done only with fear and irresolution—have again the control of his income. He came even a step towards her and acknowledged, spontaneously, that she had been right in husbanding, for all those years, their resources. He said to her one day:

'You've done right, old girl. There's nothing I like so much as to have a little to chuck away. And I can do it, thanks to you.'

That was really, she said, the happiest moment of her life. And he, seeming to realize it, had ventured to pat her on the shoulder. He had, ostensibly, come in to borrow a safety-pin of her.

And the occasion of her boxing Maisie's ears, had, after it was over, riveted in her mind the idea that there was no intrigue between Edward and Mrs Maidan. She imagined that, from henceforward, all that she had to do was to keep him well supplied with money and his mind amused with pretty girls. She was convinced that he was coming back to her. For that month she no longer repelled his timid advances that never went very far. For he certainly made timid advances. He patted her on the shoulder; he whispered into her ear little jokes about the odd figures that they saw up at the Casino. It was not much to make a little joke—but the whispering of it was a precious intimacy. . . .

And then—smash—it all went. It went to pieces at the moment when Florence laid her hand upon Edward's wrist, as it lay on the glass sheltering the manuscript of the Protest, up in the high tower with the shutters where the sunlight here and there streamed in. Or, rather, it went when she noticed the look in Edward's eyes as he gazed back into Florence's. She knew that look.

She had known—since the first moment of their meeting, since the moment of our all sitting down to dinner
together—that Florence was making eyes at Edward. But
she had seen so many women make eyes at Edward—
hundreds and hundreds of women, in railway trains, in
hotels, aboard liners, at street corners. And she had arrived
at thinking that Edward took little stock in women that
made eyes at him. She had formed what was, at that time,
a fairly correct estimate of the methods of, the reasons for,
Edward's loves. She was certain that hitherto they had
consisted of the short passion for the Dolciquita, the real
sort of love for Mrs Basil, and what she deemed the pretty
courtship of Maisie Maidan. Besides she despised Florence
so haughtily that she could not imagine Edward's being
attracted by her. And she and Maisie were a sort of bul-
wark round him.

She wanted, besides, to keep her eyes on Florence—for
Florence knew that she had boxed Maisie's ears. And
Leonora so desperately desired that her union with Edward
should appear to be flawless. But all that went. . . .

With the answering gaze of Edward into Florence's blue
and uplifted eyes, she knew that it had all gone. She knew
that that gaze meant that those two had had long conversations of an intimate kind—about their likes and dislikes,
about their natures, about their views of marriage. She
knew what it meant that she, when we all four walked out
together, had always been with me ten yards ahead of
Florence and Edward. She did not imagine that it had gone
further than talks about their likes and dislikes, about their
natures or about marriage as an institution. But, having
watched Edward all her life, she knew that that laying on
of hands, that answering of gaze with gaze, meant that the
thing was unavoidable. Edward was such a serious person.

She knew that any attempt on her part to separate those
two would be to rivet on Edward an irrevocable passion;
that, as I have before told you, it was a trick of Edward's
nature to believe that the seducing of a woman gave her
an irrevocable hold over him for life. And that touching

of hands, she knew, would give that woman an irrevocable claim—to be seduced. And she so despised Florence that she would have preferred it to be a parlour-maid. There are very decent parlour-maids.

And, suddenly, there came into her mind the conviction that Maisie Maidan had a real passion for Edward; that this would break her heart—and that she, Leonora, would be responsible for that. She went, for the moment, mad. She clutched me by the wrist; she dragged me down those stairs and across that whispering Rittersaal with the high painted pillars, the high painted chimney-piece. I guess she did not go mad enough.

She ought to have said:

'Your wife is a harlot who is going to be my husband's mistress . . .' That might have done the trick. But, even in her madness, she was afraid to go as far as that. She was afraid that, if she did, Edward and Florence would make a bolt of it, and that, if they did that, she would lose forever all chance of getting him back in the end. She acted very badly to me.

Well, she was a tortured soul who put her Church before the interests of a Philadelphia Quaker. That is all right—I daresay the Church of Rome is the more important of the two.

A week after Maisie Maidan's death she was aware that Florence had become Edward's mistress. She waited outside Florence's door and met Edward as he came away. She said nothing and he only grunted. But I guess he had a bad time.

Yes, the mental deterioration that Florence worked in Leonora was extraordinary; it smashed up her whole life and all her chances. It made her, in the first place, hopeless—for she could not see how, after that, Edward could return to her—after a vulgar intrigue with a vulgar woman. His affair with Mrs Basil, which was now all that she had to bring, in her heart, against him, she could not find it in her to call an intrigue. It was a love affair—a pure enough thing in its way. But this seemed to her to be a horror—a

wantonness, all the more detestable to her, because she so
detested Florence. And Florence talked. . . .

That was what was terrible, because Florence forced
Leonora herself to abandon her high reserve—Florence
and the situation. It appears that Florence was in two
minds whether to confess to me or to Leonora. Confess
she had to. And she pitched at last on Leonora, because if
it had been me she would have had to confess a great deal
more. Or, at least, I might have guessed a great deal more,
about her 'heart,' and about Jimmy. So she went to
Leonora one day and began hinting and hinting. And she
enraged Leonora to such an extent that at last Leonora
said:

'You want to tell me that you are Edward's mistress.
You can be. I have no use for him.'

That was really a calamity for Leonora, because, once
started, there was no stopping the talking. She tried to
stop—but it was not to be done. She found it necessary to
send Edward messages through Florence; for she would
not speak to him. She had to give him, for instance, to
understand that if I ever came to know of his intrigue she
would ruin him beyond repair. And it complicated matters
a good deal that Edward, at about this time, was really a
little in love with her. He thought that he had treated her
so badly; that she was so fine. She was so mournful that
he longed to comfort her, and he thought himself such a
blackguard that there was nothing he would not have done
to make amends. And Florence communicated these items
of information to Leonora.

I don't in the least blame Leonora for her coarseness to
Florence; it must have done Florence a world of good. But
I do blame her for giving way to what was in the end a
desire for communicativeness. You see that business cut
her off from her Church. She did not want to confess what
she was doing because she was afraid that her spiritual
advisers would blame her for deceiving me. I rather
imagine that she would have preferred damnation to

breaking my heart. That is what it works out at. She need not have troubled.

But, having no priests to talk to, she had to talk to some one, and as Florence insisted on talking to her, she talked back, in short, explosive sentences, like one of the damned. Precisely like one of the damned. Well, if a pretty period in hell on this earth can spare her any period of pain in Eternity—where there are not any periods—I guess Leonora will escape hell fire.

Her conversations with Florence would be like this. Florence would happen in on her, whilst she was doing her wonderful hair, with a proposition from Edward, who seems about that time to have conceived the naïve idea that he might become a polygamist. I daresay it was Florence who put it into his head. Anyhow, I am not responsible for the oddities of the human psychology. But it certainly appears that at about that date Edward cared more for Leonora than he had ever done before—or, at any rate, for a long time. And, if Leonora had been a person to play cards and if she had played her cards well, and if she had had no sense of shame and so on, she might then have shared Edward with Florence until the time came for jerking that poor cuckoo out of the nest.

Well, Florence would come to Leonora with some such proposition. I do not mean to say that she put it baldly, like that. She stood out that she was not Edward's mistress until Leonora said that she had seen Edward coming out of her room at an advanced hour of the night. That checked Florence a bit; but she fell back upon her 'heart' and stuck out that she had merely been conversing with Edward in order to bring him to a better frame of mind. Florence had, of course, to stick to that story; for even Florence would not have had the face to implore Leonora to grant her favours to Edward if she had admitted that she was Edward's mistress. That could not be done. At the same time Florence had such a pressing desire to talk about something. There would have been nothing else to talk about but a rapprochement between that estranged pair.

6*

So Florence would go on babbling and Leonora would go on brushing her hair. And then Leonora would say suddenly something like:

'I should think myself defiled if Edward touched me now that he has touched you.'

That would discourage Florence a bit; but after a week or so, on another morning she would have another try.

And even in other things Leonora deteriorated. She had promised Edward to leave the spending of his own income in his own hands. And she had fully meant to do that. I daresay she would have done it too; though, no doubt, she would have spied upon his banking account in secret. She was not a Roman Catholic for nothing. But she took so serious a view of Edward's unfaithfulness to the memory of poor little Maisie that she could not trust him any more at all.

So when she got back to Branshaw she started, after less than a month, to worry him about the minutest items of his expenditure. She allowed him to draw his own cheques, but there was hardly a cheque that she did not scrutinize— except for a private account of about five hundred a year which, tacitly, she allowed him to keep for expenditure on his mistress or mistresses. He had to have his jaunts to Paris; he had to send expensive cables in cipher to Florence about twice a week. But she worried him about his expenditure on wines, on fruit trees, on harness, on gates, on the account at his blacksmith's for work done to a new patent Army stirrup that he was trying to invent. She could not see why he should bother to invent a new Army stirrup, and she was really enraged when, after the invention was mature, he made a present to the War Office of the designs and the patent rights. It was a remarkably good stirrup.

I have told you, I think, that Edward spent a great deal of time, and about two hundred pounds for law fees on getting a poor girl, the daughter of one of his gardeners, acquitted of a charge of murdering her baby. That was positively the last act of Edward's life. It came at a time when Nancy Rufford was on her way to India; when the most horrible gloom was over the household; when Edward himself was in an agony and behaving as prettily as he knew how. Yet even then Leonora made him a terrible scene about this expenditure of time and trouble. She sort of had the vague idea that what had passed with the girl and the rest of it ought to have taught Edward a lesson— the lesson of economy. She threatened to take his banking account away from him again. I guess that made him cut his throat. He might have stuck it out otherwise—but the thought that he had lost his Nancy and that, in addition, there was nothing left for him but a dreary, dreary succession of days in which he could be of no public service ... Well, it finished him.

It was during those years that Leonora tried to get up a love affair of her own with a fellow called Bayham—a decent sort of fellow. A really nice man. But the affair was no sort of success. I have told you about it already....

II

Well, that about brings me up to the date of my receiving, in Waterbury, the laconic cable from Edward to the effect that he wanted me to go to Branshaw and have a chat. I was pretty busy at the time and I was half minded to send him a reply cable to the effect that I would start in a fortnight. But I was having a long interview with old Mr Hurlbird's attorneys and immediately afterwards I had to have a long interview with the Misses Hurlbird, so I delayed cabling.

I had expected to find the Misses Hurlbird excessively old—in the nineties or thereabouts. The time had passed so slowly that I had the impression that it must have been thirty years since I had been in the United States. It was only twelve years. Actually Miss Hurlbird was just sixty-one and Miss Florence Hurlbird fifty-nine, and they were both, mentally and physically, as vigorous as could be desired. They were, indeed, more vigorous, mentally, than suited my purpose, which was to get away from the United States as quickly as I could. The Hurlbirds were an exceedingly united family—exceedingly united except on one set of points. Each of the three of them had a separate doctor, whom they trusted implicitly—and each had a separate attorney. And each of them distrusted the other's doctor and the other's attorney. And, naturally, the doctors and the attorneys warned one all the time—against each other. You cannot imagine how complicated it all became for me. Of course I had an attorney of my own—recommended to me by young Carter, my Philadelphia nephew.

I do not mean to say that there was any unpleasantness of a grasping kind. The problem was quite another one— a moral dilemma. You see, old Mr Hurlbird had left all his property to Florence with the mere request that she would have erected to him in the city of Waterbury, Ill., a memorial that should take the form of some sort of institution for the relief of sufferers from the heart. Florence's money had all come to me—and with it old Mr Hurlbird's. He had died just five days before Florence.

Well, I was quite ready to spend a round million dollars on the relief of sufferers from the heart. The old gentleman had left about a million and a half; Florence had been worth about eight hundred thousand—and as I figured it out, I should cut up at about a million myself. Anyhow, there was ample money. But I naturally wanted to consult the wishes of his surviving relatives and then the trouble really began. You see, it had been discovered that Mr Hurlbird had had nothing whatever the matter with his heart. His lungs had been a little affected all through his life and he had died of bronchitis.

It struck Miss Florence Hurlbird that, since her brother had died of lungs and not of heart, his money ought to go to lung patients. That, she considered, was what her brother would have wished. On the other hand, by a kink, that I could not at the time understand, Miss Hurlbird insisted that I ought to keep the money all to myself. She said that she did not wish for any monuments to the Hurlbird family.

At the time I thought that that was because of a New England dislike for necrological ostentation. But I can figure out now, when I remember certain insistent and continued questions that she put to me, about Edward Ashburnham, that there was another idea in her mind. And Leonora has told me that, on Florence's dressing-table, beside her dead body, there had lain a letter to Miss Hurlbird—a letter which Leonora posted without telling me. I don't know how Florence had time to write to her aunt; but I can quite understand that she would not like to go out of the world without making some comments. So I guess Florence had told Miss Hurlbird a good bit about Edward Ashburnham in a few scrawled words— and that that was why the old lady did not wish the name of Hurlbird perpetuated. Perhaps also she thought that I had earned the Hurlbird money.

It meant a pretty tidy lot of discussing, what with the doctors warning each other about the bad effects of discussions on the health of the old ladies, and warning me covertly against each other, and saying that old Mr Hurlbird might have died of heart, after all, in spite of the diagnosis of *his* doctor. And the solicitors all had separate methods of arranging about how the money should be invested and entrusted and bound.

Personally, I wanted to invest the money so that the interest could be used for the relief of sufferers from the heart. If old Mr. Hurlbird had not died of any defects in that organ he had considered that it was defective. Moreover, Florence had certainly died of her heart, as I saw it. And when Miss Florence Hurlbird stood out that the money ought to go to chest sufferers I was brought to thinking that there ought to be a chest institution too, and I advanced the sum that I was ready to provide to a million and a half of dollars. That would have given seven hundred and fifty thousand to each class of invalid. I did not want money at all badly. All I wanted it for was to be able to give Nancy Rufford a good time. I did not know much about housekeeping expenses in England where, I presumed, she would wish to live. I knew that her needs at that time were limited to good chocolates, and a good horse or two, and simple, pretty frocks. Probably she would want more than that later on. But even if I gave a million and a half dollars to these institutions I should still have the equivalent of about twenty thousand a year English, and I considered that Nancy could have a pretty good time on that or less.

Anyhow, we had a stiff set of arguments up at the Hurlbird mansion, which stands on a bluff over the town. It may strike you, silent listener, as being funny if you happen to be European. But moral problems of that description and the giving of millions to institutions are immensely serious matters in my country. Indeed, they are the staple topics for consideration amongst the wealthy classes. We haven't got peerages and social climbing to occupy us much, and decent people do not take interest in politics or elderly people in sport. So that there were real tears shed by both Miss Hurlbird and Miss Florence before I left that city.

I left it quite abruptly. Four hours after Edward's telegram came another from Leonora, saying: 'Yes, do come. You could be so helpful.' I simply told my attorney that there was the million and a half; that he could invest it as he liked, and that the purposes must be decided by the Misses Hurlbird. I was, anyhow, pretty well worn out by all the discussions. And, as I have never heard yet from the Misses Hurlbird, I rather think that Miss Hurlbird, either by revelations or by moral force, has persuaded Miss Florence that no memorial to their names shall be erected in the city of Waterbury, Conn. Miss Hurlbird wept dreadfully when she heard that I was going to stay with the Ashburnhams, but she did not make any comments. I was aware, at that date, that her niece had been seduced by that fellow Jimmy before I had married her—but I contrived to produce on her the impression that I thought

Florence had been a model wife. Why, at that date I still believed that Florence had been perfectly virtuous after her marriage to me. I had not figured it out that she could have played it so low down as to continue her intrigue with that fellow under my roof. Well, I was a fool. But I did not think much about Florence at that date. My mind was occupied with what was happening at Branshaw.

I had got it into my head that the telegrams had something to do with Nancy. It struck me that she might have shown signs of forming an attachment for some undesirable fellow and that Leonora wanted me to come back and marry her out of harm's way. That was what was pretty firmly in my mind. And it remained in my mind for nearly ten days after my arrival at that beautiful old place. Neither Edward nor Leonora made any motion to talk to me about anything other than the weather and the crops. Yet, although there were several young fellows about, I could not see that any one in particular was distinguished by the girl's preference. She certainly appeared illish and nervous, except when she woke up to talk gay nonsense to me. Oh, the pretty thing that she was. . . .

I imagined that what must have happened was that the undesirable young man had been forbidden the place and that Nancy was fretting a little.

What had happened was just Hell. Leonora had spoken to Nancy; Nancy had spoken to Edward; Edward had spoken to Leonora—and they had talked and talked. And talked. You have to imagine horrible pictures of gloom and half lights, and emotions running through silent nights —through whole nights. You have to imagine my beautiful Nancy appearing suddenly to Edward, rising up at the foot of his bed, with her long hair falling, like a split cone of shadow, in the glimmer of a night-light that burned beside him. You have to imagine her, a silent, a no doubt agonized figure, like a spectre, suddenly offering herself to him—to save his reason! And you have to imagine his frantic refusal—and talk. And talk! My God!

And yet, to me, living in the house, enveloped with the

charm of the quiet and ordered living, with the silent, skilled servants whose mere laying out of my dress clothes was like a caress—to me who was hourly with them they appeared like tender, ordered and devoted people, smiling, absenting themselves at the proper intervals; driving me to meets—just good people! How the devil—how the devil do they do it?

At dinner one evening Leonora said—she had just opened a telegram:

'Nancy will be going to India, to-morrow, to be with her father.'

No one spoke. Nancy looked at her plate; Edward went on eating his pheasant. I felt very bad; I imagined that it would be up to me to propose to Nancy that evening. It appeared to me to be queer that they had not given me any warning of Nancy's departure. But I thought that that was only English manners—some sort of delicacy that I had not got the hang of. You must remember that at that moment I trusted in Edward and Leonora and in Nancy Rufford, and in the tranquillity of ancient haunts of peace, as I had trusted in my mother's love. And that evening Edward spoke to me.

What in the interval had happened had been this:

Upon her return from Nauheim Leonora had completely broken down—because she knew she could trust Edward. That seems odd but, if you know anything about break-downs, you will know that, by the ingenious torments that fate prepares for us, these things come as soon as, a strain having relaxed, there is nothing more to be done. It is after a husband's long illness and death that a widow goes to pieces; it is at the end of a long rowing contest that a crew collapses and lies forward upon its oars. And that was what happened to Leonora.

From certain tones in Edward's voice; from the long, steady stare that he had given her from his bloodshot eyes on rising from the dinner table in the Nauheim hotel, she knew that, in the affair of the poor girl, this was a case in which Edward's moral scruples, or his social code, or his idea that it would be playing it *too* low down, rendered Nancy perfectly safe. The girl, she felt sure, was in no danger at all from Edward. And in that she was perfectly right. The smash was to come from herself.

She relaxed; she broke; she drifted, at first quickly, then with an increasing momentum, down the stream of destiny. You may put it that, having been cut off from the restraints of her religion, for the first time in her life, she acted along the lines of her instinctive desires. I do not know whether to think that, in that she was no longer herself; or that, having let loose the bonds of her standards, her conventions and her traditions, she was being, for the first time, her own natural self. She was torn between her intense, maternal love for the girl and an intense jealousy of the woman who realizes that the man she loves has met what appears to be the final passion of his life. She was divided between an intense disgust for Edward's weakness in conceiving this passion, an intense pity for the miseries that he was enduring, and a feeling equally intense, but one that she hid from herself—a feeling of respect for Edward's determination to keep himself, in this particular affair, unspotted.

And the human heart is a very mysterious thing. It is impossible to say that Leonora, in acting as she then did, was not filled with a sort of hatred of Edward's final virtue. She wanted, I think, to despise him. He was, she realized gone from her for good. Then let him suffer, let him agonize; let him, if possible, break and go to that Hell that is the abode of broken resolves. She might have taken a different line. It would have been so easy to send the girl away to stay with some friends; to have taken her away herself upon some pretext or other. That would not have cured things but it would have been the decent line. . . . But, at that date, poor Leonora was incapable of taking any line whatever.

She pitied Edward frightfully at one time—and then she acted along the lines of pity; she loathed him at another and then she acted as her loathing dictated. She gasped, as a person dying of tuberculosis gasps for air. She craved madly for communication with some other human soul. And the human soul that she selected was that of the girl.

Perhaps Nancy was the only person that she could have talked to. With her necessity for reticences, with her coldness of manner, Leonora had singularly few intimates. She had none at all, with the exception of the Mrs Colonel Whelen, who had advised her about the affair with La Dolciquita, and the one or two religious, who had guided her through life. The Colonel's wife was at that time in Madeira; the religious she now avoided. Her visitors' book had seven hundred names in it; there was not a soul that she could speak to. She was Mrs Ashburnham of Branshaw Teleragh.

She was the great Mrs Ashburnham of Branshaw and she lay all day upon her bed in her marvellous, light, airy bedroom with the chintzes and the Chippendale and the portraits of deceased Ashburnhams by Zoffany and Zucchero. When there was a meet she would struggle up—supposing it were within driving distance—and let Edward drive her and the girl to the cross-roads or the country house. She would drive herself back alone; Edward would ride off with the girl. Ride Leonora could not, that season —her head was too bad. Each pace of her mare was an anguish.

But she drove with efficiency and precision; she smiled at the Gimmers and Ffoulkes and the Hedley Seatons. She threw with exactitude pennies to the boys who opened gates for her; she sat upright on the seat of the high dog-cart; she waved her hands to Edward and Nancy as they rode off with the hounds, and every one could hear her clear, high voice, in the chilly weather, saying:

'Have a good time!'

Poor forlorn woman!...

There was, however, one spark of consolation. It came from the fact that Rodney Bayham, of Bayham, followed her always with his eyes. It had been three years since she had tried her abortive love-affair with him. Yet still, on the winter mornings he would ride up to her shafts and just say: 'Good day,' and look at her with eyes that were not imploring, but seemed to say: 'You see, I am still, as the Germans say, A.D.—at disposition.'

It was a great consolation, not because she proposed ever to take him up again, but because it showed her that there was in the world one faithful soul in riding-breeches. And it showed her that she was not losing her looks.

And, indeed, she was not losing her looks. She was forty, but she was as clean run as on the day she had left the convent—as clear in outline, as clear coloured in the hair, as dark blue in the eyes. She thought that her looking-glass told her this; but there are always the doubts. ... Rodney Bayham's eyes took them away.

It is very singular that Leonora should not have aged at all. I suppose that there are some types of beauty and even of youth made for the embellishments that come with enduring sorrow. That is too elaborately put. I mean that Leonora, if everything had prospered, might have become too hard and, maybe, overbearing. As it was she was tuned down to appearing efficient—and yet sympathetic. That is the rarest of all blends. And yet I swear that Leonora, in her restrained way, gave the impression of being intensely sympathetic. When she listened to you she appeared also to be listening to some sound that was going on in the distance. But still, she listened to you and took in what you said, which, since the record of humanity is a record of sorrows, was, as a rule, something sad.

I think that she must have taken Nancy through many terrors of the night and many bad places of the day. And that would account for the girl's passionate love for the elder woman. For Nancy's love for Leonora was an admiration that is awakened in Catholics by their feeling for the Virgin Mary and for various of the saints. It is too little to say that the girl would have laid her life at Leonora's feet. Well, she laid there the offer of her virtue—and her reason. Those were sufficient instalments of her life. It would to-day be much better for Nancy Rufford if she were dead.

Perhaps all these reflections are a nuisance; but they crowd on me. I will try to tell the story.

You see—when she came back from Nauheim Leonora began to have her headaches—headaches lasting through whole days, during which she could speak no word and could bear to hear no sound. And, day after day, Nancy would sit with her, silent and motionless for hours, steeping handkerchiefs in vinegar and water, and thinking her own thoughts. It must have been very bad for her—and her meals alone with Edward must have been bad for her too—and beastly bad for Edward. Edward, of course, wavered in his demeanour. What else could he do? At times he would sit silent and dejected over his untouched food. He would utter nothing but monosyllables when Nancy spoke to him. Then he was simply afraid of the girl falling in love with him. At other times he would take a little wine; pull himself together; attempt to chaff Nancy about a stake and binder hedge that her mare had checked at, or talk about the habits of the Chitralis. That was when he was thinking that it was rough on the poor girl that he should have become a dull companion. He realized that his talking to her in the park at Nauheim had done her no harm.

But all that was doing a great deal of harm to Nancy. It gradually opened her eyes to the fact that Edward was a man with his ups and downs and not an invariably gay uncle like a nice dog, a trustworthy horse or a girl friend. She would find him in attitudes of frightful dejection, sunk into his armchair in the study that was half a gun-room. She would notice through the open door that his face was the face of an old, dead man, when he had no one to talk to. Gradually it forced itself upon her attention that there were profound differences between the pair that she regarded as her uncle and her aunt. It was a conviction that came very slowly.

It began with Edward's giving an oldish horse to a young fellow called Selmes. Selmes' father had been ruined by a fraudulent solicitor and the Selmes family had had to sell their hunters. It was a case that had excited a good deal of sympathy in that part of the country. And Edward, meeting the young man one day, unmounted, and seeing him to be very unhappy, had offered to give him an old Irish cob upon which he was riding. It was a silly sort of thing to do, really. The horse was worth from thirty to forty pounds and Edward might have known that the gift would upset his wife. But Edward just had to comfort that unhappy young man whose father he had known all his life. And what made it all the worse was that young Selmes could not afford to keep the horse even. Edward recollected this, immediately after he had made the offer, and said quickly:

'Of course I mean that you should stable the horse at Branshaw until you have time to turn round or want to sell him and get a better.'

Nancy went straight home and told all this to Leonora, who was lying down. She regarded it as a splendid instance of Edward's quick consideration for the feelings and the circumstances of the distressed. She thought it would cheer Leonora up—because it ought to cheer any woman up to know that she had such a splendid husband. That was the last girlish thought she ever had. For Leonora, whose headache had left her collected but miserably weak, turned upon her bed and uttered words that were amazing to the girl:

'I wish to God,' she said, 'that he was your husband, and not mine. We shall be ruined. We shall be ruined. Am I *never* to have a chance?' And suddenly Leonora burst into a passion of tears. She pushed herself up from the pillows with one elbow and sat there—crying, crying, crying, with her face hidden in her hands and the tears falling through her fingers.

The girl flushed, stammered and whimpered as if she had been personally insulted.

'But if Uncle Edward . . .' she began.

'That man,' said Leonora, with an extraordinary bitterness, 'would give the shirt off his back and off mine—and off yours to any . . .' She could not finish the sentence.

At that moment she had been feeling an extraordinary hatred and contempt for her husband. All the morning and all the afternoon she had been lying there thinking that Edward and the girl were together—in the field and hacking it home at dusk. She had been digging her sharp nails into her palms.

The house had been very silent in the drooping winter weather. And then, after an eternity of torture, there had invaded it the sound of opening doors, of the girl's gay voice saying:

'Well, it was only under the mistletoe.' . . . And there was Edward's gruff undertone. Then Nancy had come in, with feet that had hastened up the stairs and that tiptoed as they approached the open door of Leonora's room. Branshaw had a great big hall with oak floors and tiger skins. Round this hall there ran a gallery upon which Leonora's doorway gave. And even when she had the worst of her headaches she liked to have her door open— I suppose so that she might hear the approaching footsteps of ruin and disaster. At any rate she hated to be in a room with a shut door.

At that moment Leonora hated Edward with a hatred that was like hell, and she would have liked to bring her riding-whip down across the girl's face. What right had Nancy to be young and slender and dark, and gay at times, at times mournful? What right had she to be exactly the woman to make Leonora's husband happy? For Leonora knew that Nancy would have made Edward happy.

Yes, Leonora wished to bring her riding-whip down on Nancy's young face. She imagined the pleasure she would feel when the lash fell across those queer features; the pleasure she would feel at drawing the handle at the same moment toward her, so as to cut deep into the flesh and to leave a lasting wheal.

Well, she left a lasting wheal, and her words cut deeply into the girl's mind....

They neither of them spoke about that again. A fortnight went by—a fortnight of deep rains, of heavy fields, of bad scent. Leonora's headaches seemed to have gone for good. She hunted once or twice, letting herself be piloted by Bayham, whilst Edward looked after the girl. Then, one evening, when those three were dining alone, Edward said, in the queer, deliberate, heavy tones that came out of him in those days (he was looking at the table):

'I have been thinking that Nancy ought to do more for her father. He is getting an old man. I have written to Colonel Rufford, suggesting that she should go to him.'

Leonora called out:

'How dare you? How dare you?'

The girl put her hand over her heart and cried out: 'Oh, my sweet Saviour, help me!' That was the queer way she thought within her mind, and the words forced themselves to her lips. Edward said nothing.

And that night, by a merciless trick of the devil that pays attention to this sweltering hell of ours, Nancy Rufford had a letter from her mother. It came whilst Leonora was talking to Edward, or Leonora would have intercepted it as she had intercepted others. It was an amazing and a horrible letter....

I don't know what it contained. I just average out from its effects on Nancy that her mother, having eloped with some worthless sort of fellow, had done what is called 'sinking lower and lower'. Whether she was actually on the streets I do not know, but I rather think that she eked out a small allowance that she had from her husband by that means of livelihood. And I think that she stated as much in her letter to Nancy and upbraided the girl with living in luxury whilst her mother starved. And it must have been horrible in tone, for Mrs Rufford was a cruel sort of woman at the best of times. It must have seemed to that poor girl, opening her letter, for distraction from another grief, up in her bedroom, like the laughter of a devil.

I just cannot bear to think of my poor dear girl at that moment. . . .

And, at the same time, Leonora was lashing, like a cold fiend, into the unfortunate Edward. Or, perhaps, he was not so unfortunate; because he had done what he knew to be the right thing, he may be deemed happy. I leave it to you. At any rate, he was sitting in his deep chair, and Leonora came into his room—for the first time in nine years. She said:

'This is the most atrocious thing you have done in your atrocious life.' He never moved and he never looked at her. God knows what was in Leonora's mind exactly.

I like to think that, uppermost in it was concern and horror at the thought of the poor girl's going back to a father whose voice made her shriek in the night. And, indeed, that motive was very strong with Leonora. But I think there was also present the thought that she wanted to go on torturing Edward with the girl's presence. She was, at that time, capable of that.

Edward was sunk in his chair; there were in the room two candles, hidden by green glass shades. The green shades were reflected in the glasses of the book-cases that contained not books but guns with gleaming brown barrels and fishing-rods in green baize over-covers. There was dimly to be seen, above a mantelpiece encumbered with spurs, hooves and bronze models of horses, a dark-brown picture of a white horse.

'If you think,' Leonora said, 'that I do not know that you are in love with the girl . . .' She began spiritedly, but she could not find any ending for the sentence. Edward did not stir; he never spoke. And then Leonora said:

'If you want me to divorce you, I will. You can marry her then. She's in love with you.'

He groaned at that, a little, Leonora said. Then she went away.

Heaven knows what happened in Leonora after that. She certainly does not herself know. She probably said a good deal more to Edward than I have been able to report; but that is all that she has told me and I am not going to make up speeches. To follow her psychological development of that moment I think we must allow that she upbraided him for a great deal of their past life, whilst Edward sat absolutely silent. And, indeed, in speaking of it afterwards, she has said several times: 'I said a great deal more to him than I wanted to, just because he was so silent.' She talked, in fact, in the endeavour to sting him into speech.

She must have said so much that, with the expression of her grievance, her mood changed. She went back to her own room in the gallery, and sat there for a long time thinking. And she thought herself into a mood of absolute unselfishness, of absolute self-contempt, too. She said to herself that she was no good; that she had failed in all her efforts—in her efforts to get Edward back as in her efforts to make him curb his expenditure. She imagined herself to be exhausted; she imagined herself to be done. Then a great fear came over her.

She thought that Edward, after what she had said to him, must have committed suicide. She went out on to the gallery and listened; there was no sound in all the house except the regular beat of the great clock in the hall. But, even in her debased condition, she was not the person to hang about. She acted. She went straight to Edward's room, opened the door, and looked in.

He was oiling the breech action of a gun. It was an unusual thing for him to do, at that time of night, in his evening clothes. It never occurred to her, nevertheless, that he was going to shoot himself with that implement. She knew that he was doing it just for occupation—to keep himself from thinking. He looked up when she opened the door, his face illuminated by the light cast upwards from the round orifices in the green candle shades.

She said:

'I didn't imagine that I should find Nancy here.' She thought that she owed that to him. He answered then:

'I don't imagine that you did imagine it.' Those were the only words he spoke that night. She went, like a lame duck, back through the long corridors; she stumbled over the familiar tiger skins in the dark hall. She could hardly drag one limb after the other. In the gallery she perceived that Nancy's door was half open and that there was a light in the girl's room. A sudden madness possessed her, a desire for action, a thirst for self-explanation.

Their rooms all gave on to the gallery; Leonora's to the east, the girl's next, then Edward's. The sight of those three open doors, side by side, gaping to receive whom the chances of the black night might bring, made Leonora shudder all over her body. She went into Nancy's room.

The girl was sitting perfectly still in an armchair, very upright, as she had been taught to sit at the convent. She appeared to be as calm as a church; her hair fell, black and like a pall, down over both her shoulders. The fire beside her was burning brightly; she must have just put coals on. She was in a white silk kimono that covered her to the feet. The clothes that she had taken off were exactly folded upon the proper seats. Her long hands were one upon each arm of the chair that had a pink and white chintz back.

Leonora told me these things. She seemed to think it extraordinary that the girl could have done such orderly things as fold up the clothes she had taken off upon such a night—when Edward had announced that he was going to send her to her father, and when, from her mother, she had received that letter. The letter, in its envelope, was in her right hand.

Leonora did not at first perceive it. She said:

'What are you doing so late?'

The girl answered: 'Just thinking.'

They seemed to think in whispers and to speak below their breaths. Then Leonora's eyes fell on the envelope, and she recognized Mrs Rufford's handwriting.

It was one of those moments when thinking was impossible, Leonora said. It was as if stones were being thrown at her from every direction and she could only run. She heard herself exclaim:

'Edward's dying—because of you. He's dying. He's worth more than either of us. . . .'

The girl looked past her at the panels of the half-closed door.

'My poor father,' she said, 'my poor father.'

'You must stay here,' Leonora answered fiercely. 'You must stay here. I tell you you must stay here.'

'I am going to Glasgow,' Nancy answered. 'I shall go to Glasgow to-morrow morning. My mother is in Glasgow.'

It appears that it was in Glasgow that Mrs Rufford pursued her disorderly life. She had selected that city, not because it was more profitable but because it was the natal home of her husband to whom she desired to cause as much pain as possible.

'You must stay here,' Leonora began, 'to save Edward. He's dying for love of you.'

The girl turned her calm eyes upon Leonora.

'I know it,' she said. 'And I am dying for love of him.'

Leonora uttered an 'Ah,' that, in spite of herself, was an 'Ah' of horror and of grief.

'That is why,' the girl continued, 'I am going to Glasgow—to take my mother away from there.' She added, 'To the ends of the earth,' for, if the last months had made her nature that of a woman, her phrases were still romantically those of a schoolgirl. It was as if she had grown up so quickly that there had not been time to put her hair up. But she added: 'We're no good—my mother and I.'

Leonora said, with her fierce calmness:

'No. No. You're not no good. It's I that am no good. You can't let that man go on to ruin for want of you. You must belong to him.'

The girl, she said, smiled at her with a queer, far-away smile—as if she were a thousand years old, as if Leonora were a tiny child.

'I knew you would come to that,' she said, very slowly.
'But we are not worth it—Edward and I.'

III

Nancy had, in fact, been thinking ever since Leonora had
made that comment over the giving of the horse to young
Selmes. She had been thinking and thinking, because she
had had to sit for many days silent beside her aunt's bed.
(She had always thought of Leonora as her aunt.) And
she had had to sit thinking during many silent meals with
Edward. And then, at times, with his bloodshot eyes and
creased, heavy mouth, he would smile at her. And gradually the knowledge had come to her that Edward did not
love Leonora and that Leonora hated Edward. Several
things contributed to form and to harden this conviction.

She was allowed to read the papers in those days—or,
rather, since Leonora was always on her bed and Edward
breakfasted alone and went out early, over the estate, she
was left alone with the papers. One day, in the papers, she
saw the portrait of a woman she knew very well. Beneath
it she read the words: 'The Hon. Mrs Brand, plaintiff in
the remarkable divorce case reported on p. 8.' Nancy
hardly knew what a divorce case was. She had been so
remarkably well brought up, and Roman Catholics do not
practise divorce. I don't know how Leonora had done it
exactly. I suppose she had always impressed it on Nancy's
mind that nice women did not read these things, and that
would have been enough to make Nancy skip those pages.

She read, at any rate, the account of the Brand divorce
case—principally because she wanted to tell Leonora about
it. She imagined that Leonora, when her headache left her,
would like to know what was happening to Mrs Brand,
who lived at Christchurch, and whom they both liked very
well. The case occupied three days, and the report that
Nancy first came upon was that of the third day. Edward,
however, kept the papers of the week, after his methodical

fashion, in a rack in his gun-room, and when she had finished her breakfast Nancy went to that quiet apartment and had what she would have called a good read. It seemed to her to be a queer affair. She could not understand why one counsel should be so anxious to know all about the movements of Mr Brand upon a certain day; she could not understand why a chart of the bedroom accommodation at Christchurch Old Hall should be produced in court. She did not even see why they should want to know that, upon a certain occasion, the drawing-room door was locked. It made her laugh; it appeared to be all so senseless that grown people should occupy themselves with such matters. It struck her, nevertheless, as odd that one of the counsel should cross-question Mr Brand so insistently and so impertinently as to his feelings for Miss Lupton. Nancy knew Miss Lupton of Ringwood very well—a jolly girl, who rode a horse with two white fetlocks. Mr Brand persisted that he did not love Miss Lupton.... Well, of course he did not love Miss Lupton; he was a married man. You might as well think of Uncle Edward loving ... loving anybody but Leonora. When people were married there was an end of loving. There were, no doubt, people who misbehaved—but they were poor people—or people not like those she knew.

So these matters presented themselves to Nancy's mind.

But later on in the case she found that Mr Brand had to confess to a 'guilty intimacy' with some one or other. Nancy imagined that he must have been telling some one his wife's secrets; she could not understand why that was a serious offence. Of course it was not very gentlemanly—it lessened her opinion of Mr Brand. But since she found that Mrs Brand had condoned that offence, she imagined that they could not have been very serious secrets that Mr Brand had told. And then, suddenly, it was forced on her conviction that Mr Brand—the mild Mr Brand that she had seen a month or two before their departure to Nauheim, playing 'Blind Man's Buff' with his children and kissing his wife when he caught her—Mr Brand and Mrs

Brand had been on the worst possible terms. That was incredible.

Yet there it was—in black and white. Mr Brand drank; Mr Brand had struck Mrs Brand to the ground when he was drunk. Mr Brand was adjudged, in two or three abrupt words, at the end of columns and columns of paper, to have been guilty of cruelty to his wife and to have committed adultery with Miss Lupton. The last words conveyed nothing to Nancy—nothing real, that is to say. She knew that one was commanded not to commit adultery —but why, she thought, should one? It was probably something like catching salmon out of season—a thing one did not do. She gathered it had something to do with kissing, or holding some one in your arms. . . .

And yet the whole effect of that reading upon Nancy was mysterious, terrifying and evil. She felt a sickness—a sickness that grew as she read. Her heart beat painfully; she began to cry. She asked God how He could permit such things to be. And she was more certain that Edward did not love Leonora and that Leonora hated Edward. Perhaps, then, Edward loved some one else. It was un-thinkable.

If he could love some one else than Leonora, her fierce unknown heart suddenly spoke in her side, why could it not be herself? And he did not love her. . . . This had occurred about a month before she got the letter from her mother. She let the matter rest until the sick feeling went off; it did that in a day or two. Then, finding that Leo-nora's headaches had gone, she suddenly told Leonora that Mrs Brand had divorced her husband. She asked what, exactly, it all meant.

Leonora was lying on the sofa in the hall; she was feeling so weak that she could hardly find the words. She answered just:

'It means that Mr Brand will be able to marry again.'

Nancy said:

'But . . . but . . .' and then: 'He will be able to marry

Miss Lupton.' Leonora just moved a hand in assent. Her eyes were shut.

'Then...' Nancy began. Her blue eyes were full of horror: her brows were tight above them; the lines of pain about her mouth were very distinct. In her eyes the whole of that familiar, great hall had a changed aspect. The andirons with the brass flowers at the ends appeared unreal; the burning logs were just logs that were burning and not the comfortable symbols of an indestructible mode of life. The flame fluttered before the high fireback; the St Bernard sighed in his sleep. Outside the winter rain fell and fell. And suddenly she thought that Edward might marry some one else; and she nearly screamed.

Leonora opened her eyes, lying sideways, with her face upon the black and gold pillow of the sofa that was drawn half across the great fireplace.

'I thought,' Nancy said, 'I never imagined.... Aren't marriages sacraments? Aren't they indissoluble? I thought you were married... and...' She was sobbing. 'I thought you were married or not married as you are alive or dead.'

'That,' Leonora said, 'is the law of the church. It is not the law of the land....'

'Oh yes,' Nancy said, 'the Brands are Protestants.'

She felt a sudden safeness descend upon her, and for an hour or so her mind was at rest. It seemed to her idiotic not to have remembered Henry VIII and the basis upon which Protestantism rests. She almost laughed at herself.

The long afternoon wore on; the flames still fluttered when the maid made up the fire; the St Bernard awoke and lolloped away towards the kitchen. And then Leonora opened her eyes and said almost coldly:

'And you? Don't you think you will get married?'

It was so unlike Leonora that, for the moment, the girl was frightened in the dusk. But then, again, it seemed a perfectly reasonable question.

'I don't know,' she answered. 'I don't know that anyone wants to marry me.'

'Several people want to marry you,' Leonora said.

'But I don't want to marry,' Nancy answered. 'I should like to go on living with you and Edward. I don't think I am in the way or that I am really an expense. If I went you would have to have a companion. Or, perhaps, I ought to earn my living. . . .'

'I wasn't thinking of that,' Leonora answered in the same dull tone. 'You will have money enough from your father. But most people want to be married.'

I believe that she then asked the girl if she would not like to marry me, and that Nancy answered that she would marry me if she were told to; but that she wanted to go on living there. She added:

'If I married anyone I should want him to be like Edward.'

She was frightened out of her life. Leonora writhed on her couch and called out: 'Oh, God! . . .'

Nancy ran for the maid; for tablets of aspirin; for wet handkerchiefs. It never occurred to her that Leonora's expression of agony was for anything else than physical pain.

You are to remember that all this happened a month before Leonora went into the girl's room at night. I have been casting back again; but I cannot help it. It is so difficult to keep all these people going. I tell you about Leonora and bring her up to date; then about Edward, who has fallen behind. And then the girl gets hopelessly left behind. I wish I could put it down in diary form. Thus: On the 1st of September they returned from Nauheim. Leonora at once took to her bed. By the 1st of October they were all going to meets together. Nancy had already observed very fully that Edward was strange in his manner. About the 6th of that month Edward gave the horse to young Selmes, and Nancy had cause to believe that her aunt did not love her uncle. On the 20th she read the account of the divorce case, which is reported in the papers of the 18th and the two following days. On the 23rd she had the conversation with her aunt in the hall—about marriage in general and about her own possible marriage. Her aunt's coming to her bedroom did not occur until the 12th of November. . . .

Thus she had three weeks of introspection—for introspection beneath gloomy skies, in that old house, rendered darker by the fact that it lay in a hollow crowned by fir trees with their black shadows. It was not a good situation for a girl. She began thinking about love, she who had never before considered it as anything other than a rather humorous, rather nonsensical matter. She remembered chance passages in chance books—things that had not really affected her at all at the time. She remembered someone's love for the Princess Badrulbadour; she remembered to have heard that love was a flame, a thirst, a withering up of the vitals—though she did not know what the vitals were. She had a vague recollection that love was said to render a hopeless lover's eyes hopeless; she remembered a character in a book who was said to have taken to drink through love; she remembered that lovers' existences were said to be punctuated with heavy sighs. Once she went to the little cottage piano that was in a corner of the hall and began to play. It was a tinkly, reedy instrument, for none of that household had any turn for music. Nancy herself could play a few simple songs, and she found herself playing. She had been sitting on the window seat, looking out on the fading day. Leonora had gone to pay some calls; Edward was looking after some planting up in the new spinney. Thus she found herself playing on the old piano. She did not know how she came to be doing it. A silly, lilting, wavering tune came from before her in the dusk—a tune in which major notes with their cheerful insistence wavered and melted into minor sounds, as, beneath a bridge, the high lights on dark waters melt and waver and disappear into black depths. Well, it was a silly old tune. . . .

It goes with the words—they are about a willow tree, I think:

> Thou art to all lost loves the best
> The only true plant found.

—That sort of thing. It is Herrick, I believe, and the music with the reedy, irregular, lilting sound that goes with Herrick. And it was dusk; the heavy, hewn, dark pillars that supported the gallery were like mourning presences; the fire had sunk to nothing—a mere glow amongst white ashes. . . . It was a sentimental sort of place and light and hour. . . .

And suddenly Nancy found that she was crying. She was crying quietly; she went on to cry with long convulsive sobs. It seemed to her that everything gay, everything charming, all light, all sweetness, had gone out of life. Unhappiness; unhappiness; unhappiness was all around her. She seemed to know no happy being and she herself was agonizing. . . .

She remembered that Edward's eyes were hopeless; she was certain that he was drinking too much; at times he sighed deeply. He appeared as a man who was burning with inward flame; drying up in the soul with thirst; withering up in the vitals. Then, the torturing conviction came to her—the conviction that had visited her again and again—that Edward must love some one other than Leonora. With her little, pedagogic sectarianism she remembered that Catholics do not do this thing. But Edward was a Protestant. Then Edward loved somebody. . . .

And, after that thought, her eyes grew hopeless; she sighed as the old St Bernard beside her did. At meals she would feel an intolerable desire to drink a glass of wine, and then another and then a third. Then she would find herself grow gay. . . . But in half an hour the gaiety went; she felt like a person who is burning up with an inward flame; desiccating at the soul with thirst; withering up in the vitals. One evening she went into Edward's gun-room —he had gone to a meeting of the National Reserve Committee. On the table beside his chair was a decanter of whisky. She poured out a wineglassful and drank it off.

Flame then really seemed to fill her body; her legs swelled; her face grew feverish. She dragged her tall height up to her room and lay in the dark. The bed reeled beneath her; she gave way to the thought that she was in Edward's arms; that he was kissing her on her face that burned; on her shoulders that burned, and on her neck that was on fire.

She never touched alcohol again. Not once after that did she have such thoughts. They died out of her mind; they left only a feeling of shame so insupportable that her brain could not take it in and they vanished. She imagined that her anguish at the thought of Edward's love for another person was solely sympathy for Leonora; she determined that the rest of her life must be spent in acting as Leonora's handmaiden—sweeping, tending, embroidering, like some Deborah, some mediaeval saint—I am not, unfortunately, up in the Catholic hagiology. But I know that she pictured herself as some personage with a depressed, earnest face and tightly closed lips, in a clear white room, watering flowers or tending an embroidery frame. Or, she desired to go with Edward to Africa and to throw herself in the path of a charging lion so that Edward might be saved for Leonora at the cost of her life. Well, along with her sad thoughts she had her childish ones.

She knew nothing—nothing of life, except that one must live sadly. That she now knew. What happened to her on the night when she received at once the blow that Edward wished her to go to her father in India and the blow of the letter from her mother was this. She called first upon her sweet Saviour—and she thought of Our Lord as her sweet Saviour!—that He might make it impossible that she should go to India. Then she realized from Edward's demeanour that he was determined that she should go to India. It must then be right that she should go. Edward was always right in his determinations. He was the Cid; he was Lohengrin; he was the Chevalier Bayard.

Nevertheless her mind mutinied and revolted. She could not leave that house. She imagined that he wished her gone that she might not witness his amours with another girl.

Well, she was prepared to tell him that she was ready to witness his amours with another young girl. She would stay there—to comfort Leonora.

Then came the desperate shock of the letter from her mother. Her mother said, I believe, something like: 'You have no right to go on living your life of prosperity and respect. You ought to be on the streets with me. How do you know that you are even Colonel Rufford's daughter?' She did not know what these words meant. She thought of her mother as sleeping beneath the arches whilst the snow fell. That was the impression conveyed to her mind by the words 'on the streets.' A Platonic sense of duty gave her the idea that she ought to go to comfort her mother—the mother that bore her, though she hardly knew what the words meant. At the same time she knew that her mother had left her father with another man—therefore she pitied her father, and thought it terrible in herself that she trembled at the sound of her father's voice. If her mother was that sort of woman it was natural that her father should have had accesses of madness in which he had struck herself to the ground. And the voice of her conscience said to her that her first duty was to her parents. It was in accord with this awakened sense of duty that she undressed with great care and meticulously folded the clothes that she took off. Sometimes, but not very often, she threw them helter-skelter about the room.

And that sense of duty was her prevailing mood when Leonora, tall, clean-run, golden-haired, all in black, appeared in her doorway, and told her that Edward was dying of love for her. She knew then with her conscious mind what she had known within herself for months—that Edward was dying—actually and physically dying—of love for her. It seemed to her that for one short moment her spirit could say: '*Domine, nunc dimittis*. . . . Lord, now lettest thou thy servant depart in peace.' She imagined that she could cheerfully go away to Glasgow and rescue her fallen mother.

IV

And it seemed to her to be in tune with the mood, with the hour, and with the woman in front of her to say that she knew Edward was dying of love for her and that she was dying of love for Edward. For that fact had suddenly slipped into place and become real for her as the niched marker on a whist tablet slips round with the pressure of your thumb. That rubber at least was made.

And suddenly Leonora seemed to have become different and she seemed to have become different in her attitude towards Leonora. It was as if she, in her frail, white, silken kimono, sat beside her fire, but upon a throne. It was as if Leonora, in her close dress of black lace, with the gleaming white shoulders and the coiled yellow hair that the girl had always considered the most beautiful thing in the world—it was as if Leonora had become pinched, shrivelled, blue with cold, shivering, suppliant. Yet Leonora was commanding her. It was no good commanding her. She was going on the morrow to her mother who was in Glasgow.

Leonora went on saying that she must stay there to save Edward, who was dying of love for her. And, proud and happy in the thought that Edward loved her, and that she loved him, she did not even listen to what Leonora said. It appeared to her that it was Leonora's business to save her husband's body; she, Nancy, possessed his soul—a precious thing that she would shield and bear away up in her arms—as if Leonora were a hungry dog, trying to spring up at a lamb that she was carrying. Yes, she felt as if Edward's love were a precious lamb that she were bearing away from a cruel and predatory beast. For, at that time, Leonora appeared to her as a cruel and predatory beast. Leonora, Leonora with her hunger, with her cruelty had driven Edward to madness. He must be sheltered by his love for her and by her love—her love from a great distance and unspoken, enveloping him, surrounding him, upholding him; by her voice speaking from Glasgow,

saying that she loved, that she adored, that she passed no
moment without longing, loving, quivering at the thought
of him.

Leonora said loudly, insistently, with a bitterly imperative tone:

'You must stay here; you must belong to Edward. I will
divorce him.'

The girl answered:

'The Church does not allow of divorce. I cannot belong
to your husband. I am going to Glasgow to rescue my
mother.'

The half-opened door opened noiselessly to the full.
Edward was there. His devouring, doomed eyes were fixed
on the girl's face; his shoulders slouched forward; he was
undoubtedly half drunk and he had the whisky decanter in
one hand, a slanting candlestick in the other. He said, with
a heavy ferocity, to Nancy:

'I forbid you to talk about these things. You are to stay
here until I hear from your father. Then you will go to
your father.'

The two women, looking at each other, like beasts about
to spring, hardly gave a glance to him. He leaned against
the door-post. He said again:

'Nancy, I forbid you to talk about these things. I am the
master of this house.' And, at the sound of his voice, heavy,
male, coming from a deep chest, in the night with the
blackness behind him, Nancy felt as if her spirit bowed
before him, with folded hands. She felt that she would go
to India, and that she desired never again to talk of these
things.

Leonora said:

'You see that it is your duty to belong to him. He must
not be allowed to go on drinking.'

Nancy did not answer. Edward was gone; they heard
him slipping and shambling on the polished black oak of
the stairs. Nancy screamed when there came the sound of
a heavy fall. Leonora said again:

'You see!'

The sounds went on from the hall below; the light of the candle Edward held flickered up between the hand rails of the gallery. Then they heard his voice:

'Give me Glasgow ... Glasgow, in Scotland ... I want the number of a man called White, of Simrock Park, Glasgow ... Edward White, Simrock Park, Glasgow ... ten minutes ... at this time of night ...' His voice was quite level, normal, and patient. Alcohol took him in the legs, not the speech. 'I can wait,' his voice came again. 'Yes, I know they have a number. I have been in communication with them before.'

'He is going to telephone to your mother,' Leonora said. 'He will make it all right for her.' She got up and closed the door. She came back to the fire, and added bitterly: 'He can always make it all right for everybody, except me—excepting me!'

The girl said nothing. She sat there in a blissful dream. She seemed to see her lover sitting as he always sat, in a round-backed chair, in the dark hall—sitting low, with the receiver at his ear, talking in a gentle, slow voice, that he reserved for the telephone—and saving the world and her, in the black darkness. She moved her hand over the bareness of the base of her throat, to have the warmth of flesh upon it and upon her bosom.

She said nothing; Leonora went on talking. . . .

God knows what Leonora said. She repeated that the girl must belong to her husband. She said that she used that phrase because, though she might have a divorce, or even a dissolution of the marriage by the Church, it would still be adultery that the girl and Edward would be committing. But she said that that was necessary; it was the price that the girl must pay for the sin of having made Edward love her, for the sin of loving her husband. She talked on and on, beside the fire. The girl must become an adulteress; she had wronged Edward by being so beautiful, so gracious, so good. It was sinful to be so good. She must pay the price so as to save the man she had wronged.

In between her pauses the girl could hear the voice of Edward, droning on, indistinguishably, with jerky pauses for replies. It made her glow with pride; the man she loved was working for her. He at least was resolved; was malely determined; knew the right thing. Leonora talked on with her eyes boring into Nancy's. The girl hardly looked at her and hardly heard her. After a long time Nancy said—after hours and hours:

'I shall go to India as soon as Edward hears from my father. I cannot talk about these things, because Edward does not wish it.'

At that Leonora screamed out and wavered swiftly towards the closed door. And Nancy found that she was springing out of her chair with her white arms stretched wide. She was clasping the other woman to her breast; she was saying:

'Oh, my poor dear; oh, my poor dear.' And they sat, crouching together in each other's arms, and crying and crying; and they lay down in the same bed, talking and talking, all through the night. And all through the night Edward could hear their voices through the wall. That was how it went. . . .

Next morning they were all three as if nothing had happened. Towards eleven Edward came to Nancy, who was arranging some Christmas roses in a silver bowl. He put a telegram beside her on the table. 'You can uncode it for yourself,' he said. Then, as he went out of the door, he said:

'You can tell your aunt I have cabled to Mr Dowell to come over. He will make things easier till you leave.'

The telegram, when it was uncoded, read, as far as I can remember:

'Will take Mrs Rufford to Italy. Undertake to do this for certain. Am devotedly attached to Mrs Rufford. Have no need of financial assistance. Did not know there was a daughter, and am much obliged to you for pointing out my duty.—White.' It was something like that.

Then that household resumed its wonted course of days until my arrival.

V

It is this part of the story that makes me saddest of all. For I ask myself unceasingly, my mind going round and round in a weary, baffled space of pain—what should these people have done? What, in the name of God, should they have done?

The end was perfectly plain to each of them—it was perfectly manifest at that stage that, if the girl did not, in Leonora's phrase, 'belong to Edward,' Edward must die, the girl must lose her reason because Edward died—and, that after a time, Leonora, who was the coldest and the strongest of the three, would console herself by marrying Rodney Bayham and have a quiet, comfortable, good time. That end, on that night, whilst Leonora sat in the girl's bedroom and Edward telephoned down below—that end was plainly manifest. The girl, plainly, was half-mad already; Edward was half dead; only Leonora, active, persistent, instinct with her cold passion of energy, was 'doing things.' What then, should they have done? It worked out in the extinction of two very splendid personalities—for Edward and the girl *were* splendid personalities, in order that a third personality, more normal, should have, after a long period of trouble, a quiet, comfortable, good time.

I am writing this, now, I should say, a full eighteen months after the words that end my last chapter. Since writing the words 'until my arrival,' which I see end that paragraph, I have seen again for a glimpse, from a swift train, Beaucaire with the beautiful white tower, Tarascon with the square castle, the great Rhone, the immense stretches of the Crau. I have rushed through all Provence —and all Provence no longer matters. It is no longer in the olive hills that I shall find my Heaven; because there is only Hell. . . .

7*

Edward is dead; the girl is gone—oh, utterly gone; Leonora is having her good time with Rodney Bayham, and I sit alone in Branshaw Teleragh. I have been through Provence; I have seen Africa; I have visited Asia to see, in Ceylon, in a darkened room, my poor girl, sitting motionless, with her wonderful hair about her, looking at me with eyes that did not see me, and saying distinctly: '*Credo in unum Deum omnipotentem. . . . Credo in unum Deum omnipotentem.*' Those are the only reasonable words she uttered; those are the only words, it appears, that she ever will utter. I suppose that they are reasonable words; it must be extraordinarily reasonable for her, if she can say that she believes in an Omnipotent Deity. Well, there it is. I am very tired of it all. . . .

For, I daresay, all this may sound romantic, but it is tiring, tiring, tiring to have been in the midst of it; to have taken the tickets; to have caught the trains; to have chosen the cabins; to have consulted the purser and the stewards as to diet for the quiescent patient who did nothing but announce her belief in an Omnipotent Deity. That may sound romantic—but it is just a record of fatigue.

I don't know why I should always be selected to be serviceable. I don't resent it—but I have never been the least good. Florence selected me for her own purposes, and I was no good to her; Edward called me to come and have a chat with him, and I couldn't stop him cutting his throat.

And then, one day eighteen months ago, I was quietly writing in my room at Branshaw when Leonora came to me with a letter. It was a very pathetic letter from Colonel Rufford about Nancy. Colonel Rufford had left the army and had taken up an appointment at a tea-planting estate in Ceylon. His letter was pathetic because it was so brief, so inarticulate, and so business-like. He had gone down to the boat to meet his daughter, and had found his daughter quite mad. It appears that at Aden Nancy had seen in a local paper the news of Edward's suicide. In the Red Sea she had gone mad. She had remarked to Mrs Colonel Luton, who was chaperoning her, that she believed in an

Omnipotent Deity. She hadn't made any fuss; her eyes were quite dry and glassy. Even when she was mad Nancy could behave herself.

Colonel Rufford said the doctor did not anticipate that there was any chance of his child's recovery. It was, nevertheless, possible that if she could see some one from Branshaw it might soothe her and it might have a good effect. And he just simply wrote to Leonora: 'Please come and see if you can do it.'

I seem to have lost all sense of the pathetic; but still, that simple, enormous request of the old colonel strikes me as pathetic. He was cursed by his atrocious temper; he had been cursed by a half-mad wife, who drank and went on the streets. His daughter was totally mad—and yet he believed in the goodness of human nature. He believed that Leonora would take the trouble to go all the way to Ceylon in order to soothe his daughter. Leonora wouldn't. Leonora didn't ever want to see Nancy again. I daresay that that, in the circumstances, was natural enough. At the same time she agreed, as it were, on public grounds, that some one soothing ought to go from Branshaw to Ceylon. She sent me and her old nurse, who had looked after Nancy from the time when the girl, a child of thirteen, had first come to Branshaw. So off I go, rushing through Provence, to catch the steamer at Marseilles. And I wasn't the least good when I got to Ceylon; and the nurse wasn't the least good. Nothing has been the least good.

The doctors said, at Kandy, that if Nancy could be brought to England, the sea air, the change of climate, the voyage, and all the usual sort of things, might restore her reason. Of course, they haven't restored her reason. She is, I am aware, sitting in the hall, forty paces from where I am now writing. I don't want to be in the least romantic about it. She is very well dressed; she is quite quiet; she is very beautiful. The old nurse looks after her very efficiently.

Of course you have the makings of a situation here, but it is all very humdrum, as far as I am concerned. I should marry Nancy if her reason were ever sufficiently restored to let her appreciate the meaning of the Anglican marriage service. But it is probable that her reason will never be sufficiently restored to let her appreciate the meaning of the Anglican marriage service. Therefore I cannot marry her, according to the law of the land.

So here I am very much where I started thirteen years ago. I am the attendant, not the husband, of a beautiful girl, who pays no attention to me. I am estranged from Leonora, who married Rodney Bayham in my absence and went to live at Bayham. Leonora rather dislikes me, because she has got it into her head that I disapprove of her marriage with Rodney Bayham. Well, I disapprove of her marriage. Possibly I am jealous.

Yes, no doubt I am jealous. In my fainter sort of way I seem to perceive myself following the lines of Edward Ashburnham. I suppose that I should really like to be a polygamist; with Nancy, and with Leonora, and with Maisie Maidan and possibly even with Florence. I am no doubt like every other man; only, probably because of my American origin I am fainter. At the same time I am able to assure you that I am a strictly respectable person. I have never done anything that the most anxious mother of a daughter or the most careful dean of a cathedral would object to. I have only followed, faintly, and in my unconscious desires, Edward Ashburnham. Well, it is all over. Not one of us has got what he really wanted. Leonora wanted Edward, and she has got Rodney Bayham, a pleasant enough sort of sheep. Florence wanted Branshaw, and it is I who have bought it from Leonora. I didn't really want it; what I wanted mostly was to cease being a nurse-attendant. Well, I am a nurse-attendant. Edward wanted Nancy Rufford, and I have got her. Only she is mad. It is a queer and fantastic world. Why can't people have what they want? The things were all there to content everybody; yet everybody has the wrong thing. Perhaps you can make head or tail of it; it is beyond me.

Is there then any terrestrial paradise where, amidst the whispering of the olive-leaves, people can be with whom

they like and have what they like and take their ease in
shadows and in coolness? Or are all men's lives like the
lives of us good people—like the lives of the Ashburnhams,
of the Dowells, of the Ruffords—broken, tumultuous,
agonized, and unromantic lives, periods punctuated by
screams, by imbecilities, by deaths, by agonies? Who the
devil knows?

For there was a great deal of imbecility about the closing
scenes of the Ashburnham tragedy. Neither of those two
women knew what they wanted. It was only Edward who
took a perfectly clear line, and he was drunk most of the
time. But, drunk or sober, he stuck to what was demanded
by convention and by the traditions of his house. Nancy
Rufford had to be exported to India, and Nancy Rufford
hadn't to hear a word of love from him. She was exported
to India and she never heard a word from Edward Ashburnham.

It was the conventional line; it was in tune with the
tradition of Edward's house. I daresay it worked out for
the greatest good of the body politic. Conventions and
traditions, I suppose, work blindly but surely for the
preservation of the normal type; for the extinction of
proud, resolute, and unusual individuals.

Edward was the normal man, but there was too much of
the sentimentalist about him; and society does not need too
many sentimentalists. Nancy was a splendid creature, but
she had about her a touch of madness. Society does not
need individuals with touches of madness about them. So
Edward and Nancy found themselves steamrolled out and
Leonora survives, the perfectly normal type, married to a
man who is rather like a rabbit. For Rodney Bayham is
rather like a rabbit, and I hear that Leonora is expected to
have a baby in three months' time.

So those splendid and tumultuous creatures with their
magnetism and their passions—those two that I really
loved—have gone from this earth. It is no doubt best for
them. What would Nancy have made of Edward if she had

succeeded in living with him; what would Edward have made of her? For there was about Nancy a touch of cruelty —a touch of definite actual cruelty that made her desire to see people suffer. Yes, she desired to see Edward suffer. And, by God, she gave him hell.

She gave him an unimaginable hell. Those two women pursued that poor devil and flayed the skin off him as if they had done it with whips. I tell you his mind bled almost visibly. I seem to see him stand, naked to the waist, his forearms shielding his eyes, and flesh hanging from him in rags. I tell you that is no exaggeration of what I feel. It was as if Leonora and Nancy banded themselves together to do execution, for the sake of humanity, upon the body of a man who was at their disposal. They were like a couple of Sioux who had got hold of an Apache and had him well tied to a stake. I tell you there was no end to the tortures they inflicted upon him.

Night after night he would hear them talking; talking; maddened, sweating, seeking oblivion in drink, he would lie there and hear the voices going on and on. And day after day Leonora would come to him and would announce the results of their deliberations.

They were like judges debating over the sentence upon a criminal; they were like ghouls with an immobile corpse in a tomb beside them.

I don't think that Leonora was any more to blame than the girl—though Leonora was the more active of the two. Leonora, as I have said, was the perfectly normal woman. I mean to say that in normal circumstances her desires were those of the woman who is needed by society. She desired children, decorum, an establishment; she desired to avoid waste, she desired to keep up appearances. She was utterly and entirely normal even in her utterly un-deniable beauty. But I don't mean to say that she acted perfectly normally in this perfectly abnormal situation. All the world was mad around her and she herself, agonized, took on the complexion of a mad woman; of a woman very wicked; of the villain of the piece. What would you have?

Steel is a normal, hard, polished substance. But, if you put it in a hot fire it will become red, soft, and not to be handled. If you put it in a fire still more hot it will drip away. It was like that with Leonora. She was made for normal circumstances—for Mr Rodney Bayham, who will keep a separate establishment, secretly, in Portsmouth, and make occasional trips to Paris and to Budapest.

In the case of Edward and the girl, Leonora broke and simply went all over the place. She adopted unfamiliar and therefore extraordinary and ungraceful attitudes of mind. At one moment she was all for revenge. After haranguing the girl for hours through the night she harangued for hours of the day the silent Edward. And Edward just once tripped up, and that was his undoing. Perhaps he had had too much whisky that afternoon.

She asked him perpetually what he wanted. What did he want? What did he want? And all he ever answered was: 'I have told you.' He meant that he wanted the girl to go to her father in India as soon as her father should cable that he was ready to receive her. But just once he tripped up. To Leonora's eternal question he answered that all he desired in life was that—that he could pick himself together again and go on with his daily occupations if—the girl, being five thousand miles away, would continue to love him. He wanted nothing more. He prayed his God for nothing more. Well, he was a sentimentalist.

And the moment that she heard that, Leonora determined that the girl should not go five thousand miles away and that she should not continue to love Edward. The way she worked it was this:

She continued to tell the girl that she must belong to Edward; she was going to get a divorce; she was going to get a dissolution of marriage from Rome. But she considered it to be her duty to warn the girl of the sort of monster that Edward was. She told the girl of La Dolciquita, of Mrs Basil, of Maisie Maidan, of Florence. She spoke of the agonies that she had endured during her life with the man, who was violent, overbearing, vain, drunken, arrogant, and monstrously a prey to his sexual necessities. And, at hearing of the miseries her aunt had suffered—for Leonora once more had the aspect of an aunt to the girl— with the swift cruelty of youth and, with the swift solidarity that attaches woman to woman, the girl made her resolves. Her aunt said incessantly: 'You must save Edward's life; you must save his life. All that he needs is a little period of satisfaction from you. Then he will tire of you as he has of the others. But you must save his life.'

And, all the while, that wretched fellow knew—by a curious instinct that runs between human beings living together—exactly what was going on. And he remained dumb; he stretched out no finger to help himself. All that he required to keep himself a decent member of society was, that the girl, five thousand miles away, should continue to love him. They were putting a stopper upon that.

I have told you that the girl came one night to his room. And that was the real hell for him. That was the picture that never left his imagination—the girl, in the dim light, rising up at the foot of his bed. He said that it seemed to have a greenish sort of effect as if there were a greenish tinge in the shadows of the tall bedposts that framed her body. And she looked at him with her straight eyes of an unflinching cruelty and she said: 'I am ready to belong to you—to save your life.'

He answered: 'I don't want it; I don't want it; I don't want it.'

And he says that he didn't want it; that he would have hated himself; that it was unthinkable. And all the while he had the immense temptation to do the unthinkable thing, not from the physical desire but because of a mental certitude. He was certain that if she had once submitted to him she would remain his for ever. He knew that.

She was thinking that her aunt had said he had desired her to love him from a distance of five thousand miles. She said: 'I can never love you now I know the kind of man you are. I will belong to you to save your life. But I can never love you.'

It was a fantastic display of cruelty. She didn't in the least know what it meant—to belong to a man. But, at that, Edward pulled himself together. He spoke in his normal tones; gruff, husky, overbearing, as he would have done to a servant or to a horse.

'Go back to your room,' he said. 'Go back to your room and go to sleep. This is all nonsense.'

They were baffled, those two women.
And then I came on the scene.

VI

My coming on the scene certainly calmed things down— for the whole fortnight that intervened between my arrival and the girl's departure. I don't mean to say that the end- less talking did not go on at night or that Leonora did not send me out with the girl and, in the interval, give Edward a hell of a time. Having discovered what he wanted—that the girl should go five thousand miles away and love him steadfastly as people do in sentimental novels, she was determined to smash that aspiration. And she repeated to Edward in every possible tone that the girl did not love him; that the girl detested him for his brutality, his over- bearingness, his drinking habits. She pointed out that Edward, in the girl's eyes, was already pledged three or four deep. He was pledged to Leonora herself, to Mrs Basil, and to the memories of Maisie Maidan and to Florence. Edward never said anything.

Did the girl love Edward, or didn't she? I don't know. At that time I daresay she didn't, though she certainly had done so before Leonora had got to work upon his reputa- tion. She certainly had loved him for what I will call the public side of his record—for his good soldiering, for his saving lives at sea, for the excellent landlord that he was and the good sportsman. But it is quite possible that all those things came to appear as nothing in her eyes when she discovered that he wasn't a good husband. For, though women, as I see them, have little or no feeling of responsibility towards a county or a country or a career—although they may be entirely lacking in any kind of communal solidarity—they have an immense and automatically working instinct that attaches them to the interest of womanhood. It is, of course, possible for any woman to cut out and to carry off any other woman's husband or lover. But I rather think that a woman will only do this if she has reason to believe that the other woman has given her husband a bad time. I am certain that if she thinks the man has been a brute to his wife she will, with her instinctive feeling for suffering femininity, 'put him back,' as the saying is. I don't attach any particular importance to these generalizations of mine. They may be right, they may be wrong; I am only an ageing American with very little knowledge of life. You may take my generalizations or leave them. But I am pretty certain that I am right in the case of Nancy Rufford—that she had loved Edward Ashburnham very deeply and tenderly.

It is nothing to the point that she let him have it good and strong as soon as she discovered that he had been unfaithful to Leonora and that his public services had cost more than Leonora thought they ought to have cost. Nancy would be bound to let him have it good and strong then. She would owe that to feminine public opinion; she would be driven to it by the instinct for self-preservation, since she might well imagine that if Edward had been unfaithful to Leonora, to Mrs Basil, and to the memories of the other two, he might be unfaithful to herself. And, no doubt, she had her share of the sex instinct that makes women be intolerably cruel to the beloved person. Anyhow, I don't know whether, at this point, Nancy Rufford loved Edward Ashburnham. I don't know whether she even loved him when, on getting, at Aden, the news of his suicide she went mad. Because that may just as well have been for the sake of Leonora as for the sake of Edward. Or it may have been for the sake of both of them. I don't know. I know nothing. I am very tired.

Leonora held passionately the doctrine that the girl didn't love Edward. She wanted desperately to believe that. It was a doctrine as necessary to her existence as a belief in the personal immortality of the soul. She said that it was impossible that Nancy could have loved Edward after she had given the girl her view of Edward's career and character. Edward, on the other hand, believed maunderingly that some essential attractiveness in himself must have made the girl continue to go on loving him—to go on loving him, as it were, in underneath her official aspect of hatred. He thought she only pretended to hate him in order to save her face and he thought that her quite atrocious telegram from Brindisi was only another attempt to do that—to prove that she had feelings creditable to a member of the feminine common weal. I don't know. I leave it to you.

There is another point that worries me a good deal in the aspects of this sad affair. Leonora says that, in desiring that the girl should go five thousand miles away and yet continue to love him, Edward was a monster of selfishness. He was desiring the ruin of a young life. Edward on the other hand put it to me that, supposing that the girl's love was a necessity to his existence, and, if he did nothing by word or by action to keep Nancy's love alive, he couldn't be called selfish. Leonora replied that showed he had an abominably selfish nature even though his actions might be perfectly correct. I can't make out which of them was right. I leave it to you.

It is, at any rate, certain that Edward's actions were perfectly—were monstrously, were cruelly—correct. He sat still and let Leonora take away his character, and let Leonora damn him to deepest hell, without stirring a finger. I daresay he was a fool; I don't see what object there was in letting the girl think worse of him than was necessary. Still there it is. And there it is also that all those three presented to the world the spectacle of being the best

of good people. I assure you that during my stay for that
fortnight in that fine old house, I never so much as noticed
a single thing that could have affected that good opinion.
And even when I look back, knowing the circumstances,
I can't remember a single thing any of them said that could
have betrayed them. I can't remember, right up to the
dinner, when Leonora read out that telegram—not the
tremor of an eyelash, not the shaking of a hand. It was
just a pleasant country house-party.

And Leonora kept it up jolly well, for even longer
than that—she kept it up as far as I was concerned until
eight days after Edward's funeral. Immediately after that
particular dinner—the dinner at which I received the
announcement that Nancy was going to leave for India
on the following day—I asked Leonora to let me have a
word with her. She took me into her little sitting-room and
I then said—I spare you the record of my emotions—that
she was aware that I wished to marry Nancy; that she had
seemed to favour my suit and that it appeared to be rather
a waste of money upon tickets and rather a waste of time
upon travel to let the girl go to India if Leonora thought
that there was any chance of her marrying me.

And Leonora, I assure you, was the absolutely perfect
British matron. She said that she quite favoured my suit;
that she could not desire for the girl a better husband; but
that she considered that the girl ought to see a little more
of life before taking such an important step. Yes, Leonora
used the words 'taking such an important step.' She was
perfect. Actually, I think she would have liked the girl to
marry me enough but my programme included the buying
of the Kershaws' house about a mile away upon the
Fordingbridge road, and settling down there with the girl.
That didn't at all suit Leonora. She didn't want to have
the girl within a mile and a half of Edward for the rest of
their lives. Still, I think she might have managed to let me
know, in some periphrasis or other, that I might have the
girl if I would take her to Philadelphia or Timbuctoo. I
loved Nancy very much—and Leonora knew it.

However, I left it at that. I left it with the understanding that Nancy was going away to India on probation. It
seemed to me a perfectly reasonable arrangement and I am
a reasonable sort of man. I simply said that I should follow
Nancy out to India after six months' time or so. Or, perhaps, after a year. Well, you see, I did follow Nancy out to
India after a year. . . .

I must confess to having felt a little angry with Leonora
for not having warned me earlier that the girl would be
going. I took it as one of the queer, not very straight
methods that Roman Catholics seem to adopt in dealing
with matters of this world. I took it that Leonora had been
afraid I should propose to the girl or, at any rate, have
made considerably greater advances to her than I did, if I
had known earlier that she was going away so soon. Perhaps
Leonora was right; perhaps Roman Catholics, with their
queer, shifty ways, are always right. They are dealing with
the queer, shifty thing that is human nature. For it is quite
possible that, if I had known Nancy was going away so
soon, I should have tried making love to her. And that
would have produced another complication. It may have
been just as well.

It is queer the fantastic things that quite good people
will do in order to keep up their appearance of calm poco-
curantism. For Edward Ashburnham and his wife called
me half the world over in order to sit on the back seat of a
dog-cart whilst Edward drove the girl to the railway station
from which she was to take her departure to India. They
wanted, I suppose, to have a witness of the calmness of
that function. The girl's luggage had been already packed
and sent off before. Her berth on the steamer had been
taken. They had timed it all so exactly that it went like
clockwork. They had known the date upon which Colonel
Rufford would get Edward's letter and they had known
almost exactly the hour at which they would receive his
telegram asking his daughter to come to him. It had all
been quite beautifully and quite mercilessly arranged, by

Edward himself. They gave Colonel Rufford, as a reason for telegraphing, the fact that Mrs Colonel Somebody or other would be travelling by that ship and that she would serve as an efficient chaperon for the girl. It was a most amazing business, and I think that it would have been better in the eyes of God if they had all attempted to gouge out each other's eyes with carving knives. But they were 'good people.'

After my interview with Leonora I went desultorily into Edward's gun-room. I didn't know where the girl was and I thought I might find her there. I suppose I had a vague idea of proposing to her in spite of Leonora. So, I presume, I don't come of quite such good people as the Ashburnhams. Edward was lounging in his chair smoking a cigar and he said nothing for quite five minutes. The candles glowed in the green shades; the reflections were green in the glasses of the book-cases that held guns and fishing-rods. Over the mantelpiece was the brownish picture of the white horse. Those were the quietest moments that I have ever known. Then, suddenly, Edward looked me straight in the eyes and said:

'Look here, old man, I wish you would drive with Nancy and me to the station to-morrow.'

I said that of course I would drive with him and Nancy to the station on the morrow. He lay there for a long time, looking along the line of his knees at the fluttering fire, and then suddenly, in a perfectly calm voice, and without lifting his eyes, he said:

'I am so desperately in love with Nancy Rufford that I am dying of it.'

Poor devil—he hadn't meant to speak of it. But I guess he just had to speak to somebody and I appeared to be like a woman or a solicitor. He talked all night.

Well, he carried out the programme to the last breath.

It was a very clear winter morning, with a good deal of frost in it. The sun was quite bright, the winding road between the heather and the bracken was very hard. I sat on the back seat of the dog-cart; Nancy was beside Edward. They talked about the way the cob went; Edward pointed out with the whip a cluster of deer upon a coombe three-quarters of a mile away. We passed the hounds in the level bit of road beside the high trees going into Fordingbridge and Edward pulled up the dog-cart so that Nancy might say good-bye to the huntsman and cap him a last sovereign. She had ridden with those hounds ever since she had been thirteen.

The train was five minutes late and they imagined that that was because it was market-day at Swindon or wherever the train came from. That was the sort of thing they talked about. The train came in; Edward found her a first-class carriage with an elderly woman in it. The girl entered the carriage, Edward closed the door and then she put out her hand to shake mine. There was upon those people's faces no expression of any kind whatever. The signal for the train's departure was a very bright red; that is about as passionate a statement as I can get into that scene. She was not looking her best; she had on a cap of brown fur that did not very well match her hair. She said:

'So long,' to Edward.

Edward answered: 'So long.'

He swung round on his heel and, large, slouching, and walking with a heavy deliberate pace, he went out of the station. I followed him and got up beside him in the high dog-cart. It was the most horrible performance I have ever seen.

And, after that, a holy peace, like the peace of God which passes all understanding, descended upon Branshaw Teleragh. Leonora went about her daily duties with a sort of triumphant smile—a very faint smile, but quite triumphant. I guess she had so long since given up any idea of getting her man back that it was enough for her to have got the girl out of the house and well cured of her infatuation. Once, in the hall, when Leonora was going out, Edward said, beneath his breath—but I just caught the words:

'Thou hast conquered, O pale Galilean.'

It was like his sentimentality to quote Swinburne.

But he was perfectly quiet and he had given up drinking. The only thing that he ever said to me after that drive to the station was:

'It's very odd. I think I ought to tell you, Dowell, that I haven't any feelings at all about the girl now it's all over. Don't you worry about me. I'm all right.' A long time afterwards he said: 'I guess it was only a flash in the pan.' He began to look after the estates again; he took all that trouble over getting off the gardener's daughter who had murdered her baby. He shook hands smilingly with every farmer in the market-place. He addressed two political meetings; he hunted twice. Leonora made him a frightful scene about spending the two hundred pounds on getting the gardener's daughter acquitted. Everything went on as if the girl had never existed. It was very still weather.

Well, that is the end of the story. And, when I come to look at it I see that it is a happy ending with wedding bells and all. The villains—for obviously Edward and the girl were villains—have been punished by suicide and madness. The heroine—the perfectly normal, virtuous, and slightly deceitful heroine—has become the happy wife of a perfectly normal, virtuous and slightly deceitful husband. She will shortly become a mother of a perfectly normal, virtuous, slightly deceitful son or daughter. A happy ending, that is what it works out at.

I cannot conceal from myself the fact that I now dislike Leonora. Without doubt I am jealous of Rodney Bayham. But I don't know whether it is merely a jealousy arising from the fact that I desired myself to possess Leonora or whether it is because to her were sacrificed the only two persons that I have ever really loved—Edward Ashburnham and Nancy Rufford. In order to set her up in a modern mansion, replete with every convenience and dominated by a quite respectable and eminently economical master of the house, it was necessary that Edward and Nancy Rufford should become, for me at least, no more than tragic shades.

I seem to see poor Edward, naked and reclining amidst darkness, upon cold rocks, like one of the ancient Greek damned, in Tartarus or wherever it was.

And as for Nancy . . . Well, yesterday at lunch she said suddenly:

'Shuttlecocks!'

And she repeated the word 'shuttlecocks' three times. I know what was passing in her mind, if she can be said to have a mind, for Leonora has told me that, once, the poor girl said she felt like a shuttlecock being tossed backwards and forwards between the violent personalities of Edward and his wife. Leonora, she said, was always trying to deliver her over to Edward, and Edward tacitly and silently forced her back again. And the odd thing was that Edward himself considered that those two women used *him* like a shuttlecock. Or, rather, he said that they sent him backwards and forwards like a blooming parcel that someone didn't want to pay the postage on. And Leonora also imagined that Edward and Nancy picked her up and threw her down as suited their purely vagrant moods. So there you have the pretty picture. Mind, I am not preaching anything contrary to accepted morality. I am not advocating free love in this or any other case. Society must go on, I suppose, and society can only exist if the normal, if the virtuous, and the slightly deceitful flourish, and if the passionate, the headstrong, and the too-truthful are condemned to suicide and to madness. But I guess that I myself, in my fainter way, come into the category of the passionate, of the headstrong, and the too-truthful. For I can't conceal from myself the fact that I loved Edward Ashburnham—and that I love him because he was just myself. If I had had the courage and the virility and possibly also the physique of Edward Ashburnham I should, I fancy, have done much what he did. He seems to me like a large elder brother who took me out on several excursions and did many dashing things whilst I just watched him robbing the orchards, from a distance. And, you see, I am just as much of a sentimentalist as he was. . . .

Yes, society must go on; it must breed, like rabbits. That is what we are here for. But then, I don't like society —much. I am that absurd figure, an American millionaire, who has bought one of the ancient haunts of English peace. I sit here, in Edward's gun-room, all day and all day in a house that is absolutely quiet. No one visits me, for I visit no one. No one is interested in me, for I have no interests. In twenty minutes or so I shall walk down to the village, beneath my own oaks, alongside my own clumps of gorse, to get the American mail. My tenants, the village boys and the tradesmen will touch their hats to me. So life peters out. I shall return to dine and Nancy will sit opposite me with the old nurse standing behind her. Enigmatic, silent, utterly well-behaved as far as her knife and fork go, Nancy will stare in front of her with the blue eyes that have over them strained, stretched brows. Once, or perhaps twice, during the meal her knife and fork will be suspended in mid-air as if she were trying to think of something that she had forgotten. Then she will say that she believes in an Omnipotent Deity or she will utter the one word 'shuttlecocks,' perhaps. It is very extraordinary to see the perfect flush of health on her cheeks, to see the lustre of her coiled black hair, the poise of the head upon the neck, the grace of the white hands— and to think that it all means nothing—that it is a picture without a meaning. Yes, it is queer.

But, at any rate, there is always Leonora to cheer you up; I don't want to sadden you. Her husband is quite an economical person of so normal a figure that he can get quite a large proportion of his clothes ready-made. That is the great desideratum of life, and that is the end of my story. The child is to be brought up as a Romanist.

It suddenly occurs to me that I have forgotten to say how Edward met his death. You remember that peace had descended upon the house; that Leonora was quietly triumphant and that Edward said his love for the girl had been merely a passing phase. Well, one afternoon we were in the stables together, looking at a new kind of flooring that Edward was trying in a loose-box. Edward was talking with a good deal of animation about the necessity of getting the numbers of the Hampshire territorials up to the proper standard. He was quite sober, quite quiet, his skin was clear-coloured; his hair was golden and perfectly brushed; the level brick-dust red of his complexion went clean up to the rims of his eyelids; his eyes were porcelain blue and they regarded me frankly and directly. His face was perfectly expressionless; his voice was deep and rough. He stood well back upon his legs and said:

'We ought to get them up to two thousand three hundred and fifty.'

A stable-boy brought him a telegram and went away. He opened it negligently, regarded it without emotion, and, in complete silence, handed it to me. On the pinkish paper in a sprawled handwriting I read: 'Safe Brindisi. Having rattling good time. Nancy.'

Well, Edward was the English gentleman; but he was also, to the last, a sentimentalist, whose mind was compounded of indifferent poems and novels. He just looked up to the roof of the stable, as if he were looking to Heaven, and whispered something that I did not catch.

Then he put two fingers into the waistcoat pocket of his grey, frieze suit; they came out with a little neat pen-knife—quite a small pen-knife. He said to me:

'You might just take that wire to Leonora.' And he looked at me with a direct, challenging, brow-beating glare. I guess he could see in my eyes that I didn't intend to hinder him. Why should I hinder him?

I didn't think he was wanted in the world, let his confounded tenants, his rifle-associations, his drunkards, reclaimed and unreclaimed, get on as they liked. Not all the hundreds and hundreds of them deserved that that poor devil should go on suffering for their sakes.

When he saw that I did not intend to interfere with him his eyes became soft and almost affectionate. He remarked:

'So long, old man, I must have a bit of a rest, you know.'

I didn't know what to say. I wanted to say, 'God bless you,' for I also am a sentimentalist. But I thought that perhaps that would not be quite English good form, so I trotted off with the telegram to Leonora. She was quite pleased with it.

SELECTED MEMORIES

Drawn from *Return to Yesterday,*
Ancient Lights, Mightier than the Sword,
and *The Heart of the Country*

THE EARLY YEARS

MY GRANDFATHER'S HOUSE

Says Thackeray:

'On his way to the City, Mr Newcome rode to look at the new house, No. 120, Fitzroy Square, which his brother, the colonel, had taken in conjunction with that Indian friend of his, Mr Binnie.... The house is vast but, it must be owned, melancholy. Not long since it was a ladies' school, in an unprosperous condition. The scar left by Madame Latour's brass plate may still be seen on the tall black door, cheerfully ornamented, in the style of the end of the last century, with a funereal urn in the centre of the entry, and garlands and the skulls of rams at each corner.... The kitchens were gloomy. The stables were gloomy. Great black passages; cracked conservatory; dilapidated bath-room, with melancholy waters moaning and fizzing from the cistern; the great large blank stone staircase—were all so many melancholy features in the general countenance of the house; but the Colonel thought it perfectly cheerful and pleasant, and furnished it in his rough-and-ready way.' *The Newcomes.*

And it was in this house of Colonel Newcome's that my eyes first opened, if not to the light of day, at least to any visual impression that has not since been effaced. I can remember vividly, as a very small boy, shuddering as I stood upon the door-step at the thought that the great stone urn, lichened, soot-stained, and decorated with a great ram's head by way of handle, elevated only by what looked like a square piece of stone of about the size and shape of a folio book, might fall upon me and crush me

223

entirely out of existence. Such a possible happening, I remember, was a frequent subject of discussion among Madox Brown's friends.

Ford Madox Brown, the painter of the pictures called *Work* and *The Last of England,* and the first painter in England, if not in the world, to attempt to render light exactly as it appeared to him, was at that time at the height of his powers, of his reputation, and of such prosperity as he enjoyed. His income from his pictures was considerable, and since he was an excellent talker, an admirable host, extraordinarily and indeed unreasonably open-handed, the great, formal, and rather gloomy house had become a meeting-place for almost all the intellectually unconventional of that time. Between 1870 and 1880 the real Pre-Raphaelite Movement was long since at an end: the Aesthetic Movement, which also was nicknamed Pre-Raphaelite, was, however, coming into prominence, and at the very heart of this movement was Madox Brown. As I remember him, with a square white beard, with a ruddy complexion, and with thick white hair parted in the middle and falling to above the tops of his ears, Madox Brown exactly resembled the king of hearts in a pack of cards. In passion and in emotions—more particularly during one of his fits of gout—he was a hard-swearing, old-fashioned Tory: his reasoning, however, and circumstances made him a revolutionary of the romantic type. I am not sure, even, that toward his later years he would not have called himself an anarchist, and have damned your eyes if you had faintly doubted this obviously extravagant assertion. But he loved the picturesque, as nearly all his friends loved it.

About the inner circle of those who fathered and sponsored the Aesthetic Movement there was absolutely nothing of the languishing. They were, to a man, rather burly, passionate creatures, extraordinarily enthusiastic, extraordinarily romantic, and most impressively quarrelsome. Neither about Rossetti nor about Burne-Jones, neither about William Morris nor P. P. Marshall—and

these were the principal upholders of the firm of Morris
& Company which gave aestheticism to the Western world
—was there any inclination to live upon the smell of the
lily. It was the outer ring, the disciples, who developed
this laudable ambition for poetic pallor, for clinging garments, and for ascetic countenances. And it was, I believe,
Mr Oscar Wilde who first formulated this poetically vege-
tarian theory of life in Madox Brown's studio at Fitzroy
Square. No, there was little of the smell of the lily about
the leaders of this movement! Thus it was one of Madox
Brown's most pleasing anecdotes—at any rate it was one
that he related with the utmost gusto—how William
Morris came out on to the landing in the house of the
'Firm' in Red Lion Square and roared downstairs:

'Mary, those six eggs were bad. I've eaten them, but
don't let it occur again.'

Morris, also, was in the bait of lunching daily off roast
beef and plum pudding, no matter at what season of the
year, and he liked his puddings large. So that, similarly,
upon the landing one day he shouted:

'Mary, do you call that a pudding?'

He was holding upon the end of a fork a plum pudding
about the size of an ordinary breakfast cup, and having
added some appropriate objurgations, he hurled the edible
downstairs on to Red-Lion Mary's forehead. This anecdote
should not be taken to evidence settled brutality on the
part of the poet-craftsman. Red-Lion Mary was one of the
loyalest supporters of the 'Firm' to the end of her days.
No, it was just in the full-blooded note of the circle. They
liked to swear, and, what is more, they liked to hear each
other swear. Thus, another of Madox Brown's anecdotes
went to show how he kept Morris sitting monumentally
still, under the pretence that he was drawing his portrait,
while Mr Arthur Hughes tied his long hair into knots for
the purpose of enjoying the explosion that was sure to
come when the released Topsy—Morris was always Topsy
to his friends—ran his hands through his hair. This anecdote always seemed to me to make considerable calls upon

one's faith. Nevertheless, it was one that Madox Brown used most frequently to relate, so that no doubt something of the sort must have occurred.

No, the note of these aesthetes was in no sense ascetic. What they wanted in life was room to expand and to be at ease. Thus I remember, in a sort of golden vision, Rossetti lying upon a sofa in the back studio with lighted candles at his feet and lighted candles at his head, while two extremely beautiful ladies dropped grapes into his mouth. But Rossetti did this, not because he desired to present the beholder with a beautiful vision, but because he liked lying on sofas, he liked grapes, and he particularly liked beautiful ladies. They desired, in fact, all of them, room to expand. And when they could not expand in any other directions they expanded enormously into their letters. And—I don't know why—they mostly addressed their letters abusing each other to Madox Brown. There would come one short, sharp note, and then answers occupying reams of note-paper. Thus one great painter would write:

'Dear Brown, Tell Gabriel that if he takes my model Fanny up the river on Sunday I will never speak to him again.'

Gabriel would take the model Fanny up the river on Sunday, and a triangular duel of portentous letters would ensue.

Or again, Swinburne would write:

'Dear Brown, if P. says that I said that Gabriel was in the habit of . . . , P. lies.'

The accusation against Rossetti being a Gargantuan impossibility which Swinburne, surely the most loyal of friends, could impossibly have made, there ensued a Gargantuan correspondence. Brown writes to P. how, when, and why the accusation was made; he explains how he went round to Jones, who had nothing to do with the matter, and found that Jones had eaten practically nothing for the last fortnight, and how between them they had decided that the best thing that they could do would be to go and tell Rossetti all about it, and of how Rossetti had had a painful interview with Swinburne, and how unhappy everybody was. P. replies to Brown that he had never uttered any such words upon any such occasion: that upon that occasion he was not present, having gone round to Ruskin, who had the toothache, and who read him the first hundred and twenty pages of *Stones of Venice*; that he could not possibly have said anything of the sort about Gabriel, since he knew nothing whatever of Gabriel's daily habits, having refused to speak to him for the last nine months because of Gabriel's intolerable habit of backbiting, which he was sure would lead them all to destruction, and so deemed it prudent not to go near him. Gabriel himself then enters the fray, saying that he has discovered that it is not P. at all who made the accusation, but Q., and that the accusation was made not against him, but about O.X., the Academician. If, however, he, P., accuses him, Gabriel, of backbiting, P. must be perfectly aware that this is not the case, he, Gabriel, having only said a few words against P.'s wife's mother, who is a damned old cat. And so the correspondence continues, Jones and Swinburne and Marshall and William Rossetti and Charles Augustus Howell and a great many more joining in the fray, until at last everybody withdraws all charges, six months having passed, and Brown invites all the contestants to dinner, Gabriel intending to bring old Plint, the picture-buyer, and to make him, when he has had plenty of wine, buy P.'s picture of the *Lost Shepherd* for two thousand pounds.

These tremendous quarrels, in fact, were all storms in teacups, and although the break-up of the 'Firm' did cause a comparatively lasting estrangement between several of the partners, it has always pleased me to remember that at the last private view that Madox Brown held of one of his pictures, every one of the surviving Pre-Raphaelite brothers came to his studio, and every one of the surviving partners of the original firm of Morris & Company.

The arrival of Sir Edward Burne-Jones and his wife brought up a characteristic passion of Madox Brown's. Sir Edward had persuaded the president of the Royal Academy to accompany them in their visit. They were actuated by the kindly desire to give Madox Brown the idea that thus at the end of his life the Royal Academy wished to extend some sort of official recognition to a painter who had persistently refused for nearly half a century to recognize their existence. Unfortunately it was an autumn day and the twilight had set in very early. Thus not only were the distinguished visitors rather shadowy in the dusk, but the enormous picture itself was entirely indistinguishable. Lady Burne-Jones, with her peculiarly persuasive charm, whispered to me, unheard by Madox Brown, that I should light the studio gas, and I was striking a match, when I was appalled to hear Madox Brown shout, in tones of extreme violence and of apparent alarm:

'Damn and blast it all, Fordie! Do you want us all blown into the next world?'

And he proceeded to explain to Lady Burne-Jones that there was an escape of gas from a pipe. When she suggested candles or a paraffin lamp, Madox Brown declared with equal violence that he couldn't think how she could imagine that he could have such infernally dangerous things in the house. The interview thus concluded in a gloom of the most tenebrous, and shortly afterward we went downstairs, where, in the golden glow of a great many candles set against a golden and embossed wallpaper, tea was being served. The fact was that Madox Brown was determined that no 'damned academician' should see his picture. Nevertheless, it is satisfactory to me to think that there was among these distinguished and kindly men still so great a feeling of solidarity. They had come, many of them from great distances, to do honour, or at least to be kind, to an old painter who at that time was more entirely forgotten than he has ever been before or since.

The 'lily' tradition of the disciples of these men is, I should imagine, almost entirely extinguished. But the other day, at a particularly smart wedding, there turned up one staunch survivor in garments of prismatic hues— a mustard-coloured ulster, a green wide-awake, a blue shirt, a purple tie, and a suit of tweed. This gentleman moved distractedly among groups of correctly attired people. In one hand he bore an extremely minute painting by himself. It was, perhaps, of the size of a visiting-card set in an ocean of white mount. In the other he bore an enormous spray of Madonna lilies. That, I presume, was why he had failed to remove his green hat. He was approached by the hostess, and he told her that he wished to place the picture, his wedding gift, in the most appropriate position that could be found for it. And upon her suggesting that she would attend to the hanging after the ceremony was over, he brushed her aside. Finally he placed the picture upon the ground beneath a tall window, and perched the spray of lilies on top of the frame. He then stood back and, waving his emaciated hands and stroking his brown beard, surveyed the effect of his decoration. The painting, he said, symbolized the consolation that the arts would afford the young couple during their married life, and the lily stood for the purity of the bride. This is how in the 'seventies and the 'eighties the outer ring of the aesthetes really behaved. It was as much in their note as were the plum pudding and the roast beef in William Morris's. The reason for this is not very far to seek. The older men, the Pre-Raphaelites and the members of the 'Firm,' had too rough work to do to bother much about the trimmings.

It is a little difficult nowadays to imagine the acridity with which any new artistic movement was opposed when Victoria was Queen of England. Charles Dickens, as I have elsewhere pointed out, called loudly for the immediate imprisonment of Millais and the other Pre-Raphaelites, including my grandfather, who was not a Pre-Raphaelite. Blasphemy was the charge alleged against them, just as it was the charge alleged against the earliest upholders of Wagner's music in England. This may seem incredible, but I have in my possession three letters from three different members of the public addressed to my father, Dr Francis Hueffer, a man of great erudition and force of character, who, from the early 'seventies until his death, was the musical critic of *The Times*. The writers stated that unless Doctor Hueffer abstained from upholding the blasphemous music of the future—and in each case the writer used the word blasphemous—he would be respectively stabbed, ducked in a horse-pond, and beaten to death by hired roughs. Yet to-day I never go to a place of popular entertainment where miscellaneous music is performed for the benefit of the poorest classes without hearing at least the overture to *Tannhäuser*. Nowadays it is difficult to discern any new movement in any of the arts. No doubt there is movement, no doubt we who write and our friends who paint and compose are producing the arts of the future. But we never have the luck to have the word 'blasphemous' hurled at us. It would, indeed, be almost inconceivable that such a thing could happen, that the frame of mind should be reconstructed. But to the Pre-Raphaelites this word was blessed in the extreme. For human nature is such—perhaps on account of obstinacy or perhaps on account of feelings of justice— that to persecute an art, as to persecute a religion, is simply to render its practitioners the more stubborn and its advocates in their fewness the more united and the more effective in their union. It was the injustice of the attack upon the Pre-Raphaelites, it was the fury and outcry, that won for them the attention of Mr Ruskin. And Mr Ruskin's attention being aroused, he entered on that splendid and efficient championing of their cause which at last established them in a position of perhaps more immediate importance than, as painters, they exactly merited. As pioneers and as sufferers they can never sufficiently be recommended. Mr Ruskin, for some cause which my grandfather was used to declare was purely personal, was the only man intimately connected with these movements who had no connection at all with Madox Brown. I do not know why this was, but it is a fact that, although Madox Brown's pictures were in considerable evidence at all places where the pictures of the Pre-Raphaelites were exhibited, Mr Ruskin in all his works never once mentioned his name. He never blamed him; he never praised him; he ignored him. And this was at a time when Ruskin must have known that a word from him was sufficient to make the fortune of any painter. It was sufficient, not so much because of Mr Ruskin's weight with the general public, as because the small circle of buyers, wealthy and assiduous, who surrounded the painters of the Movement, hung upon Mr. Ruskin's lips and needed at least his printed sanction for all their purchases.

Madox Brown was the most benevolent of men, the most helpful and the kindest. His manifestations, however, were apt at times to be a little thorny. I remember an anecdote which Madox Brown's housemaid of that day was in the habit of relating to me when she used to put me to bed. Said she—and the exact words remain upon my mind:

'I was down in the kitchen waiting to carry up the meat, when a cabman comes down the area steps and says: "I've got your master in my cab. He's very drunk." I says to him'—and an immense intonation of pride would come into Charlotte's voice—' "My master's a-sitting at the head of his table entertaining his guests. That's Mr [Swinburne]. Carry him upstairs and lay him in the bath." '

Madox Brown, whose laudable desire it was at many stages of his career to redeem poets and others from dipsomania, was in the habit of providing several of them with labels upon which were inscribed his own name and address. Thus, when any of these geniuses were found incapable in the neighbourhood they would be brought by cabmen or others to Fitzroy Square. This, I think, was a stratagem more characteristic of Madox Brown's singular

and quaint ingenuity than any that I can recall. The poet
being thus recaptured would be carried upstairs by Charlotte and the cabman and laid in the bath—in Colonel
Newcome's very bath-room, where, according to Thackeray, the water moaned and gurgled so mournfully in the
cistern. For me, I can only remember that room as an
apartment of warmth and lightness: it was a concomitant
to all the pleasures that sleeping at my grandfather's meant
for me. And indeed, to Madox Brown as to Colonel Newcome—they were very similar natures in their chivalrous,
unbusinesslike, and naïve simplicity—the house in Fitzroy
Square seemed perfectly pleasant and cheerful.

The poet having been put into the bath would be reduced to sobriety by cups of the strongest coffee that could
be made (the bath was selected because he would not be
able to roll out and to injure himself). And having been
thus reduced to sobriety, he would be lectured, and he
would be kept in the house, being given nothing stronger
than lemonade to drink, until he found the régime intolerable. Then he would disappear, the label sewn inside
his coat collar, to reappear once more in the charge of a
cabman.

Of Madox Brown's acerbity I witnessed myself no instances at all, unless it be the one that I have lately
narrated. A possibly too stern father of the old school,
he was as a grandfather extravagantly indulgent. I remember his once going through the catalogue of his
grandchildren and deciding, after careful deliberation, that
they were all geniuses with the exception of one, as to
whom he could not be certain whether that one was a
genius or mad. Thus I read with astonishment the words
of a critic of distinction with regard to the exhibition of
Madox Brown's works that I organized at the Grafton
Gallery ten years ago. They were to the effect that Madox
Brown's pictures were very crabbed and ugly—but what
was to be expected of a man whose disposition was so
harsh and distorted? This seemed to me to be an amazing
statement. But upon discovering the critic's name I found

that Madox Brown once kicked him downstairs. The gentleman in question had come to Madox Brown with the proposal from an eminent firm of picture-dealers that the painter should sell all his works to them for a given number of years at a very low price. In return they were to do what would be called nowadays 'booming' him, and they would do their best to get him elected as Associate of the Royal Academy. That Madox Brown should have received with such violence a proposition that seemed to the critic so eminently advantageous for all parties, justified that gentleman in his own mind in declaring that Madox Brown had a distorted temperament. Perhaps he had.

But if he had a rough husk he had a sweet kernel, and for this reason the gloomy house in Fitzroy Square did not, I think, remain as a shape of gloom in the minds of many people. It was very tall, very large, very grey, and in front of it towered up very high the mournful plane-trees of the square. And over the porch was the funereal urn with the ram's heads. This object, dangerous and threatening, has always seemed to me to be symbolical of this circle of men, so practical in their work and so romantically unpractical, as a whole, in their lives. They knew exactly how, according to their lights, to paint pictures, to write poems, to make tables, to decorate pianos, rooms, or churches. But as to the conduct of life they were a little sketchy, a little romantic, perhaps a little careless. I should say that of them all Madox Brown was the most practical. But his way of being practical was always to be quaintly ingenious. Thus we had the urn. Most of the Pre-Raphaelites dreaded it: they all of them talked about it as a possible danger, but never was any step taken for its removal. It was never even really settled in their minds whose would be the responsibility for any accident. It is difficult to imagine the frame of mind, but there it was and there to this day the urn remains. The question could have been settled by any lawyer, or Madox Brown might have had some clause that provided for his

8*

indemnity inserted in his lease. And, just as the urn itself set the tone of the old immense Georgian mansion fallen from glory, so perhaps the fact that it remained for so long the topic of conversation set the note of the painters, the painter-poets, the poet-craftsmen, the painter-musicians, the filibuster verse-writers, and all that singular collection of men versed in the arts. They assembled and revelled comparatively modestly in the rooms where Colonel Newcome and his fellow directors of the Bundelcund Board had partaken of mulligatawny and spiced punch before the sideboard that displayed its knife-boxes with the green-handled knives in their serried phalanxes.

But, for the matter of that, Madox Brown's own sideboard also displayed its green-handled knives, which always seemed to me to place him as the man of the old school in which he was born and remained to the end of his days. If he was impracticable, he hadn't about him a touch of the Bohemian; if he was romantic, his romances took place along ordered lines. Every friend's son of his who went into the navy was destined in his eyes to become, not a pirate, but at least a port-admiral. Every young lawyer that he knew was certain, even if he were only a solicitor, to become Lord Chancellor, and every young poet who presented him with a copy of his first work was destined for the laureateship. And he really believed in these romantic prognostications, which came from him without end as without selection. So that if he was the first to give a helping hand to D. G. Rossetti, his patronage in one or two other instances was not so wisely bestowed.

He was, of course, the sworn foe of the Royal Academy. For him they were always, the members of that august body, 'those *damned* academicians,' with a particular note of acerbity upon the expletive. Yet I very well remember, upon the appearance of the first numbers of the *Daily Graphic*, that Madox Brown, being exceedingly struck by the line engravings of one of the artists whom that paper regularly employed to render social functions, exclaimed: 'By Jove! if young Cleaver goes on as well as he has

begun, those damned academicians, supposing they had
any sense, would elect him president right away!' Thus
it will be seen that the business of romance was not to
sweep away the Royal Academy, was not to found an
opposing salon. It was to capture the established body by
storm, leaping as it were on to the very quarter-deck, and
setting to the old ship a new course. The characteristic,
in fact, of all these men was their warm-heartedness, their
enmity for the formal, for the frigid, for the ungenerous.
It cannot be said that any of them despised money. I
doubt whether it would even be said that any of them did
not, at one time or another, seek for popularity, or try to
paint, write, or decorate pot-boilers. But they were naïvely
unable to do it. To the timid—and the public is always
the timid—what was individual in their characters was
always alarming. It was alarming even when they tried to
paint the conventional dog-and-girl pictures of the Christmas supplement. The dogs were too like dogs and did not
simper; the little girls were too like little girls. They would
be probably rendered as just losing their first teeth.

In spite of the Italianism of Rossetti, who was never in
Italy, and the mediaevalism of Morris, who had never
looked mediaevalism, with its cruelties, its filth, its
stenches, and its avarice, in the face—in spite of these
tendencies that were forced upon them by those two con-
tagious spirits, the whole note of this old, romantic circle
was national, was astonishingly English, was Georgian
even. They seemed to date from the Regency, and to have
skipped altogether the baneful influences of early Vic-
torianism and of the commerciality that the Prince Consort
spread through England. They seem to me to resemble
in their lives—and perhaps in their lives they were greater
than their works—to resemble nothing so much as a group
of old-fashioned ships' captains. Madox Brown, indeed,
was nominated for a midshipman in the year 1827. His
father had fought on the famous *Arethusa* in the classic
fight with the *Belle Poule*. And but for the fact that his
father quarrelled with Commodore Coffin, and so lost all

hope of influence at the Admiralty, it is probable that Madox Brown would never have painted a picture or have lived in Colonel Newcome's house. Indeed, on the last occasion when I saw William Morris I happened to meet him in Portland Place. He was going to the house of a peer that his firm was engaged in decorating, and he took me with him to look at the work. He was then a comparatively old man, and his work had grown very flamboyant, so that the decoration of the dining-room consisted, as far as I can remember, of one huge acanthus-leaf design. Morris looked at this absent-mindedly, and said that he had just been talking to some members of a ship's crew whom he had met in Fenchurch Street. They had remained for some time under the impression that he was a ship's captain. This had pleased him very much, for it was his ambition to be taken for such a man. I have heard, indeed, that this happened to him on several occasions, on each of which he expressed an equal satisfaction. With a grey beard like the foam of the sea, with grey hair through which he continually ran his hands erect and curly on his forehead, with a hooked nose, a florid complexion, and clean, clear eyes, dressed in a blue serge coat, and carrying, as a rule, a satchel, to meet him was always, as it were, to meet a sailor ashore. And that in essence was the note of them all. When they were at work they desired that everything they did should be shipshape; when they set their work down they became like Jack ashore. And perhaps that is why there is, as a rule, such a scarcity of artists in England. Perhaps to what is artistic in the nation the sea has always called too strongly.

MY NURSE, MRS ATTERBURY

My nurse, Mrs Atterbury, had one singularity—she had come in contact with more murders and deaths by violence than any person I ever met—at any rate until 1914. In consequence, I imagine, my childhood was haunted by imaginary horrors and was most miserable. I can still see the shadows of wolves if I lie awake in bed with a fire in the room. And indeed I had the fixed belief for years that except for myself the world was peopled with devils. I used to peep through the cracks of doors to see the people within in their natural forms.

Mrs Atterbury had been in the great railway accident near Doncaster where innumerable persons were burned to death; she had seen seven people run over and killed and her milder conversations abounded in details of deaths by drowning. I don't think she was present at the sinking of the *Princess Alice* but she talked about it as if she had been. Her normal conversations ran:

'When I lived with meyuncle Power in the Minories time of the Crimea Wower, meyuncle let 'is top front to a master saddler. N'wen wower broke out the master saddler 'e worked niteanday, niteanday fer sevin weeks without stop er stay. N'e took 'is saddles to the Wower Orfis 'n drawed his pay. All in gowlden sovrins in a Gled-stun beg. N'wen 'e got 'ome 'e cut 'is froat on the top front landin' 'n the blood 'n the gowld run down the staircase together like the awtificial cascades in Battersea Pawk.'... 'The blood 'n the gowld!'... she would repeat and catch my wrist in her skinny fingers.

She was a witness—or an almost witness—of one of the Jack the Ripper murders in Whitechapel. She certainly came on the body of one of the victims and claimed to have seen a man vanish into the fog. I never actually heard the details of that. My mother, worried by the advent of a questioning police sergeant and the hysterics of the household below stairs, forbade the old lady to tell us children about it. But her impressive and mysterious absence in her best black bonnet and jet beaded cloak, and the whispers of the household, made me fully aware that she was giving evidence at the Inkwedge. For long

afterwards heaven knew what horrors were not concealed
for me in the pools of shadow beneath the lamp-posts. In
solitary streets your footsteps echoing and a smudge of
fog in the gaslight!

The last time I saw the old lady she was sitting—as she
did day in day out for years—in the window of a parlour
that occupied the apex of a corner lot in an outer suburb.
She could look right up and down two long streets.

She greeted me with great vivacity. The day before there
had been a tremendous thunderstorm. The streets up
which she looked had been almost obscured by falling
water. She said to me:

'I calls out to Lizzie. . . . Good gracious me! That
man! " 'E's struck dead!" . . . N'e *was*!' she added
triumphantly.

MY COUSINS, THE ROSSETTIS

My cousins, the Rossettis, were horrible monsters of pre-
cocity. Let me set down here with what malignity I viewed
their proficiency in Latin and Greek at ages incredibly
small. Thus, I believe, my cousin Olive wrote a Greek play
at the age of something like five. And, they were perpetually being held up to us—or perhaps to myself alone,
for my brother was always very much the sharper of the
two—as marvels of genius whom I ought to thank God for
merely having the opportunity to emulate. For my cousin
Olive's infernal Greek play which had to do with Theseus
and the Minotaur, draped in robes of the most flimsy butter
muslin, I was drilled, a lanky boy of twelve or so, to wander
round and round the back drawing-room of Endsleigh
Gardens, imbecilely flapping my naked arms before an
audience singularly distinguished who were seated in the
front room. The scenery which had been designed and

painted by my aunt was, I believe, extremely beautiful;
and the chinoiseries, the fine furniture and the fine pictures
were such that had I been allowed to sit peaceably amongst
the audience, I might really have enjoyed the piece. But it
was my unhappy fate to wander round in the garb of a
captive before an audience that consisted of Pre-Raphaelite
poets, ambassadors of foreign powers, editors, poets
laureate, and Heaven knows what. Such formidable beings
at least did they appear to my childish imagination. From
time to time the rather high voice of my father would
exclaim from the gloomy depths of the auditorium, 'Speak
up, Fordie!' Alas, my aptitude for that sort of sport being
limited, the only words that were allotted to me were the
Greek lamentation, 'Theu! Theu! Theu!' and in the
meanwhile my cousin Arthur Rossetti, who appeared only
to come up to my knee, was the hero Theseus, strode
about with a large sword, slew dragons and addressed
perorations in the Tennysonian 'o' and 'a' style, to the
candle-lit heavens, with their distant view of Athens.
Thank God, having been an adventurous youth whose sole
idea of true joy was to emulate the doings of the hero of
a work called *Peck's Bad Boy and His Pa*, or at least to
attain to the lesser glories of Dick Harkaway, who had a
repeating rifle and a tame black jaguar and who bathed in
gore almost nightly—thank God, I say, that we succeeded
in leading our unsuspecting cousins into dangerous situa-
tions from which they only emerged by breaking limbs. I
seem to remember the young Rossettis as perpetually
going about with fractured bones. I distinctly remember
the fact that I bagged my cousin Arthur with one collar-
bone, broken on a boat slide in my company, whilst my
younger sister brought down her cousin Mary with a
broken elbow fractured in a stone hall. Olive Rossetti, I
also remember with gratification, cut her head open at a
party given by Miss Mary Robinson because she wanted
to follow me down some dangerous steps and fell on to a
flower-pot.

POETESSES IN FOUR-WHEELERS

The poet—and still more the poetess—of the 'seventies and 'eighties, though an awful, was a frail creature who had to be carried about from place to place, and generally in a four-wheeled cab. Indeed, if my recollection of these poetesses in my very earliest days was accompanied always by thunders and expostulations, my images of them in slightly later years, when I was not so strictly confined to the nursery—my images of them were always those of somewhat elderly ladies, forbidding in aspect, with grey hair, hooked noses, flashing eyes, and continued trances of indignation against reviewers. They emerged ungracefully —for no one ever yet managed to emerge gracefully from the door of a four-wheeler—sometimes backwards from one of those creaking and dismal tabernacles and pulling behind them odd-shaped parcels. Holding the door open, with his whip in one hand, would stand the cabman. He wore an infinite number of little capes on his overcoat; a grey worsted muffler would be coiled many times round his throat and the lower part of his face, and his top hat would be of some unglossy material that I have never been able to identify. After a short interval his hand would become extended, the flat palm displaying such coins as the poetess had laid in it. And, when the poetess with her odd bundles was three-quarters of the way up the door-steps, the cabman, a man of the slowest and most deliberate, would be pulling the muffler down from about his mouth and exclaiming:

'Wot's this?'

The poetess without answering, but with looks of enormous disdain, would scuffle into the house and the front door would close. Then upon the knocker the cabman would commence his thunderous symphony.

Somewhat later more four-wheelers would arrive with more poetesses. Then still more four-wheelers with elderly poets; untidy-looking young gentlemen with long hair and wide-awake hats, in attitudes of dejection and fatigue would ascend the steps; a hansom or two would drive up containing rather smarter, stout elderly gentlemen wearing, as a rule, black coats with velvet collars and most usually black gloves. These were reviewers, editors of the *Athenaeum* and of other journals. Then there would come quite smart gentlemen with an air of prosperity in their clothes, and with deference somewhat resembling that of undertakers in their manners. These would be publishers.

You are to understand that what was about to proceed was the reading to this select gathering of the latest volume of poems by Mrs Clara Fletcher—that is not the name—the authoress of what was said to be a finer sequence of sonnets than those of Shakespeare. And before a large semicircle of chairs occupied by the audience that I have described, and, with Mr Clara Fletcher standing obsequiously behind her to hand her, from the odd-shaped bundles of manuscripts, the pages that she required, Mrs Clara Fletcher, with her regal head regally poised, having quelled the assembly with a single glance, would commence to read.

Mournfully then, up and down the stone staircases there would flow two hollow sounds. For in those days it was the habit of all poets and poetesses to read aloud upon every possible occasion, and whenever they read aloud to employ an imitation of the voice invented by the late Lord Tennyson, and known in those days as the *ore rotundo*—'with the round mouth mouthing out their hollow o's and a's.'

The effect of this voice heard from outside a door was to a young child particularly awful. It went on and on, suggesting the muffled baying of a large hound that is permanently dissatisfied with the world. And this awful rhythm would be broken in upon from time to time by the

thunders of the cabman. How the housemaid—the housemaid was certainly Charlotte Kirby—dealt with this man
of wrath I never could rightly discover. Apparently the
cabman would thunder upon the door; Charlotte, keeping
it on the chain, would open it for about a foot. The cabman
would exclaim, 'Wot's this?' and Charlotte would shut the
door in his face. The cabman would remain inactive for
four minutes in order to recover his breath. Then once
more his stiff arm would approach the knocker and again
the thunders would resound. The cabman would exclaim:
'A bob and a tanner from the Elephant and Castle to
Tottenham Court Road!' and Charlotte would again close
the door in his face. This would continue for perhaps half
an hour. Then the cabman would drive away to meditate.
Later he would return and the same scenes would be gone
through. He would retire once more for more meditation
and return in the company of a policeman. Then Charlotte
would open the front door wide and by doing no more than
ejaculate 'My good man!' she would appear to sweep out
of existence policeman, cab, cabhorse, cabman, and whip.
A settled peace would descend upon the house, lulled into
silence by the reverberation of the hollow o's and a's. In
about five minutes' time the policeman would return and
converse amiably with Charlotte for three-quarters of an
hour, through the area railings. I suppose that was really
why cabmen were always worsted and poetesses protected
from these importunities in the dwelling over whose
destinies Charlotte presided for forty years.

THE ABBÉ LISZT

When I was a very small boy indeed I was taken to a
concert. In those days, as a token of my Pre-Raphaelite
origin, I wore very long golden hair, a suit of greenish-

yellow corduroy velveteen with gold buttons, and two
stockings of which the one was red and the other green.
These garments were the curse of my young existence and
the joy of every street-boy who saw me. I was taken to this
concert by my father's assistant on *The Times* newspaper.
Mr Rudall was the most kindly, the most charming, the
most gifted, the most unfortunate—and also the most
absent-minded—of men. Thus, when we had arrived in
our stalls—and in those days the representative of *The
Times* always had the two middle front seats—Mr Rudall
discovered that he had omitted to put on his neck-tie that
day. He at once went out to purchase one, and, having
become engrossed in the selection, he forgot all about the
concert, went away to the Thatched House Club, and
passed there the remainder of the evening. I was left, in
the middle of the front row, all alone and feeling very tiny
and deserted, the sole representative of the august organ
that in those days was known as the Thunderer.

Immediately in front of me, standing in the vacant space
before the platform, which was all draped in red, there
were three gilt arm-chairs and a gilt table. In the hall there
was a great and continuing rustle of excitement. Then,
suddenly, this became an enormous sound of applause. It
volleyed and rolled round and round the immense space;
I had never heard such a sound and I have never again
heard such another. Then I perceived that from beneath
the shadow of the passage that led into the artistes' room—
in the deep shadow—there had appeared a silver head, a
dark brown face, hook-nosed, smiling the enigmatic,
Jesuit's smile, the long locks falling backwards so that
the whole shape of the apparition was that of the Sphynx
head. Behind this figure came two others that excited no
proportionate attention, but, small as I then was, I recognized in them the late King and the present Queen
Mother.

They came closer and closer to me; they stood in front
of the three gilt arm-chairs; the deafening applause

continued. The old man with the terrible enigmatic face made gestures of modesty. He refused, smiling all the time, to sit in one of the gilt arm-chairs. And suddenly he bowed down upon me. He stretched out his hands; he lifted me out of my seat, he sat down in it himself and left me standing, the very small lonely child with the long golden curls, underneath all those eyes and stupefied by the immense sounds of applause.

The King sent an equerry to entreat the Master to come to his seat; the Master sat firmly planted there smiling obstinately. Then the Queen came and took him by the hand. She pulled him—I don't know how much strength she needed—right out of his seat and—to prevent his returning to it she sat down there. After all it was *my* seat. And then, as if she realized my littleness and my loneliness, she drew me to her and set me on her knee. It was a gracious act.

There is a passage in Pepys's *Diary* in which he records that he was present at some excavations in Westminster Abbey when they came upon the skull of Jane Seymour, and he kissed the skull on the place where once the lips had been. And in his *Diary* he records: 'It was on such and such a day of such and such a year that I did kiss a Queen,' and then, his feelings overcoming him, he repeats: 'It was on such and such a day of such and such a year that I did kiss a Queen'—I have forgotten what was the date when I sat in a Queen's lap. But I remember very well that when I came out into Piccadilly the cabmen, with their three-tiered coats, were climbing up the lamp-posts and shouting out: 'Three cheers for the Habby Liszt!' And indeed the magnetic personality of the Abbé Liszt was incredible in its powers of awakening enthusiasm.

A few days later my father took me to call at the house where Liszt was staying—it was at the Lytteltons', I suppose. There were a number of people in the drawing-room and they were all asking Liszt to play. Liszt steadfastly refused. A few days before he had had a slight accident that had hurt one of his hands. Suddenly he turned his eyes upon me, and then, bending down, he said in my ear:

'Little boy, I will play for you, so that you will be able to tell your children's children that you have heard Liszt play.'

And he played the first movement of the *Moonlight Sonata*. I do not remember much of his playing, but I remember very well that I was looking, whilst Liszt played, at a stalwart, florid Englishman who is now an earl. And suddenly I perceived that tears were rolling down his cheeks. And soon all the room was in tears. It struck me as odd that people should cry because Liszt was playing the *Moonlight Sonata*.

Ah! that wonderful personality; there was no end to the enthusiasms it aroused. I had a distant connection—oddly enough an English one—who became by marriage a lady-in-waiting at the Court of Saxe-Weimar. I met her a few years ago, and she struck me as a typically English and unemotional personage. But she had always about her a disagreeable odour that persisted to the day of her death. When they came to lay her out, they discovered that round her neck she wore a sachet, and in that sachet there was the half of a cigar that had been smoked by Liszt. Liszt had lunched with her and her husband thirty years before.

A PRE-RAPHAELITE POETESS

One of the other most unpleasant memories of mine were the incursions made upon me by a Pre-Raphaelite poetess, Miss Mathilde Blind. Miss Blind was descended from a distinguished family of revolutionaries. Indeed, one of the brothers attempted to assassinate Bismarck, and

disappeared, without any trace of him ever again being heard
of, in the dungeons of a Prussian fortress. She was, moreover, a favourite pupil of Mazzini the liberator of Italy, and
a person, in her earlier years, of extreme beauty and fire.
Upon the death of their son and the marriage of their two
daughters, the late Mrs William Rossetti and Mrs Francis
Hueffer, the Madox Browns adopted Mathilde Blind who
from thenceforward spent most of her time with them. As
a boy—I wrote my first book when I was sixteen and its
success alas! was more tremendous than any that I can
ever again know—I would be sitting in my little study
intent either upon my writing or my school tasks, when
ominous sounds would be heard at the door. Miss Blind,
with her magnificent aquiline features and fine grey hair,
would enter, alarming slip proofs dangling from both her
hands. 'Fordie,' she would say, 'I want a synonym for
"dun." ' On page 152 of her then volume of poems she
would have written of dun cows standing in green streams.
She was then correcting the proofs of page 154 to find that
she had spoken of the dun cows returning homewards over
the leas. Some other adjective would have to be found for
this useful quadruped. Then my bad quarter of an hour
would commence. I would suggest 'strawberry-coloured'
and she would say that that would not fit the metre. I
would try 'roan' but she would say that that would spoil
the phonetic syzygy. I did not know what that was but I
would next suggest 'heifers,' whereupon she would say that
heifers did not give milk and that, anyhow, the accentua-
tion was wrong. I would be reduced to a miserable mute-
ness; Miss Blind frightened me out of my life. And rising
up and gathering her proof-sheets together, the poetess,
with her Medusa head, would regard me with indignant
and piercing brown eyes. 'Fordie,' she would say with an
awful scrutiny, 'your grandfather says you are a genius,
but I have never been able to discover in you any signs
but those of your being as stupid as a donkey.' I never
could escape from being likened to that other useful
quadruped.

MY UNHAPPIEST NIGHT

I remember as a boy being set somewhat inconsiderately the task of convoying home a very distinguished artist, practising, however, an art other than that of poetry. We had been at a musical evening in the neighbourhood of Swiss Cottage and arrived at the Underground Station just before the last train came in. My enormously distinguished temporary ward was in the habit of filling one of his trouser pockets with chocolate creams and the other with large, unset diamonds. With the chocolate creams he was accustomed to solace his sense of taste whilst he sat in the artistes' room waiting for his turn to play. With the diamonds on similar occasions he solaced his sense of touch, plunging his hand amongst them and moving them about luxuriously. He would have sometimes as many as twenty or thirty large and valuable stones. On this occasion M., always an excitable person, was in a state of extreme rage. For at the party where he had played M. Saint-Saens the composer had also been invited to play the piano. As far as I can remember Saint-Saens was not a very good pianist; he had the extremely hard touch of the organist, and M. considered that to have invited him to sit down on the same piano-stool was an insult almost beyond bearing.

The platform of the Underground Railway was more than usually gloomy, since, the last down train having gone, the lamps upon the other platform had been extinguished. M. volleyed and thundered, and at last, just as the train came in, he thrust both his hands into his trouser pockets and then waved them wildly above his head in execration of my insufficient responsiveness. There flew from the one pocket a shower of chocolate creams, from the other a shower of diamonds. M. gave a final scream upon a very high note and plunged into a railway carriage. I was left divided as to whether my duty were towards the maestro or his jewels. I suppose it was undue materialism in myself, but I stayed to look after the diamonds. It was a long and agonizing search. The station-master, who imagined that I was as mad as the vanished musician, insisted that there were no diamonds and extinguished the station lamps. A friendly porter, however, assisted me with a hand-lantern and eventually we recovered about five diamonds, each perhaps as large as my little finger-nail. Whether any more remained upon the platform I never knew, for M. also never knew how many jewels he possessed or carried about him. It was a night certainly of nightmare, for being so young a boy I had not sufficient money to take a cab and the last train into Town had gone. I had, therefore, to walk to Claridge's Hotel, a distance of perhaps four miles, and arriving there I could not discover that the porter had seen anything of M. I therefore thought it wise to arouse his wife. Mme. —— was accustomed to being awakened at all hours of the night. Her distinguished husband was in the habit of dragging her impetuously out of bed to listen to his latest rendering of a passage of Chopin; and indeed upon this account, she subsequently divorced the master, such actions being held by the French courts to constitute incompatibility of temperament. She did not, however, take my arousing her with any the greater equanimity, and when I produced the diamonds she upbraided me violently for having lost the master. There ensued a more agonizing period of driving about in cabs before we discovered M. detained at the police station nearest Baker Street. He had in his vocabulary no English at all except some very startling specimens of profanity. Upon arriving at Baker Street Station he had spent a considerable amount of time and energy in attempting to explain to the ticket collector in French that he had lost a sacred charge, a weakly little boy incapable of taking care of himself; and as he did not even know the name of his hotel the police had taken charge of him and were attempting kindly to keep him soothed by singing popular songs to him in the charge-room where we found him quite contented and happy, beating time with his feet to the melody of 'Two Lovely Black Eyes.' I think this was upon the whole the unhappiest night I ever spent.

THE MUSIC CRITIC OF *THE TIMES*

In England, at any rate in the musical world, as in the world of all the other arts, a general change seems gradually to have come over the atmosphere in the last quarter of a century. Jealousies amongst executants, amongst composers, have diminished; and along with them have diminished the enthusiasm and the partisanships of the public. In the 'fifties and 'sixties there was an extraordinary outcry against the Pre-Raphaelite movement, in the 'seventies and 'eighties there was an outcry almost more extraordinary against what was called the Music of the Future. As I have said elsewhere, Charles Dickens attempted to get the authorities to imprison the Pre-Raphaelite painters because he considered that their works were blasphemous. And he was backed by a whole, great body of public opinion. In the 'seventies and 'eighties there were cries for the imprisonment alike of the critics who upheld and the artistes who performed the Music of the Future. The compositions of Wagner were denounced as being atheistic, sexually immoral, and tending to further socialism and the throwing of bombs. Wagnerites were threatened with assassination, and assaults between critics of the rival schools were things not unknown in the foyer of the opera. I really believe that my father, as the chief exponent of Wagner in these islands, did go in some personal danger. Extraordinary pressures were brought to bear upon the more prominent critics of the day, the pressure coming, as a rule, from the exponents of the school of Italian opera. Thus, at the openings of the opera seasons packing-cases of large dimensions and considerable in number would arrive at the house of the ferocious critic of the chief newspaper of England. They would contain singular assortments of comestibles and of objects of art. Thus I remember half a dozen hams, the special product of some north Italian town, six cases of Rhine wine, which were no doubt intended to propitiate the malignant Teuton; a reproduction of the Medici Venus in marble, painted with phosphoric paint so that it gleamed blue and ghostly in the twilight; a case of Bohemian glass and several strings of Italian sausages. And these packing cases, containing no outward sign of their senders, would have to be unpacked and then once more repacked, leaving the servants with fingers damaged by nails and passages littered with straw. Inside would be found the cards of Italian *prime donne*, tenors or basses, newly arrived in London, and sending servile homage to the illustrious critic of the 'Giornale Times.' On one occasion a letter containing bank-notes for £50 arrived from a *prima donna* with a pathetic note begging the critic to absent himself from her first night. Praise from a Wagnerite she considered to be impossible, but she was ready to pay for silence. I do not know whether this letter inspired my father with the idea of writing to the next suppliant that he was ready to accept her present—it was the case of Bohemian glass—but that in that case he would never write a word about her singing. He meant the letter, of course, as a somewhat clumsy joke, but the lady—she was not, however, an Italian—possessing a sense of humour, at once accepted the offer. This put my father rather in a quandary, for Mme. H—— was one of the greatest exponents of emotional tragic music that there had ever been, and the occasion on which she was to appear was the first performance in England of one of the great operas of the world. I do not exactly know whether my father went through any conscientious troubles—I presume he did, for he was a man of singular moral niceness. At any rate he wrote an enthusiastic notice of the opera and an enthusiastic and deserved notice of the impersonatrix of Carmen. And since the Bohemian glass—or the poor remains of the breakages of a quarter of a century—still decorate my sideboard, I presume that he accepted the present. I do not really see what else he could have done.

Pressure of other sorts was also not unknown. Thus, there was an opera produced by a foreign baron who was a distinguished figure in the diplomatic service, and who was very well looked on at Court. In the middle of the performance my father received a command to go into the royal box, where a royal personage informed him that in his august opinion the work was one of genius. My father replied that he was sorry to differ from so distinguished a connoisseur—but that in his opinion the music was absolute rubbish—*Lauter Klatsch*. The reply was undiplomatic and upon the whole regrettable, but my father had been irritated by the fact that a good deal of Court pressure had already been brought to bear upon him. I believe that there were diplomatic reasons for desiring to flatter the composer of the opera, who was attached to a foreign embassy—the embassy of the nation with whom for the moment the diplomatic relations of Great Britain were somewhat strained. So that without doubt His Royal Highness was as patriotically in the right as my father was in a musical sense. Eventually, the notice of the opera was written by another hand. The performance of this particular opera remains in my mind because during one of its scenes, which represented the frozen circle of Hell, the cotton wool, which figures as snow on the stage, caught fire and began to burn. An incipient panic took place among the audience, but the orchestra, under a firm composer whose name I have unfortunately forgotten, continued to play, and the flames were extinguished by one of the singers using his cloak. But I still remember being in the back of the box and seeing in the foreground, silhouetted against the lights of the stage, the figures of my father and of some one else— I think it was William Rossetti—standing up and shouting down into the stalls: 'Sit down, brutes! Sit down, cowards!'

On the other hand, it is not to be imagined that acts of kindness and good-fellowship were rare under this seething mass of passions and of jealousies. Thus at one of the Three Choir Festivals, my father, having had the misfortune to sprain his ankle, was unable to be present in the cathedral. His notice was written for him by the critic of the paper which was most violently opposed to views at all Wagnerian—a gentleman whom till that moment my father regarded as his bitterest personal enemy. This critic happened to be staying in the same hotel, and having heard of the accident volunteered to write the notice out of sheer good feeling. This gentleman, an extreme *bon vivant* and a man of an excellent and versatile talent, has since told me that he gave himself particular trouble to imitate my father's slightly cumbrous Germanic English and his extreme modernist views. This service was afterwards repaid by my father in the following circumstances. It was again one of the Three Choir Festivals—at Worcester, I think, and we were stopping at Malvern—my father and Mr S—— going in every day to the cathedral city. Mr S—— was either staying with us or in an adjoining house, and on one Wednesday evening, his appetite being sharpened by an unduly protracted performance of 'The Messiah,' Mr S—— partook so freely of the pleasures of the table that he omitted altogether to write his notice. This fact he remembered just before the closing of the small local telegraph office, and although Mr S—— was by no means in a condition to write his notice, he was yet sufficiently mellow with wine to be lachrymose and overwhelmed at the idea of losing his post. We rushed off at once to the telegraph office and did what we could to induce the officials to keep the wires open whilst the notice was being written. But all inducements failed. My father hit upon a stratagem at the last moment. At that date it was a rule of the Post Office that if the beginning of a long message were handed in before eight o'clock the office must be kept open until its conclusion as long as there was no break in the handing in of slips. My father therefore commanded me to telegraph anything that I liked to the newspaper office as long as I kept it up whilst he was writing the notice of 'The Messiah.' And the only thing that came into my head at the moment was the Church Service. The newspaper was therefore astonished to receive a long telegram beginning! *When the wicked man turneth away from the sin that he has committed* and continuing through the *Te Deum* and the *Nunc Dimittis,* till suddenly it arrived at 'The Three Choirs Festival. Worcester, Wednesday, July 27th, 1887.'

A GERMAN MASTER

At the last public school which I attended—for my at-tendances at schools were varied and singular, according as my father ruined himself with starting new periodicals or happened to be flush of money on account of new legacies—at my last public school I was permitted to with-draw myself every afternoon to go to concerts. This brought down upon me the jeers of one particular German master who kept order in the afternoons, and upon one occasion he set for translation the sentence:

'Whilst I was idling away my time at a concert, the rest of my classmates were diligently engaged in study of the German language.'

Proceeding mechanically with the translation—for I paid no particular attention to Mr P——, because my father, in his reasonable tones, had always taught me that schoolmasters were men of inferior intelligence to whom personally we should pay little attention, though the rules for which they stood must be exactly observed—I had got as far as *Indem ich faulenzte . . .* when it suddenly occurred to me that Mr P—— in setting this sentence to the class was aiming a direct insult not only at myself, but at Beethoven, Bach, Mozart, Wagner, and Robert Franz.

An extraordinary and now inexplicable fury overcame me.
At all my schools I was always the good boy of my respec-
tive classes, but on this occasion I rose in my seat pro-
pelled by an irresistible force, and I addressed Mr P——
with words the most insulting and the most contemptuous.
I pointed out that music was the most divine of all arts,
that German was a language fit only for horses; that
German literature contained nothing that any sensible
person could want to read except the works of Schopen-
hauer, who was an anglomaniac, and in any case was much
better read in an English translation; I pointed out that
Victor Hugo has said that to utter the lowest type of
inanities, '*il faut être stupide comme un maître d'école
qui n'est bon à rien que pour planter des choux.*' I can
still feel the extraordinary indignation that filled me,
though I have to make an effort of the imagination to
understand why I was so excited; I can still feel the way
the breath poured through my distended nostrils. With,
I suppose, some idea of respect for discipline I had carefully spoken in German which none of my classmates
understood. My harangue was suddenly ended by Mr
P——'s throwing his large inkpot at me; it struck me
upon the shoulder and ruined my second-best coat and
waistcoat.

THE PINES, PUTNEY

Well, Time went on; my father died; Mr Watts-Dunton
became my mother's trustee and my guardian. He also
threw his comether over Mr Swinburne and took him to
live with him in the Pines, Putney. There they both grew
deaf together under the housekeepership of Mr Watts-
Dunton's sister, the widow of an attorney who had not
made good—in a white, high, widow's cap, white mittens,
and a black silk shoulder-cape. Deaf, too.... You may

imagine all three deaf people sitting together in the dusk
of the Pines waiting for the argand colza-oil lamp to be
lighted, when Mr Swinburne and Mrs Mason would play
cribbage whilst the poet sipped his glass of Worcester
Sauce and Mr Watts-Dunton pored over a crabbed volume
of forgotten gipsy lore . . . or made pretence so to do.

The Pines, Putney, as its name shows, was no place
for the stabling of Pegasus. It was, upon the whole, the
most lugubrious London semi-detached villa that it was
ever my fate to enter. It was spacious enough, but, built
at the time of the 1850–60 craze for Portland cement, its
outer surfaces had collected enough soot to give it the
aspect of the dwelling of a workhouse master or chief
gaoler. In the sooty garden grew a single fir that, in my
time at least, could have gone as a Christmas tree into
the villa's dining-room. In the next garden there had been
another, but that had died.

I don't mean to say that the house was poverty-stricken.
It was the residence of the highly prosperous family lawyer
that Mr Watts-Dunton was, well staffed with servants, the
windows and furniture always kept at a high pitch of
polish, the cut steel fire implements always shining . . . I
imagine the walls must have been covered with brown
paper in the proper aesthetic fashion of the advanced of
the day and that that drank up the light. . . . At any rate
the rooms of the Pines, Putney, were always dim . . . I
had occasion to go there pretty frequently . . . once a
quarter at least when my mother's dividends were due;
and on occasion when she had outrun the constable and
needed an advance . . . or when I myself did! . . . So it was
pretty often.

Then I would be received with an extraordinary pomp
of praise by Mr Watts-Dunton. He would address to me
studied periods of adulation of my latest published book.
. . . I had published I think six before I came of age . . . and
Mr Watts-Dunton addressed me as if I were a public
meeting. And Mr Swinburne would add some nervous
phrases to the effect that he intended to read my book

as soon as time served. . . . He would be floating somewhere about in the dimnesses like a shaft of golden
light. . . . But when I came seriously to prefer my request
for a cheque and Mr Watts-Dunton had exhausted the
praise with which he put me off . . . then, if I was at all
insistent, extraordinary things would happen. . . . Loud
bells would ring all over the establishment. Housemaids
would rush in, their cap-strings floating behind, bearing
the orange envelopes of telegrams on silver salvers. And
Mr Watts-Dunton would start like a ship suddenly struck
by a gale, would tear open an envelope and exclaim
dramatically:

'Sorry, me dear faller. . . . Extraordinarily sorry, me dear
faller. . . . Tallegram from Haslemere. From Lord Tennyson. . . . Have to go . . . ah . . . and correct his proofs at
once. . . . M'm, m'm, m'm. . . . Desolated to be unable
to be further delighted by most int'rustin' conversa. . . .'
And he would have disappeared, the dimnesses swallowing
him up with improbable velocity. . . .

When it wasn't Lord Tennyson, it would be Browning
. . . or Coventry Patmore or Lewis Morris. . . .

And you are not to believe that Mr Watts-Dunton was
merely a toady. He was an extraordinarily assiduous and
skilful family lawyer and adviser as to investments and
solvent of brawls and poets' fallings out. . . . So that where
those poor Pre-Raphaelites would have been without him
there is no knowing. . . . His one novel . . . *Aylwin* . . . had
the largest sale ever enjoyed by any novel up to that date
and for decades after. It was what his friends called bilge,
and his innumerable poems seemed to be all devoted to
proving that he had once been kissed by a Romany lal . . .
a sort of watered-down Isopel Berners. . . . But what else
could the poems and novels of the proprietor of the Pines,
Putney, be? . . . And when reading his poems aloud to
Mr Swinburne, he would coyly hold his head on one side
as if the better to afford you the view of the spot on the
side of his jaw where the gipsy maiden had kissed him. . . .
And I really believe one must have done so once. . . . But

he did save ever so many of those outrageous poet-painters from the workhouse or the gaol and kept as many more on this side of delirium tremens. . . .

On the less dramatic occasions when Mr Watts-Dunton really produced a cheque I would be invited to stay to lunch. . . . And owing to the increasing deafness of the two friends and of Mrs Mason the meals passed in ever deeper and deeper silence. . . . Mr Swinburne ate, lost in his dreams, with beside his plate an enormous Persian cat to whom he fed alternate forksful of food. Mr Watts-Dunton gobbled his meats with voracity. The cooking was exquisite, the wines quite impeccable—though Mr Swinburne touched none. Mrs Mason addressed inaudible remarks to the maids. . . .

At a given point she would catch the eye of non-existent ladies and rise stiffly. . . . Immediately, with an extremely jerky movement so rapid as to be almost imperceptible, Mr Swinburne would be on his toe-points, positively running to the door, his coat-tails flapping behind him. . . . It was the singular action of an extremely active man. At one moment he was sitting sunk in his chair; at the next he was on the points of his toes and in extraordinarily rapid motion. . . . Mrs Mason would be passing out of the doorway with a rigid inclination of the head to Mr Swinburne, who had opened the door for her; and slowly and meditatively the poet would regain his chair . . . with the litheness of a slow cat . . . and would begin to talk in long, wonderful monologues . . . about the *Bacchae* or the *Birds.*

A MR HARDY

I was keenly aware of a Mr Hardy who was a kind, small man, with a thin beard, in the background of London tea parties. . . and in the background of my mind . . . I remember very distinctly the tea party at which I was introduced to him by Mrs Lynn Lynton with her paralysing, pebble-blue eyes, behind gleaming spectacles. Mrs Lynn Lynton, also a novelist, was a Bad Woman, my dear. One of the Shrieking Sisterhood! And I could never have her glance bent on me from behind those glasses without being terrified at the fear that she might shriek ... or be Bad. I think it was Rhoda Broughton who first scandalized London by giving her heroine a latchkey. But Mrs Lynn Lynton had done something as unspeakably wicked. ... And I was a terribly proper young man.

So, out of a sort of cloud of almost infantile paralysis— I must have been eighteen to the day—I found myself telling a very very kind, small, ageless, soft-voiced gentleman with a beard the name of my first book, which had been published a week before. And he put his head on one side and uttered, as if he were listening to himself, the syllables: 'Ow. ... Ow. ...'

I was petrified with horror ... not because I thought he had gone mad or was being rude to me, but because he seemed to doom my book to irremediable failure. ...

I do not believe I have ever mentioned the name of one of my own books in my own print ... at least I hope I have been too much of a little gentleman ever to have done so. But I do not see how I can here avoid mentioning that my first book was called *The Brown Owl* and that it was only a fairy tale ... I will add that the publisher —for whom Mr Edward Garnett was literary adviser— paid me ten pounds for it and that it sold many thousands more copies than any other book I ever wrote ... and keeps on selling to this day.

And on that day I had not got over the queer feeling of having had a book published ... I hadn't wanted to have a book published. I hadn't tried to get it published. My grandfather had, as it were, ordered Mr Garnett to get it published. ... I can to this day hear my grandfather's voice saying to Mr Garnett, who was sitting to him on a model's throne:

'Fordie has written a book, too.... Go and get your book, Fordie!'... and the manuscript at the end of Mr Garnett's very thin wrist disappearing into his capacious pocket.... And my mother let me have ten shillings of the money paid by Mr Garnett's employer.... And that I thought authorship was on the whole a mug's game and concealed as well as I could from my young associates the fact that I was an Author. I should have told you that that was my attitude and should have believed it. My ambition in those days was to be an Army Officer!

And then suddenly, in Mrs Lynn Lynton's dim, wicked drawing-room, in face of this kind, bearded gentleman, I was filled with consternation and grief. Because it was plain that he considered that the vowel sounds of the title of my book were ugly and that, I supposed, would mean that the book could not succeed. So I made the discovery that I—but tremendously!—wished that the book should succeed ... even though I knew that if the book should succeed it would for ever damn my chances as one of Her Majesty's officers....

And I could feel Mr Hardy feeling the consternation and grief that had come up in me, because he suddenly said in a voice that was certainly meant to be consolatory:

'But of course you meant to be onomatopoeic. Ow—ow—representing the lamenting voices of owls.... Like the repeated double O's of the opening of the Second Book of *The Aeneid*....'

I was struck as dumb as a stuck pig. I could not get out a word whilst he went on talking cheerfully. He told me some anecdotes of the brown owl and then remarked that it might perhaps have been better if, supposing I had wanted to represent in my title the cry of the brown owl, instead of two 'ow' sounds I could have found two 'oo's.'.... And he reflected and tried over the sound of 'the brooding coots' and 'the muted lutes....'

And then he said, as if miraculously to my easement:

'But of course you're quite right.... One shouldn't talk of one's books at tea parties.... Drop in at Max Gate when you are passing and we'll talk about it all in peace. . . .'

Marvellously kind . . . and leaving me still with a new emotional qualm of horror. . . . Yes, I was horrified . . . because I had let that kind gentleman go away thinking that my book was about birds . . . whereas it was about Princesses and Princes and magicians and such twaddle. . . . I had written it to amuse my sister Juliet. . . . So I ran home and wrote him a long letter telling him that the book was not about birds and begging his pardon in several distinct ways. . . .

SOME WRITERS
AND ARTISTS

FORD MADOX BROWN

I

MADOX BROWN has been dead for twenty years now, or getting on for that. I would not say that the happiest days of my life were those that I spent in his studio, for I have spent in my life days as happy since then; but I will say that Madox Brown was the finest man I ever knew. He had his irascibilities, his fits of passion when, tossing his white head, his mane of hair would fly all over his face, and when he would blaspheme impressively after the manner of our great-grandfathers. And in these fits of temper he would frequently say the most unjust things. But I think that he was never either unjust or ungenerous in cold blood, and I am quite sure that envy had no part at all in his nature. Like Rossetti and like William Morris, in his very rages he was nearest to generosities. He would rage over an injustice to someone else to the point of being bitterly unjust to the oppressor. I do not think that I would care to live my life over again—I have had days that I would not again face for a good deal—but I would give very much of what I possess to be able, having still such causes for satisfaction as I now have in life, to be able to live once more some of those old evenings in the studio.

The lights would be lit, the fire would glow between the red tiles; my grandfather would sit with his glass of weak whisky-and-water in his hand, and would talk for hours. He had anecdotes more lavish and more picturesque than any man I ever knew. He would talk of Beau Brummel, who had been British Consul at Calais when Madox Brown was born there, of Paxton who built the Crystal Palace, and of the mysterious Duke of Portland who lived underground, but who, meeting Madox Brown in Baker Street outside Druce's, and hearing that Madox Brown suffered from gout, presented him with a large quantity of colchicum grown at Welbeck. . . .

Well, I would sit there on the other side of the rustling fire, listening, and he would revive the splendid ghosts of Pre-Raphaelites, going back to Cornelius and Overbeck and to Baron Leys and Baron Wappers, who taught him first to paint in the romantic grand manner. He would talk on. Then Mr William Rossetti would come in from next door but one, and they would begin to talk of Shelley and Browning and Mazzini and Napoleon III, and Mr Rossetti, sitting in front of the fire, would sink his head nearer and nearer the flames. His right leg would be crossed over his left knee, and, as his head went down, so, of necessity, his right foot would come up and out. It would approach nearer and nearer to the fire-irons which stood at the end of the fender. The tranquil talk would continue. Presently the foot would touch the fire-irons and down they would go into the fender with a tremendous clatter of iron. Madox Brown, half dozing in the firelight, would start and spill some of his whisky. I would replace the fire-irons in their stand.

The talk would continue, Mr Rossetti beginning again to sink his head towards the fire, and explaining that, as he was not only bald but an Italian, he liked to have his head warmed. Presently, bang! would go the fire-irons again. Madox Brown would lose some more whisky and would exclaim:

'Really, William!'

Mr Rossetti would say:

'I am very sorry, Brown.'

I would replace the fire-irons again, and the talk would continue. And then for the third time the fire-irons would go down. Madox Brown would hastily drink what little whisky remained to him, and jumping to his feet would shout:

'God damn and blast you, William, can't you be more careful?'

To which his son-in-law, always the most utterly calm of men, would reply:

'Really, Brown, your emotion appears to be excessive. If Fordie would leave the fire-irons lying in the fender there would be no occasion for them to fall.'

The walls were covered with gilded leather; all the doors were painted dark green; the room was very long, and partly filled by the great picture that was never to be finished, and, all in shadow, in the distant corner was the table covered with bits of string, curtain knobs, horse-shoes, and odds and ends of iron and wood.

II

It was a few days after this, in the evening, that Madox Brown, painting at his huge picture, pointed to the top of the frame that already surrounded the canvas. Upon the top was inscribed 'Ford Madox Brown,' and on the bot-tom, *Wycliffe on his Trial before John of Gaunt. Presented to the National Gallery by a Committee of Admirers of the Artist*. In this way the 'X' of Madox Brown came exactly over the centre of the picture. It was Madox Brown's practice to begin a painting by putting in the eyes of the central figure. This, he considered, gave him the requisite strength of tone that would be applied to the whole canvas. And indeed I believe that, once he had painted in those eyes, he never in any picture altered them, however much he might alter the picture itself. He used them, as it were, to work up to. Having painted in those eyes he would begin at the top left-hand corner of the canvas, and would go on painting downwards in a nearly straight line until the picture was finished. He would of course have made a great number of studies before commencing the picture itself. Usually there was an exceedingly minute and conscientious pencil-drawing, then a large charcoal cartoon, and after that, for the sake of the colour scheme, a version in water-colour, in pastels, and generally one in oil. In the case of the Manchester frescoes almost every one was preceded by a small version painted in oils upon a panel, and this was the case with the large Wycliffe.

On this, the last evening of his life, Madox Brown pointed with his brush to the 'X' of his name. Below it, on the left-hand side the picture was completely filled in; on the right it was completely blank—a waste of slightly yellow canvas that gleamed in the dusky studio. He said:

'You see I have got to that "X." I am glad of it, for half the picture is done and it feels as if I were going home.'

Those, I think, were his last words. He laid his brushes upon his painting cabinet, scraped his palette of all mixed paints, laid his palette upon his brushes and his spectacles upon his palette. He took off the biretta that he always wore when he was painting—he must have worn such a biretta for upwards of half a century—ever since he had been a French student. And so having arrived at his end-of-the-day routine which he had followed for innumerable years, he went upstairs to bed. He probably read a little of the *Mystères de Paris*, and died in his sleep, the picture with its inscriptions remaining downstairs, a little ironic, a little pathetic, and unfinished.

MR HOWELL AND MR ROSSETTI

Rossetti wanted to fill his house with anything that was odd, Chinese, or sparkling. If there was something gruesome about it, he liked it all the better. Thus at his death, two marauders, out of the shady crew that victimized him and one honest man, each became possessed of the dark

lantern used by Eugene Aram. I mean to say that quite
lately there were in the market three dark lanterns each of
which was supposed to have come from Rossetti's house
at his death, only one of which had been bought with
honest money at Rossetti's sale. Even this one may not
have been the relic of the murderer which Rossetti had
purchased with immense delight. He bought in fact just
anything or everything that amused him or tickled his
fancy, without the least idea of making his house resemble
anything but an old curiosity shop.

This collection was rendered still more odd by the
eccentricities of Mr Charles Augustus Howell, an extraordinary personage who ought to have a volume all to
himself. There was nothing in an odd-jobbing way that
Mr Howell was not up to. He supported his family for
some time by using a diving bell to recover treasure from
a lost galleon off the coast of Portugal, of which country
he appears to have been a native. He became Ruskin's
secretary and he had a shop in which he combined the
framing and the forging of masterpieces. He conducted
the most remarkable of dealers' swindles with the most
consummate ease and grace, doing it indeed so lovably
that when his misdeeds were discovered he became only
more beloved. Such a character would obviously appeal to
Rossetti, and as, at one period of his career, Rossetti's
income ran well into five figures, whilst he threw gold out
of all the windows and doors, it is obvious that such a
character as Rossetti's must have appealed very strongly
to Mr Charles Augustus Howell. The stories of him are
endless. At one time whilst Rossetti was collecting
chinoiseries, Howell happened to have in his possession a
nearly priceless set of Chinese tea-things. These he
promptly proceeded to have duplicated at his establishment, where forging was carried on more wonderfully
than seems possible. This forgery he proceeded to get
one of his concealed agents to sell to Rossetti for an
enormously high figure. Coming to tea with the poet-artist
on the next day, he remarked to Rossetti:

9*

'Hallo, Gabriel, where did you get those clumsy imitations?'

Rossetti of course was filled with consternation, whereupon Howell remarked comfortingly: 'Oh, it's all right, old chap, I've got the originals, which I'll let you have for an old song.'

And eventually, he sold the originals to Rossetti for a figure very considerably over that at which Rossetti had bought the forgeries. Howell was then permitted to take away the forgeries as of no value, and Rossetti was left with the originals. Howell, however, was for some time afterwards more than usually assiduous in visiting the painter-poet. At each visit he brought one of the forged cups in his pocket and whilst Rossetti's back was turned he substituted the forgery for one of the genuine cups which he took away in his pocket. At the end of the series of visits, therefore, Rossetti once more possessed the copies and Howell the genuine set which he sold, I believe, to M. Tissot.

A SETTLEMENT OF ALIENS

Winchelsea stands on a long bluff, in shape like that of Gibraltar. Two miles of marsh separate it from Rye. Once it was sea where the Marsh now is: one day it will be so again. When it was sea all the navies of England could ride in that harbour. And the Five Ports and the two Antient Towns provided all the navies of the King of England. As against certain privileges. A Baron of the Cinque Ports can still drive through all toll-gates without payment and sell in all markets toll-free.

In the face of the cliff that Winchelsea turns to Rye there is a spring forming a dip—St Leonard's Well, or the Wishing Well. The saying is that once you have drunk of those dark waters you will never rest till you drink again.

I have seen—indeed I have induced them to it—Henry James, Stephen Crane, and W. H. Hudson drink there from the hollows of their hands. So did Conrad. They are all dead now.

It was perhaps those waters that induced their frequentations of those two towns. But indeed there were sufficient other inducements. Historic patina covers their buildings more deeply than any others, in England at least. Indeed, I know of no places save for Paris, where memories seem so thick on every stone. The climate too is very mild. There is practically no day throughout the year on which a proper man cannot eat his meals under a south wall out of doors. Then, it is near France. On most days you can see the French cliffs. Once, by an effect of mirage, the city of Boulogne was brought so near to Hastings which is next door to Rye, that the promenaders on the parade of the English town could discern the faces of the tourists inspecting the column of Napoleon on the Boulogne sward over the sea. Napoleon erected that to celebrate his invasion of England. That was as near as anything of his ever got to the coasts of the Five Ports.

At any rate it is an infectious and holding neighbourhood. Once you go there you are apt there to stay. Or you will see in memory, the old walled towns, the red roofs, the grey stones, the country sweeping back in steps from the Channel to the North Downs, the great stretch of the Romney Marsh running out to Dungeness. In the Middle Ages they used to say: 'These be the four quarters of the world: Europe, Asia, Africa, and the Romney Marsh.' But that was before Columbus committed his indiscretion. Hendrik Hudson drew many of his sailors from Rye town. A Rye man was the first European to lose his life by an arrow, in Manhattan; on the shores of the Hudson, I should imagine, beneath where Grant's grave is. . . .

Some years ago my friend Mr H. G. Wells wrote to the papers to say that for many years he was conscious of a ring of foreign conspirators plotting against British letters at no great distance from his residence, Spade House,

Sandgate.... For indeed, those four men—three Americans and one Pole—lit in those days in England a beacon that posterity shall not easily die. You have only got to consider how empty, how lacking a nucleus, English literature would to-day be if they had never lived, to see how discerning were Mr Wells' views of that foreign penetration at the most vulnerable point of England's shores.

At that date Henry James was clean-shaven. As clean-shavenness was then comparatively rare he had in his relatively quiet moments the air of a divine; when, which was more frequent, he was animated, he was nearly always humorous and screwed his sensitive lips into amused or sardonic lines. Then he was like a comedian. His skin was dark, his face very clear cut, his brow domed and bare. His eyes were singularly penetrating, dark and a little prominent. On their account he was regarded by the neighbouring poor as having the qualities of a Wise Man—a sorcerer. My servants used to say: 'It always gives me a turn to open the door for Mr James. His eyes seems to look you through to the very back-bone.'

His vitality was amazing. You might put it that he was very seldom still and almost never silent. Occasionally when he desired information and you were giving him what he wanted he would sit gazing at you with his head leaning back against his grandfather's chair. But almost immediately he would be off with comment and elucidation—or with more questions accompanied by gestures, raising of the eyebrows and the humorous twisting of his lips. His peculiarities were carefully thought out by himself. A distinguished man in the 'fifties must have peculiarities if he has a strong personality. His conversation used to contain a great many compliments to his interlocutor, male or female. They were the current coin of his conversation, learned in France and having no real significance but the fact that they were agreeable. Every woman from the Lady Maude Warrender on the hill to Meary Walker in the marshes was 'dear lady'; every man, 'my dear fellow.' If you did or produced anything it was always admirable: 'Your admirable verses, your admirable still lifes, tea-cakes, knowledge of stock-exchange operations, market gardening.' It was agreeable when you were used to it but many people it bewildered or repelled because of a supposed insincerity. Until you know a person well it is perhaps not ethically better to say to him or her: '*Muy hermosa senora beso los manos de usted*,' than to employ a universal 'buddy' for social contacts. But it is not insincere.

On the other hand if he liked or were intimate with you his manner changed at once. You would not lack for censure, criticism, or exhortations along with exactly calculated praise. He liked to live with people of leisure who were intellectually no wasters of time. At times he was unreasonably cruel—and that to the point of vindictiveness when his nerves were set on edge. I remember him at a tea-party given by one of his most gentle and modest admirers. He was talking to the young man's equally gentle, modest, and adoring wife. The young man interrupted him by several times offering him sugar, tea-cakes, cigars. The things that he at last spat out to that young man I will not repeat. He indicted his manners, his hospitality, his dwelling, his work, with a cold fury in voice and eyes.

I was once walking with him and Mr John Galsworthy along the Rye Road to Winchelsea. His dachshund, Maximilian, ran sheep, so, not to curtail the animal's exercise, the Master had provided it with a leash at least ten yards long. Mr Galsworthy and I walked one on each side of James listening obediently whilst he talked. In order to round off an immense sentence the great man halted, just under Winchelsea Hill beneath the windows of acquaintances of us all. He planted his stick firmly into the ground and went on and on and on. Maximilian passed between our six legs again and again, threading his leash behind him. Mr Galsworthy and I stood silent. In any case we must have resembled the *Laocoon*, but when

Maximilian had finished the resemblance must have been overwhelming. The Master finished his reflections, attempted to hurry on, found that impossible. Then we liberated ourselves with difficulty. He turned on me, his eyes fairly blazing, lifting his cane on high and slamming it into the ground:

'H...' he exclaimed, 'you are painfully young, but at no more than the age to which you have attained, the playing of such tricks is an imbecility! An im...be...cility!'

The politenesses of Conrad to James and of James to Conrad were of the most impressive kind. Even if they had been addressing each other from the tribune of the Académie Française their phrases could not have been more elaborate or delivered more *ore rotundo*. James always addressed Conrad as '*Mon cher confrère*,' Conrad almost bleated with the peculiar tone that the Marseillaise get into their compliments '*Mon cher Maître*.'... Every thirty seconds! When James spoke of me to Conrad he always said: '*Votre ami, le jeune homme modeste*.' They always spoke French together, James using an admirably pronounced, correct, and rather stilted idiom such as prevailed in Paris of the 'seventies. Conrad spoke with extraordinary speed, fluency, and some incomprehensibility, a meridional French with as strong a Southern accent as that of garlic in *aioli*.... I speak French with a strong British accent and much too correctly. When I was a boy my grandfather who was French by birth and had a strong French tinge to his English used to say to me: 'Fordie, you must speak French with absolute correctness and without slang which would be an affectation. But with the strongest possible British accent to show that you are an English gentleman.'

We talked in those days, with those distinctions of language, for many hours on end. Or rather, I listened whilst they talked.

Conrad had the most unbounded, the most generous, and the most understanding admiration for the Master's work but he did not much like James personally. I imagine

that was because at bottom James was a New Englander
pur sang, though he was actually born in New York. James
on the other hand liked neither Conrad nor his work very
much, mostly, I imagine, because at bottom Conrad was a
Pole, a Roman Catholic and Romantic and Slav pessimist.
It was hardly to be expected that James should like,
say, *Lord Jim*, for, though that may less appear to-day,
the technique of Conrad's work was then singularly revolutionary. James on the other hand never made fun of
Conrad in private. Conrad was never for him 'poor dear
old' as were Flaubert, Mrs Humphry Ward, Meredith,
Hardy, or Sir Edmund Gosse. He once expressed to me as
regards Conrad something like an immense respect for his
character and achievements. I cannot remember his exact
words, but they were something to the effect that Conrad's
works impressed him very disagreeably, but he could find
no technical fault or awkwardness about them. So that
since so many men whose judgment he affected regarded
Conrad even then as a great master he must not be taken
as uttering any literary censure....

The Conrad of those days was Romance. He was dark,
black bearded, passionate in the extreme and at every
minute; rather small but very broad shouldered and long
in the arm. Speaking English he had so strong a French
accent that few who did not know him well could understand him at first. His gestures were profuse and continuous, his politenesses Oriental and at times almost servile.
Like James he would address a Society lady, if he ever met
one, or an old woman in the lane, or his own servants, or
the ostler at an inn, or myself who was for many years little
more than his cook, slut, and butler in literary matters, or
Sir Sidney Colvin, or Sir Edmund Gosse, all with the
same profusion of endearing adjectives. On the other hand
his furies would be sudden, violent, blasting, and incomprehensible to his victim. At one of my afternoon
parties in London he objurgated the unfortunate Charles
Lewis Hind—a thin, slightly stuttering nervous, dark
fellow who was noted as a critic, mostly of paintings. Hind

in a perfectly sincere mood had congratulated him because his name was on all the hoardings in London. Conrad's *Nostromo* was then being serialized in a journal that gave the fact unusual prominence in its advertisements.

Conrad on the other hand despised the journal, and himself more for letting his work appear in it. His hatred of the publicity was as real as if it were an outrage on the honour of his family. From the windows of my house his name was visible on a hoarding that some house-breakers had erected—visible in letters three feet long. This had driven him nearly mad and he had really taken the congratulations of Mr Hind as gloatings over his bitter poverty. Mr Hind had a sardonic manner and spoke with a rictus; bitter and dreadfully harassing poverty alone had driven Conrad, mercilessly, to consent to that degradation of his art.

In the event, next day Conrad was very ill with mortification and I had to write the part of the serial that remained to make up the weekly instalment. Our life was like that. That manuscript of mine is in the hands of an American collector.*

Otherwise he was the most marvellous raconteur in the world. There was no country he could not make you see when he talked, from Poland to the palms of Palembang. He suffered at that time and till towards the end of his life from agonies of poverty. He was terribly concerned for the material future of his family to whom he was almost unbelievably attached. Crane and Hudson he really loved personally. His admiration for their works was unbounded. When their books came it was as if he bounded into them like a schoolboy running from the school door. I do not think he took much real stock in other writers of English. He would utter elaborate politenesses to them if he met them.

But you could always tell when he really admired work. It would manifest itself in two ways. You would be read-

* The long instalment of *Nostromo* in Ford's handwriting without any corrections by Conrad is now in Yale University Library.

ing at one end of the room and he at the other. It would
be a new book he was reading—or perhaps a Flaubert, a
Turgenev, or a Maupassant. He would begin to groan and
roll about on the couch where he was extended. After a
time he would say:

'What is the use? I ask you what is the use of writing?
When this fellow can write like this. There's no room for
us.' He would go on groaning. Then he would, after a
time, spring up, holding his book. 'Listen to this!' he
would exclaim in sheer joy; laughing with it as if with his
whole body; 'By God,' he would cry out, 'There was never
anything like this.' And he would read out a phrase of
Crane's 'The waves were barbarous and abrupt'; or a
short passage of Hudson in which he shows you dandelion
globes, when you are lying on your back on Lewes Downs,
globes illuminated by the sun against the blue sky, in
millions, for miles up into the blue. Or he would close a
book by Henry James, sigh deeply and say: 'I don't know
how the Old Man does it. There's nothing he does not
know; there's nothing he can't do. That's what it is when
you have been privileged to go about with Turgenev.'

Hudson immensely admired Conrad personally. He was
very lean, *very* tall, high-boned, long-limbed, grey. He was
slow in his motions. You have to be if you are a field
naturalist. His head was smallish for his great frame, but
as if chiselled by the wind as rocks are; his cheeks weather-
beaten. His eyes were small and keen, usually a little closed
as if he were looking up along a strong wind. His voice
was very gentle, soft as a rule, sometimes a little high and
reedy, his accent neither English nor American, but very
scrupulous. He had a little, short, pointed, grey hidalgo's
beard and a heavy grey moustache. He was all gentleness
and infinite patience. I have been with him in circumstances of ill-natured companionship and querulousness
in which his patience was unending. He would stroll along,
swinging his shoulders, stooping a little, mostly silent,
occasionally putting in a word of dissent. To show that he
was paying attention. He suggested, the immensely long

fellow, a man holding in his hand a frightened bird, but making his examination with such gentleness that the bird's little heart would soon cease to beat fast. If he stood against an old grey wall in a field he was so grey that he would be almost invisible from a few yards away unless you looked specially for him.

He knew on the surface little about books. He would say again and again, indignantly: 'I am no writer. I am a naturalist.' He looked at books from afar. It was perhaps long-sightedness but it gave the idea that he was mentally aloof. He would stand up, holding *Heart of Darkness* and say: 'Yes, the river's all right. The trees are all right. Yes, not so bad. No doubt he's a master.' James personally a little alarmed him. Hudson was used to high society, moving in aloof realms that are usually closed to imaginative writers. They were then open to almost all Americans, because they committed you to nothing socially. The Greys of Fallodon loved Hudson because he loved birds. So he would look at James enigmatically, breathing rather uncertainly through his nose. James was a Society figure all right—but a little too flamboyant. Like an unusual species of a familiar genus. The early works of James in their first versions Hudson liked and he was ready to acknowledge that the Old Man was the Master of us all. Old Man means 'captain' on a ship, a colonel in a regiment, a head foreman in a gang of stevedores, a master shepherd on a farm.

Crane was the most beautiful spirit I have ever known. He was small, frail, energetic, at times virulent. He was full of phantasies and fantasticisms. He would fly at and deny every statement before it was out of your mouth. He wore breeches, riding leggings, spurs, a cowboy's shirt, and there was always a gun near him in the mediaeval building that he inhabited seven miles from Winchelsea. In that ancient edifice he would swat flies with precision and satisfaction with the bead-sight of his gun. He proclaimed all day long that he had no use for corner lots nor battlefields, but he got his death in a corner, on the most

momentous of all battlefields for Anglo-Saxons. Brede
Manor saw the encampment of Harold before Hastings.

He was an American, pure blooded, and of ostentatious
manners when he wanted to be. He used to declare at one
time that he was the son of an uptown New York bishop,
at another, that he had been born in the Bowery and there
dragged up. At one moment his voice would be harsh, like
a raven's, uttering phrases like: 'I'm a fly-guy that's wise
to the all-night push,' if he wanted to be taken for a
Bowery tough, or 'He was a mangy, sheep-stealing coyote'
if he desired to be thought of cowboy ancestry. At other
times he would talk rather low in very selected English.
That was all boyishness.

But he was honourable, physically brave, infinitely hope-
ful, generous, charitable to excess, observant beyond belief,
morally courageous, of unswerving loyalty, a beautiful poet
—and of untiring industry. With his physical frailty, his
idealism, his love of freedom and of truth he seemed to me
to be like Shelley. His eyes with their long fringes of
lashes were almost incredibly beautiful—and as if vengeful.
Of his infinite industry he had need.

It was delightful to go to Brede Place, because Steevie
was there, but nothing was more depressing than to drive
down into the hollow. In the Middle Ages they built in
bottoms to be near water and Brede, though mostly an
Elizabethan building, in the form of an E out of compliment to Great Eliza, was twelfth-century in site. The
sunlight penetrated, pale, like a blight into that damp
depression. The great house was haunted. It had stood
empty for half a century, the rendezvous of smugglers. On
the green banks played fatherless children—and number-
less parasites. Crane never forgot a friend, even if it were
merely a fellow who had passed a wet night with him
under an arch. His wife was minded to be a mediaeval
chatelaine. A barrel of beer and a baron of beef stood
waiting in the rear hall for every hobo that might pass that
way. The house was a nightmare of misplaced hospitality,

of lugubrious dissipation in which Crane himself had no part. Grub Street and Greenwich Village did.

The effect on James of poor Steevie was devastating. Crane rode about the countryside on one of two immense coach-horses that he possessed. On their rawboned carcases his frail figure looked infinitely tiny and forlorn. At times he would rein up before the Old Man's door and going in would tell the Master's titled guests that he was a fly-guy that was wise to all the all-night pushes of the world. The Master's titled guests liked it. It was, they thought, characteristic of Americans. If the movies had then existed they would have thought themselves confronted with someone from Hollywood. James winced and found it unbearable.

Steevie he stood and would have stood a great deal more from. The boy for him was always: 'My young compatriot of genius.' But he would explain his wincings to English people by: 'It's as if . . . oh dear lady it's as if you should find in a staid drawing-room on Beacon Hill or Washington Square or at an intimate reception at an Embassy at Washington a Cockney—oh, I admit of the greatest genius —but a Cockney, still, Costermonger from Whitechapel. And, oh heavens, received, surrounded, and adulated . . . by, ah, the choicest, the loveliest, the most sympathetic, and, ah, the most ornamental. . . .'

And the joke—or, for the Old Man the tragedy—was that Crane assumed his Bowery cloak for the sole purpose of teasing the Master. In much the same way, taking me for a Pre-Raphaelite poet, at the beginning of our friendship, he would be for ever harshly denouncing those who paid special prices for antiquities. To Conrad or to Hudson, on the other hand, he spoke and behaved as a reasoning and perceptive human being.

And indeed the native beauty of his nature penetrated sufficiently to the Old Man himself. I never heard James say anything intimately damaging of Crane, and I do not believe he ever said anything of that sort to other people. But what made the situation really excruciating to James was the raids made by Crane's parasites on Lamb House. No doors could keep them out, nor no butler. They made hideous the still levels of the garden with their cachinations, they poked the Old Man in the ribs before his servants, caricatured his speeches before his guests, and extracted from him loans that were almost never refused. There were times when he would hang about in the country outside Rye Walls rather than make such an encounter.

The final tragedy of poor Steevie did not find him wanting. It was tragedy. The sunlight fell blighted into that hollow, the spectres waved their draped arms of mist, the parasites howled and belched on the banks at Brede. That was horrible. But much more horrible was the sight of Crane at his labours. They took place in a room in the centre bar of the E of the Place, over the arched entry. Here Crane would sit writing, hour after hour and day after day, racked with the anxiety that he would not be able to keep going with his pen alone all that fantastic crew. His writing was tiny: he used great sheets of paper. To see him begin at the top of the sheet with his tiny words was agonizing; to see him finish a page filled you with concern. It meant the beginning of one more page, and so till his death. Death came slowly, but Brede was a sure death trap to the tuberculous.

Then James's agonies began. He suffered infinitely for that dying boy. I would walk with him for hours over the Marsh trying to divert his thoughts. But he would talk on and on. He was for ever considering devices for Crane's comfort. Once he telegraphed to Wanamaker's for a whole collection of New England delicacies from pumpkin pie to apple butter and sausage meat and clams and soft shell crabs and mincemeat and ... everything thinkable, so that the poor lad should know once more and finally those fierce joys. Then new perplexities devastated him. Perhaps the taste of those far off meats might cause Steevie to be homesick and so hasten his end. He wavered backwards and forwards between the alternatives beneath the grey walls of Rye Town. He was not himself for many days after Crane's death.

So the first of those four men to die was the youngest. Taken altogether they were, those four, all gods for me. They formed, when I was a boy, my sure hope in the eternity of good letters. They do still. Long ago the greatest pride of my life used to be that Crane once wrote of me to a friend; I had presumably upset him by some want of Oriental deference:

> 'You must not mind Hueffer, that is his way. He patronises me, he patronises Mr Conrad, he patronises Mr James. When he goes to Heaven he will patronise God Almighty. But God Almighty will get used to it, for Hueffer is all right.'

And the words are my greatest pride after so many years.

They are now all dead, a fact which seems to me incredible still. For me they were the greatest influence on the literature that has followed after them that has yet been vouchsafed to that literature. That fourfold tradition will not soon part. To that tradition I will one day return. For the moment I have been trying to make them live again in your eyes. . . . 'It is above all to make you see.'

THE OLD MAN

I daresay, if we could only perceive it, Life has a pattern. I don't mean that of birth, apogee, and death, but a woven symbolism of its own. The Pattern in the Carpet, Henry James called it—and that he saw something of the sort was no doubt the secret of his magic. But, though I walked with and listened to the Master day after day, I remember only one occasion on which he made a remark that was a revelation of his own aims and

methods. . . . For the rest, our intercourse resolved itself
into my listening silently and wondering unceasingly at
his observation of the littlest things of life.

'Are you acquainted,' he would begin, as we strolled
under the gateway down Winchelsea Hill towards Rye. . . .
Ellen Terry would wave a gracious hand from her garden
above the old Tower, the leash of Maximilian would
require several readjustments, and the dog himself a great
many *sotto voce* admonitions as to his expensive habit of
chasing sheep into dykes. 'Are you acquainted,' the Master
would begin again, 'with the terrible words. . . .'

A higgler, on a cart burdened with crates of live poultry,
would pass us. The Master would drive the point of his
cane into the roadway. 'Now *that* man!' he would exclaim.
And he would break off to say what hideous, what appalling, what bewildering, what engrossing, Affairs were
going on all round us in the little white cottages and farms
that we could see, dotting Playden Hill and the Marsh
to the verge of the great horizon. 'Terrible things!' he
would say. 'Appalling!' . . . 'Now that man who just passed
us. . . .' And then he would dig his stick into the road again
and hurry forward, like the White Queen escaping from
disaster, dropping over his shoulder the words: 'But that
probably would not interest you. . . .'

I don't know what he thought *would* interest me!

So he would finish his sentence before the door above
the high steps of Lamb House:

'Are you acquainted with the terrible, the devastating
words, if I may call them so, the fiat of Doom: "I don't
know if you know, sir?" As when the housemaid comes
into your bedroom in the morning and says: "I don't
know if you know, sir, that the bath has fallen through
the kitchen ceiling." '

It was held in Rye that he practised black magic behind
the high walls of Lamb House. . . .

I think I will, after reflection, lay claim to a very considerable degree of intimacy with Henry James. It was
a winter, and a wholly non-literary intimacy. That is to

say, during the summers we saw little of each other. He had his friends, and I mine. He was too often expecting 'my friend Lady Maude,' or some orthodox critic to tea, and I, modern poets whom he could not abide. Occasionally, even during the summer, he would send from Rye to Winchelsea, a distance of two miles, telegrams such as the following which I transcribe:

'To Ford Madox Hueffer, Esq.,
'The Bungalow, Winchelsea, near Rye, Sussex.
    'May I bring four American ladies, of whom one a priest, to tea today?
                    'Yours sincerely,
                            'Henry James.'

And he would come.

But in the winters, when London visitors were scarce, he would come to tea every other day with almost exact regularity, and I would walk back with him to Rye. On the alternate days I would have tea with him and he would walk back to Winchelsea, in all weathers, across the wind-swept marshes. That was his daily, four miles, constitutional.

But it was, as I have said, an almost purely non-literary intimacy. I could, I think, put down on one page all that he ever said to me of books—and, although I used, out of respect, to send him an occasional book of my own on publication, and he an occasional book of his to me, he never said a word to me about my writings and I do not remember ever having done more than thank him in letters for his volume of the moment. I remember his saying of *Romance* that it was an immense English Plum Cake which he kept at his bedside for a fortnight and of which he ate a nightly slice.

He would, if he never talked of books, frequently talk of the personalities of their writers—not infrequently in terms of shuddering at their social excess, much as he shuddered at contact with Crane. He expressed intense dislike for Flaubert who 'opened his own door in his dressing-gown' and he related, not infrequently, unrepeatable stories of the *ménages* of Maupassant—but he much preferred Maupassant to 'poor dear old Flaubert.' Of Turgenev's appearance, personality and habits, he would talk with great tenderness of expression—he called him nearly always 'the beautiful Russian genius,' and would tell stories of Turgenev's charming attentions to his peasant mistresses. He liked, in fact, persons who were suave when you met them—and I daresay that his preference of that sort coloured his literary tastes. He preferred Maupassant to Flaubert because Maupassant was *homme du monde*—or at any rate had *femmes du monde* for his mistresses; and he preferred Turgenev to either because Turgenev was a quiet aristocrat and invalid of the German Bathing Towns, to the finger-tips. And he liked—he used to say so—people who treated him with deep respect.

Flaubert he hated with a lasting, deep rancour. Flaubert had once abused him unmercifully—over a point in the style of Prosper Merimée, of all people in the world. You may read about it in the *Correspondence* of Flaubert, and James himself referred to that occasion several times. It seemed to make it all the worse that, just before the outbreak, Flaubert should have opened the front door of his flat to Turgenev and James, in his dressing-gown.

Myself, I suppose he must have liked, because I treated him with deep respect, had a low voice—appeared in short, a *jeune homme modeste*. Occasionally he would burst out at me with furious irritation—as if I had been a stupid nephew. This would be particularly the case if I ventured to have any opinions about the United States —which, at that date, I had visited much more lately than he had. I remember one occasion very vividly—the place, beside one of the patches of thorn on the Rye road, and his aspect, the brown face with the dark eyes rolling in the whites, the compact, strong figure, the stick raised so as to be dug violently into the road. He had been talking two days before of the provincialism of Washington

in the 'sixties. He said that when one descended the steps
of the Capitol in those days *on trébuchait sur des vaches*
—one stumbled over cows, as if on a village green. Two
days later, I don't know why—I happened to return to
the subject of the provincialism of Washington in the
'sixties. He stopped as if I had hit him and, with the
coldly infuriated tone of a country squire whose patriotism
had been outraged, exclaimed:

'Don't talk such *damnable* nonsense!' He really shouted
these words with a male fury. And when, slightly outraged myself I returned to the charge with his own *on
trébuchait sur des vaches*, he exclaimed: 'I should not
have thought you would have wanted to display such
ignorance,' and hurried off along the road.

I do not suppose that this was as unreasonable a manifestation of patriotism as it appears. No doubt he imagined
me incapable of distinguishing between material and cul-
tural poverties and I am fairly sure that, at the bottom
of his mind lay the idea that in Washington of the 'sixties
there had been some singularly good cosmopolitan and
diplomatic conversation and society, whatever the cows
might have done outside the Capitol. Indeed I know that
towards the end of his life, he came to think that the
society of early, self-conscious New England, with its
circumscribed horizon and want of exterior decoration or
furnishings, was a spiritually finer thing than the mannered
Europeanism that had so taken him to its bosom. As these
years went on, more and more, with a sort of trepidation,
he hovered round the idea of a return to the American
Scene. When I first knew him you could have imagined
no oak more firmly planted in European soil. But, little
by little, when he talked about America there would come
into his tones a slight tremulousness that grew with the
months. I remember, once he went to see some friends—
Mrs and Miss Lafarge, I think—off to New York from
Tilbury Dock. He came back singularly excited, bringing
out a great many unusually uncompleted sentences. He
had gone over the liner: 'And once aboard the lugger....

And if.... Say a toothbrush.... And circular notes....
And something for the night....' All this with a sort of
diffident shamefacedness.

I fancy that his mannerisms—his involutions, whether
in speech or in writing, were due to a settled conviction
that, neither in his public nor in his acquaintance, would
he ever find anyone who would not need talking down to.
The desire of the Artist, of the creative writer, is that his
words and his 'scenes' shall suggest—of course with precision—far more than they actually express or project.
But, having found that his limpidities, from *Daisy Miller*
to *The Real Thing*, not only suggested less than he desired,
but carried suggestions entirely unmeant, he gave up the
attempt at Impressionism of that type—as if his audiences
had tired him out. So he talked down to us, explaining and
explaining, the ramifications of his mind. He was aiming
at explicitness, never at obscurities—as if he were talking
to children.

At any rate, then, he had none of that provincialism of
the literary mind which must forever be dragging in
allusions to some book or local custom. If he found it
necessary to allude to one or the other he explained them
and their provenance. In that you saw that he had learned
in the same school as Conrad and Stephen Crane. And
indeed he had.

It has always seemed to me inscrutable that he should
have been so frequently damned for his depicting only
one phase of life; as if it were his fault that he was not
also Conrad, to write of the sea, or Crane, to project the
life of the New York slums. The Old Man knew consum-
mately one form of life; to that he restricted himself. I
have heard him talk with extreme exactness and insight
of the life of the poor—at any rate of the agricultural
poor, for I do not remember ever to have heard him
discuss industrialism. But he knew that he did not know
enough to treat of farm labourers in his writing. So that,
mostly, when he discoursed of these matters he put his

observations in the form of question: 'Didn't I agree to this?' 'Hadn't I found that?'

But indeed, although I have lived amongst agricultural labourers a good deal at one time or another, I would cheerfully acknowledge that his knowledge—at any rate of their psychologies—had a great deal more insight than my own. He had such an extraordinary gift for observing minutiae—and a gift still more extraordinary for making people talk. I have heard the secretary of a golf club, a dour silent man who never addressed five words to myself though I was one of his members, talk for twenty minutes to the Master about a new bunker that he was thinking of making at the fourteenth hole. And James had never touched a niblick in his life. It was the same with market-women, tram-conductors, ship-builders' labourers, auctioneers. I have stood by and heard them talk to him for hours. Indeed, I am fairly certain that he once had a murder confessed to him. But he needed to stand on extraordinarily firm ground before he would think that he knew a world. And what he knew he rendered, along with its amenities, its gentlefolkishness, its pettinesses, its make-believes. He gives you an immense—and an increasingly tragic picture of a Leisured Society that is fairly unavailing, materialist, emasculated—and doomed. No one was more aware of all that than he.

Steevie used to rail at English Literature, as being one immense petty, Parlour Game. Our books he used to say were written by men who never wanted to go out of drawing-rooms for people who wanted to live at perpetual tea-parties. Even our adventure stories, colonial fictions and tales of the boundless prairie were conducted in that spirit. The criticism was just enough. It was possible that James never wanted to live outside tea-parties—but the tea-parties that he wanted were debating circles of a splendid aloofness, of an immense human sympathy, and of a beauty that you do not find in Putney—or in Passy!

It was his tragedy that no such five o'clock ever sounded for him on the timepieces of this world. And that is no doubt the real tragedy of all of us—of all societies—that we never find in our Spanish Castle our ideal friends living in an assured and permanent republic. Crane's Utopia, but not his literary method, was different. He gave you the pattern in—and the reverse of—the carpet in physical life—in wars, in slums, in Western saloons, in a world where the 'gun' was the final argument. The life that Conrad gives you is somewhere halfway between the two: it is dominated—but less dominated—by the revolver than that of Stephen Crane, and dominated, but less dominated, by the moral scruple than that of James. But the approach to life is the same with all these three: they show you that disillusionment is to be found alike at the tea-table, in the slum and on the tented field. That is of great service to our Republic.

It occurs to me that I have given a picture of Henry James in which small personal unkindlinesses may appear to sound too dominant a note. That is the misfortune of wishing to point a particular moral. I will not say that loveableness was the predominating feature of the Old Man: he was too intent on his own particular aims to be lavishly sentimental over surrounding humanity. And his was not a character painted in the flat, in water-colour, like the caricatures of Rowlandson. For some protective reason or other, just as Shelley used to call himself the Atheist, he loved to appear in the character of a sort of Mr Pickwick—with the rather superficial benevolences, and the mannerisms of which he was perfectly aware. But below that protective mask was undoubtedly a plane of nervous cruelty. I have heard him be—to simple and quite unpretentious people—more diabolically blighting than it was quite decent for a man to be—for he was always an artist in expression. And it needed a certain fortitude when, the studied benevolence and the chuckling, savouring, enjoyment of words, disappearing suddenly from his personality, his dark eyes rolled in their whites and he spoke very brutal and direct English. He chose in fact to appear as Henrietta Maria—but he could be atrocious to those who behaved as if they took him at that valuation.

And there was yet a third depth—a depth of religious, of mystical benevolence such as you find just now and again in the stories that he 'wanted' to write—in *The Great Good Place*. . . . His practical benevolences were innumerable, astonishing—and indefatigable. To do a kindness when a sick cat or dog of the human race *had* 'got through' to his mind as needing assistance he would exhibit all the extraordinary ingenuities that are displayed in his most involved sentences.

I have said that my relation with James was in no sense literary—and I never knew what it *was*. I am perfectly sure that I never in my life addressed to the Master one word of praise or of flattery and, as far as I know, he called me *le jeune homme modeste* and left it at that. He did indeed confess to having drawn my externals in Merton Densher of *The Wings of the Dove*—the longish, leanish, loosish, rather vague Englishman who, never seeming to have anything to do with his days, occupied in journalism his night hours.

I daresay he took me to be a journalist of a gentle disposition, too languid to interrupt him. Once, after I had sent him one of my volumes of poems, he just mentioned the name of the book, raised both his hands over his head, let them slowly down again, made an extraordinary, quick grimace, and shook with an immense internal joke. . . . Shortly afterwards he began to poke fun at Swinburne.

In revenge, constantly and with every appearance of according weight to my opinions, though he seldom waited for an answer, he would consult me about practical matters —investments now and then, agreements once or twice— and, finally, unceasingly as to his fantastic domestic arrangements. He had at one stage portentous but increasingly unsatisfactory servants of whom, in his kindness of heart, he would not get rid until their conduct became the talk of the Antient Town of Rye.

So, one day he came over to Winchelsea to ask me if

I thought a Lady Help would be a desirable feature in an eminent bachelor's establishment.... Going as we seemed eternally in those days to be doing, down Winchelsea Hill under the Strand Gate, he said:

'H ... you seem worried!' I said that I was worried. I don't know how he knew. But he knew everything.

Ellen Terry waved her gracious hand from the old garden above the tower; the collar of Maximilian the dachshund called for adjustment. He began another interminable, refining, sentence—about housemaids and their locutions. It lasted us to the bridge at the western foot of Rye.

In Rye High Street he exclaimed—he was extraordinarily flustered:

'I perceive a compatriot. Let us go into this shop!' And he bolted into a fruiterer's. He came out holding an orange and, eventually, throwing it into the air in an ecstasy of nervousness and stuttering like a schoolboy:

'If it's money H ...' he brought out. *'Mon sac n'est pas grand ... Mais puisez dans mon sac!'*

I explained that it was not about money that I was worried, but about the 'form' of a book I was writing. His mute agony was a painful thing to see. He became much more appalled, but much less nervous. At last he made the great sacrifice:

'Well, then,' he said, 'I'm supposed to be.... Um, um.... There's Mary ... Mrs Ward ... does me the honour.... I'm supposed to know.... In short: Why not let me look at the manuscript!'

I had the decency not to take up his time with it.... *Les beaux jours quand on était bien modeste!* And how much I regret that I did not.

The last time I saw him was, accidentally, in August of 1915—on the fourteenth of that month, in St James's Park. He said:

'Tu vas te battre pour le sol sacré de Mme. de Stael!'

I suppose it was characteristic that he should say 'de Mme. de Stael'—and not of Stendhal, or even of George

Sand! He added—and how sincerely and with what passion—putting one hand on his chest and just bowing, that he loved and had loved France as he had never loved a woman!

I have said that I remember only one occasion on which Henry James spoke of his own work. That was like this: He had published *The Sacred Fount,* and was walking along beside the little shipyard at the foot of Rye Hill. Suddenly he said:

'You understand. . . . I *wanted* to write *The Great Good Place* and *The Altar of the Dead.* . . . There are things one wants to write all one's life but one's artist's conscience prevents one. . . . And then . . . perhaps one allows oneself. . . .'

I don't know what he meant. . . . Or I do! For there *are* things one wants to write all one's life—only one's artist's conscience prevents one. That is the first—or the final, bitter—lesson that the Artist has to learn.

MR JAMES AND MR KIPLING

Lamb House was a majestic Georgian building of the type that Henry James had gone to England more especially to seek. Its best front gave on to the garden. The garden had an immense smooth lawn and was shut in by grey stone walls against which grew perennial flowers. It contained also a massively built white-panelled pavilion. In that, during the summer at least, the Master usually sat and worked.

In Rye church you could see the remains of a criminal hung in chains. It was that of a murderer, a butcher, who set out to kill a Mr Lamb and killed a Mr Greville. Or it may have been the other way round. Rye Town was prouder of its murderer than of its two literary lights, Fletcher and Henry James, but he always seemed to me to have been a clumsy fellow. Lamb House had belonged to the family of the gentleman who was—or wasn't—killed. But Henry James most gloated over the other legend according to which the house had been occupied by a mistress of George IV. The King, sailing down channel on a battleship, was said to have been rowed ashore to visit the lady in the garden pavilion. I always used to wonder at the prodigious number of caps, gloves, canes and hats that were arranged on a table—or it may have been a great chest—in the hall. How, I used to say to myself, can he need so prodigious a number of head-coverings? And I would wonder what thoughts revolved in his head whilst he selected the cap or the stick of the day. I never myself possessed more than one cloth cap at a time.

When I was admitted into his presence by the astonishingly ornate manservant he said:

'A writer who unites—if I may use the phrase—in his own person an enviable popularity to—as I am told—considerable literary gifts and whom I may say I like because he treats me'—and here Mr James laid his hand over his heart, made the slightest of bows and, rather cruelly rolling his dark and liquid eyes and moving his lower jaw as if he were rolling in his mouth a piquant tit-bit, Mr James continued, 'because he treats me—if again I may say any such thing—with proper respect'—and there would be an immense humorous gasp before the word 'respect'— ... 'I refer of course to Mr Kipling ... has just been to see me. And—such are the rewards of an enviable popularity!—a popularity such as I—or indeed you my young friend if you have any ambitions which I sometimes doubt—could not dream of far less imagine to ourselves—such are the rewards of an enviable popularity that Mr Kipling is in the possession of a magnificent one thousand two hundred guinea motor car. And, in the course of conversation as to characteristics of motor cars in general and those of the particular one thousand two hundred guinea motor car in the possession of our

friend. . . . But what do I say? . . . Of our cynosure! Mr
Kipling uttered words which have for himself no doubt
a particular significance but which to me at least convey
almost literally nothing beyond their immediate sound. . . .
Mr Kipling said that the motor car was calculated to make
the Englishman . . . '—and again came the humorous gasp
and the roll of the eyes—'was calculated to make the Englishman . . . think.' And Mr James abandoned himself for
part of a second to low chuckling. 'And,' he continued,
'the conversation dissolved itself, after digressions on the
advantages attendant on the possession of such a vehicle,
into what I believe are styled golden dreams—such as
how the magnificent one thousand two hundred guinea
motor car after having this evening conveyed its master
and mistress to Batemans Burwash of which the proper
pronunciation is Burridge would to-morrow devotedly return here and reaching here at twelve would convey me
and my nephew Billiam to Burridge in time to lunch and
having partaken of that repast to return here in time to
give tea to my friend Lady Maud Warrender who is
honouring that humble meal with her presence to-morrow
under my roof. . . . And we were all indulging in—what
is it?—delightful anticipations and dilating on the agree-
ablenesses of rapid—but not for fear of the police and
consideration for one's personal safety *too* rapid—speed
over country roads and all, if I may use the expression,
was gas and gingerbread when. . . . There is a loud knocking on the door and—*avec des yeux éffarés* . . . ' and here
Mr James really did make his prominent and noticeable
eye almost stick out of his head . . . ' in rushes the chauffeur. . . . And in short the chauffeur has omitted to lubri-
cate the wheels of the magnificent one thousand two hundred guinea motor car with the result that its axles have
become one piece of molten metal. . . . The consequence
is that its master and mistress will return to Burwash
which should be pronounced Burridge by train, and the
magnificent one thousand two hundred guinea motor car
will *not* devotedly return here at noon and will *not* in

time for lunch convey me and my nephew Billiam to
Burwash and will *not* return here in time for me to give
tea to my friend Lady Maud Warrender who is honouring
that humble meal with her presence to-morrow beneath
my roof or if the whether is fine in the garden. . . .'

'Which,' concluded the Master after subdued 'ho, ho,
ho's' of merriment, 'is calculated to make Mr Kipling
think.'

COLLABORATING WITH CONRAD

I

I may as well dispose, once and for all, of the legend that
I had any part in teaching Conrad English, though on
the face of it it may well look plausible enough since he
was a foreigner who never till the end of his life spoke
English other than as a foreigner. But when it came to
writing, it was at once quite a different matter. As I said
elsewhere a little time ago, the moment he got a pen in
his hand and had no eye to publication, Conrad could
write English with a speed, a volubility, and a banal
correctness that used to amaze me. So you have his
immense volume of letters. On the other hand, when, as
it were, he was going before the public, a species of stage
fright would almost completely paralyse him so that his
constructions were frequently very un-English.

In his letters, that is to say, he just let himself go without precision of phrase as without *arrière pensée*, pouring
out supplications, abuse of third parties, eternal and un-
varying complaints, so that in the end the impression is
left of a weak, rather whining personality. But no impression could be more false. Conrad was a man, a He-man
if you like, who fought against enormous odds with un-
dying—with almost unfaltering courage. And his courage
was all the more impressive in that by birth, race, and

temperament he was an unshakable pessimist. Life for him was predestined to end tragically, or, if not, in banality; literature was foredoomed to failure. These were his *choses données,* his only certain truths. In face of that creed, his struggles were unceasing.

And it was astonishing what small things could call down to his underlying buoyancy. I remember once we had been struggling with *Romance* for hours and hours, and he had been in complete despair, and everything that I had suggested had called forth his bitterest gibes, and he was sick, and over ears in debt, and penniless. And we had come to a blank full-stop—one of those intervals when the soul *must* pause to breathe and love itself have rest. And Mrs Conrad came in and said that the mare had trotted from Postling Vents to Sandling in five minutes—say, twelve miles an hour! At once, there in the room was Conrad-Jack-ashore! The world was splendid; hope nodded from every rosebud that looked over the window-sill of the low room. We were going to get a car and go to Canterbury; the mare should have a brand-new breeching strap. And in an incredibly short space of time—say, three hours—at least half a page of *Romance* got itself written.

That was how it went, day in day out, for years—the despair, the lamentations continuing for hours, and then the sudden desperate attack on the work—the attack that would become the fabulous engrossment. We would write for whole days, for half nights, for half the day, or all the night. We would jot down passages on scraps of paper or on the margins of books, handing them one to the other or exchanging them. We would roar with laughter over passages that would have struck no other soul as humorous; Conrad would howl with rage and I would almost sigh over others that no other soul perhaps would have found as bad as we considered them. We would recoil one from the other and go each to our own cottage—our cottages at that period never being further the one from the other than an old mare could take us in an afternoon. In those cottages we would prepare other drafts and so drive backwards and forwards with packages of manuscript under the dog-cart seats. We drove in the heat of summer, through the deluges of autumn, with the winter snows blinding our eyes. But always, always with manuscripts. Heavens, don't my fingers still tingle with the feeling of undoing the stiff buckles, long past midnight, of a horse streaming with rain—and the rubbing down in the stable and the backing the cart into the coach-house. And with always at the back of the mind, the consideration of some unfinished passage, the puzzledom to avoid some too-used phrase that yet seemed hypnotically inevitable.

II

He used to come in in the mornings and, having climbed the many stairs to my small, dreadful study, would sit for hours motionless and numb with a completely expressionless face. Every now and then he would say:

'I can't do it. It can't be done. *Je suis foutu!*' Then he would launch out into a frightful diatribe against the English language. It was a language for dogs and horses. It was incapable of conveying human thoughts. He had given up the attempt. For good. The damn paper must go without its damn serial. Who would care? No one.

I would stand in the window, looking right over London: a grey expanse with sparkling points. From there—in the middle West—one could see Greenwich Observatory in the extreme East. It was looking over that view that I first told Conrad the story that he turned into *The Secret Agent.*

But in those moments I would have a perfectly vacant mind. It just stopped. There was really nothing to say. English is not a good language for prose. You cannot make a direct statement in literary English. At any rate in those days you could not and I doubt if you can now —in English English. In American English you almost can, but you shock elegant ears. Conrad's English however was literary. I had nothing with which to console him.

He would declare that he had written the last word of that serial. I would manoeuvre him towards writing as the drake manoeuvres the sitting duck back to the nest when she has abandoned her eggs. I would read over his last sentence to him. If it provoked no beginnings on his part I would displace him at the desk and write a sentence or two. There are five words that seem horrible to me. They are *The Silver of the Mine*. That was the title of the part of *Nostromo* over which we then wrestled.

He would groan:

'No, it's no use. I'm going to France. I tell you I am going to set up as a French writer. French is a language: it is not a collection of grunted sounds.'

I would say:

'*Nostromo* would go admirably in French. Let us get it blocked out. Then you could re-write it very easily in French.'

The hospital nurse would come in:

'Now, Mr Ford, it is time you got back to bed again.' I would have been up an hour.

Conrad liked the society of that nurse. Inscrutably. She was a flail. She had a face like a Cockney camel. Words that I hardly understood poured out of it incessantly. Conrad however did understand her. He had served before the mast with Cockney deckhands. He would ask her how her other patients were. That would give her an excuse to get going.

'Last peetien I ad wus Lord Northcliffe. Hoperishun on is leg! Lie in bed e would wiv the telephone on is chess. Sweer into the telephone e would. Sweer . . . somethin' awful. . . . Sweer wen hi chinged im . . . oh terrible. Sweer at the pines an then onto the telephone. At the *Dily Mile*. Sech lengwidge. Houtrageous. Then wen hi was going: "Nurse," e sez to me, "Nurse. . . . Whenever you hear men speak against me you will say: 'He bore his illness like a Christian and a gentleman.' " . . . Peetient

bifor that was an old maid ... bifor er they ad swingin
doors. Between the quality staircase and the servants'. ...
Green bize. ...' She had been standing on the top landing
of the house. A servant let the green baize door swing
against her. It had precipitated her down several flights
of stone stairs. She lay at the bottom with her skull
smashed and her brains protruding. The servants put
sheets of newspaper under her head. They wanted to protect their mistress's staircase. When the surgeon came
he could read the imprint of the paper on her brain—
an account of the dispersal of the works of art from the
collection of the Hon. Matthew L. Oldroyd.

That was her story—one of hundreds. Of thousands,
perhaps. Her appearance used to drive me frantic. It meant
that Conrad would not get to work for hours. Neither
could I. I need a certain period of quiet and collection
before words will come.

I would slip away downstairs and dust the dining-room
against lunch. When I returned Conrad would be writing
contentedly at my desk. The nurse with her lack-lustre
eyes and untidy strands of hair hanging from beneath
her cap was detrimental to all her patients. Conrad she
seemed to stimulate. He would listen to her singular tarra-
diddles for hours with an expression of the utmost interest
and deference. Perhaps *Nostromo* would never have got
itself written but for her. Or perhaps Conrad's next book
would have borne a Parisian imprint.

W. H. HUDSON

Hudson was born of American parentage in a place called
Quilmes in the Argentine, about 1840, and coming to
London in the 'eighties of the last century, he was accustomed to declare—in order to account for his almost
impassioned love for the English countryside—that no

member of his family had been in England for over two hundred and fifty years. After his death his industrious and devoted biographer, Mr Morley Roberts, ferreted out that Hudson's father had been born in the State of Maine about 1814, his paternal grandfather having gone there from the West of England a little before the Declaration of Independence. On his mother's side he was, however, of very old United States descent. In any case his youth and young manhood had been passed in Spanish-American countries and that no doubt gave him his gravity of behaviour ... and of prose. For he remained always an extraordinarily closed-up person and the legends that grew up about him could hardly be distinguished from the little biographical truths that one knew. The truths always came in asides. You would be talking about pumas. For this beast he had a great affection, calling it the friend of man. He would declare that the puma would follow a traveller for days over the pampas or through the forest, watch over him and his horse whilst he slept, and drive away the jaguar ... who was the enemy of man. He said that this had happened to him many times. Once he had been riding for two months on the pampas, sleeping beneath the *ombu* trees that seem to cover half a county, and three times a puma had driven off a jaguar. It had been a period of drought. For a whole week he had not been able to wash his face. One asked what it was like not to wash one's face for a week and he would reply: 'Disagreeable. ... Not so bad ... as if cobwebs touched you here and there.' You would say that that must have been a disagreeable week all the same and he would slip out: 'Not so bad as a week I've known ... when Mrs Hudson and I passed a whole ten days in a garret with nothing but a couple of tins of cocoa and some oatmeal to eat. ...'

He shared with Turgenev the quality that makes you unable to find out how he got his effects. Like Turgenev he was utterly undramatic in his methods, and his books have that same quality that have those of the author of *Fathers and Children*. When you read them you forget the

lines and the print. It is as if a remotely smiling face
looked up at you out of the page and told you things.
And those things become part of your own experience.
It is years and years since I first read *Nature in Downland*.
Yet, as I have already said somewhere or other, the first
words that I there read have become a part of my own
life. They describe how, lying on the turf of the high sunlit downs above Lewes in Sussex, Hudson looked up into
the perfect, limpid blue of the sky and saw, going to infinite distances one behind the other, the eye picking up
one, then another beyond it, and another and another,
until the whole sky was postulated ... little shining globes,
like soap bubbles. They were thistledown floating in an
almost windless heaven.

Now that is part of my life. I have never had the
patience—the contemplative tranquillity—to lie looking
up into the heavens. I have never in my life done it. Yet
that is I, not Hudson, looking up into the heavens, the
eye discovering more and more tiny, shining globes until
the whole sky is filled with them, and those thistle-seed
globes seem to be my globes.

For that is the quality of great art—and its use. It is
you, not another, who at night with the stars shining have
leaned over a Venice balcony and talked about patines
of bright gold; you, not anyone else, saw the parents of
Bazarov realize that their wonderful son was dead. And
you yourself heard the voice cry, *Eli, Eli, lama sabac-
thani*!... because of the quality of the art with which
those scenes were projected....

His wife then—and it was at least true that in her
day she had been a celebrated singer—kept a boarding-
house. She was twenty years older than Hudson and did
not come up to his elbow. And it was more or less true
that after her marriage to him she sang very little, because
her voice was leaving her. But otherwise she was very
normal and quick-witted, if a little quick-tempered and
not a good business woman. For all the great money she
had earned in her day had gone and shortly after their

marriage her boarding-house went bankrupt too. It was then that they had known days of real starvation and it is not the least romantic part of Hudson's career, the desperate and courageous efforts he made to keep them going. He was a stranger in London with nothing to earn a living by but his pen; and it is curious to think that one of the ways by which he did earn money was by ferreting out genealogical tables for Americans of English origins. Then he also did hack-work descriptions of South American birds for scientific ornithologists who had never seen a bird. And then magazines began to commission him for articles about birds; his wife inherited a fantastically gloomy house in the most sooty neighbourhood of London and a small sum of money with which she set up a boarding-house that this time did not fail. And it was touching to see how Hudson made another gentle legend for himself amongst Shetland-shawled old maids and broken-down Indian colonels. And then he was granted a pension on the King's Civil List, and then fame came to him in London and money from New York. And he and his wife lived together until she died, a little before him, at the great age of a hundred years.... That, too, was Romance.

I am ashamed to say that I did not see it at the time, and I disliked the atmosphere of the boarding-house so much that whenever I could I used to insist on Hudson's coming out with me to Kensington Gardens. He was not a good walker in those days in spite of the fact that he had spent the greater part of his life on his feet, watching birds. We used to pace very slowly up and down beneath the tall elms of the Broad Walk and in front of the little palace, amongst the children of the wealthy. We would watch the grey squirrels that had come from New York and that were monstrously at home in the Gardens, having bitten off the tails of all the aboriginal red squirrels. And he would talk of how the Liberator carried his whip and reviewed his troops; and of the birds and herds and great trees of the pampas, far away and long ago. And *Far Away and Long Ago* is the most self-revelatory of all his books.

I do not think that I would much like to recapture many
of the atmospheres of my own past. The present days are
better. But I would be glad, indeed, if once again I could
walk slowly along the dingy streets that led from that Bays-
water boarding-house to Paddington Station . . . slowly beside Hudson and his wife who would be going away
towards English greennesses, through the most lugubrious
streets the world could imagine, let alone know. And
Huddie would be expressing theories as to the English
rain and far below him his tiny wife would be incessantly
telling him that he was going the wrong way.

Hudson had lived in that district for forty years, continuing to stay there after fortune had a little smiled on
him—because it was near the great terminus of Paddington
and they could slip away from there to the country without
attracting attention by their singular disproportion in size.
In spite of this they never could go to that exit from
London without her telling him that he was going the
wrong way . . . I suppose because she had lived there for
nearly a century. And she would keep on and on at it,
bickering like a tiny wren threatening some great beast
approaching her nest in the gorse. Her great age only
affected her coloration so that she seemed to recede
further and further into the mists of St Luke's Road
until she was almost invisible. But her vivacity was un-
conquerable, and appropriate. It was as if, having framed
that romantic giant, the force of nature could go no further,
and to frame a fitting mate must compound for him that
singular and elfish humming-bird.

A KIND OF CRITICISM

It is goodwill that is needed if the Humaner Letters are
to come into their own. No amount of praise from
Academicians will make a bad book have a permanent life

whilst ill-natured comment on a good one will delay its entry into its kingdom. Thus people die without having read it and the writer is discouraged. These are the two worst things that can happen to humanity. You may die reconciled to your fate without having seen Carcassonne but what would it be like to leave the world without having read . . . oh, *The Playboy of the Western World*? And what is the place in the hereafter reserved for the gentleman who checked the activities of Keats? For myself I would rather see the worst popular writer roll in gold than a fraudulent pill maker or a Wall Street bear. He at least is only doing what Shakespeare tried to do.

The only human activity that has always been of extreme importance to the world is imaginative literature. It is of supreme importance because it is the only means by which humanity can express at once emotions and ideas. To avoid controversy I am perfectly ready to concede that the other arts are of equal importance. But nothing that is not an art is of any lasting importance at all, the meanest novel being humanly more valuable than the most pompous of factual works, the most formidable of material achievements or the most carefully thought out of legal codes. Samuel Butler wrote an immense number of wasted words in the attempt to avenge himself for some fancied slight at the hands of Darwin. But, in spite of these follies, *The Way of All Flesh* is of vastly more use to us to-day than is *The Origin of Species*. Darwin as scientist is as superseded as the poor alchemist in the Spessart inn: so is Butler in the same department of human futility. But *The Way of All Flesh* cannot be superseded because it is a record of humanity. Science changes its aspect as every new investigator gains sufficient publicity to discredit his predecessors. The stuff of humanity is unchangeable. I do not expect the lay reader to agree with me in this pronouncement but it would be better for him if he did. The world would be a clearer place to him.

From that point of view the activities of the old *Athenaeum* under Maccoll were unmitigatedly harmful—

and singularly adroit. Mr Maccoll was to all appearances,
a nearly imbecile, blond, bald, whiskered individual. He
wore black gloves on every occasion indoors or out, and if
you addressed him his eyes wandered round the cornice
of the ceiling as if the mere fact of being spoken to had
driven him into a panic. As far as I know he never wrote
anything except perhaps the biography of some obscure
theologian or diplomatist but his bulky figure with its
black kid gloves—and its hand in addition always in the
pockets of his reefer jacket as if he had doubly to hide
some grotesque and shameful disease—his panic-stricken
and bulky figure comes back to me as containing one of
the most potent and disastrous forces of his day.

He had got his job, I think, from having been the
travelling tutor of Sir Charles Dilke, the politician and
owner of the journal. But having made his singular and
bemused apparition at a public or private function he
would return to his office and with unerring and diabolical
skill would send out books to the reviewers for whom they
were exactly unsuited. The policy of his journal was to
regard all novels as tawdry trifles to be dismissed in a few
notes. It considered that no poetry had been written or
could have been written by persons born after 1820,
except when Mr Watts-Dunton got hold of a volume by
D. G. Rossetti whose solicitor he was or by Swinburne to
whom he acted as keeper. The body of the paper was given
up to tremendous and sesquipedalian reviews of works with
titles like: *The Walcheren Expedition and the Manoeuvres
in the Low Countries* in three volumes, post quarto. If its
reviewer could discover three misprints, the name of a
Dutch village spelt wrong, two real inaccuracies, and a
nine which the printer had inverted in a date so that it
looked like a six—then the joy of the journal was un-
measured. It pronounced in Olympian tones that this
immense undertaking was completely worthless to the
student of the subject and nothing could better display its
infallibility. It once received a novel of mine with the
words:

'From the fact that on page 276 Mr Hueffer misspells the word *herasia* the reader will be able to judge of the value of his piece of fiction,' and most novels received as summary treatment at its hands.

THE APOTHEOSIS OF JOHN GALSWORTHY

He made towards supreme honours a tranquil course that suggested that of a white-sailed ship progressing inevitably across a halcyon sea. You would have said that he had every blessing that kings and peoples and Providence had to bestow. Having refused a knighthood he was awarded the highest honour that the King had at his disposal—that of the Order of Merit. He presided in Paris at the dinner of the international P.E.N. Club, which is the highest honour that the members of his craft could find for him; and, in the end, the Nobel Prize Committee honoured itself by selecting him for one of its laureates. It seemed, all this, appropriate and inevitable, for, in honouring him, the world honoured one of its noblest philanthropists.

The last time I saw him was in Paris when he gave his presidential address to his beloved P.E.N. And singularly, as he emerged above the shadow of all those hard French writers, there re-emerged at any rate for me the sense of his frailty ... of his being something that must be shielded from the harder earnestnesses of the world. I don't know that he was conscious on that last public triumph of the really bad nature of the hard men who surrounded him. The world had moved onward since the days when he had read Maupassant and Turgenev for what he could learn of them. Both those writers were what he called dissolvents and the Paris *littérateurs* now wanted above all constructive writing and would have agreed with him if he had said—as he did in one of the last letters that he wrote—that Tolstoi was a greater writer than Turgenev.

But, there, he said nothing of the sort. He seemed to
float, above all those potential assassins, like a white swan
above a gloomy mere, radiating bright sunlight...and
with his gentle, modest French words he made statements
that ran hissing through Paris as if he had drawn a whip
across all those listening faces.

For the French writer of to-day, Maupassant is the
Nihilist Enemy—an enemy almost as hated as the late
M. Anatole France.

And Turgenev is an alien ugly duckling who once disgusted the paving-stones of Paris with his foreign footsteps. Nothing indeed so infuriates the French of to-day
as to say that Turgenev was really a French writer.... And
there, enthroned and smiling, poor Galsworthy told that
audience that shivered like tigers in a circus cage that, if
he had trained himself to have any art, and if that training
had landed him where he was, that art had been that of
French writers.

A sort of buzzing of pleasurable anticipation went all
round that ferocious assembly. The author of *Fort Comme
La Paix* looked at the author of *Nuits Ensoleillées* and
thought: 'Aha, my friend, this is going to be a bitter
moment for you. When I consider the *dédicace* of the
ignoble volume that this barbarian chieftain presented
yesterday to me...when I consider the fulsome, but
nevertheless deserved, praise that he wrote on that fly-leaf,
I don't have to doubt whom he is going to claim as his
Master....' And the author of *Nuits Ensoleillées* looked
back at the author of the other classic and thought exactly
the same thing—with the necessary change in the identity
of the author. And every French author present looked at
every other French author and thought thoughts similar.
And when the applause subsided poor Jack went on:

Yes, he repeated, all the art he had had he had had of
the French. If he stood where he was, if he was honoured
as he was, it was because all his long life he had studied
the works, he had been guided by the examples of... Guy
de Maupassant and of him who though a foreigner by

birth was yet more French in heart than any Frenchman—Ivan Turgenev!

I have never seen an audience so confounded. If an invisible force had snatched large, juicy joints of meat from the very jaws of a hundred Bengal tigers the effect would have been the same. They simply could not believe their ears. . . . As for me, I was so overwhelmed with confusion that I ran out of that place and plunged, my cheeks still crimson, into the salon of the author of *Vasco*, who was preparing to give a tea-party at the end of the Île St Louis. And the news had got there before me. It was in the salon of every author of the Île, of the Rue Guynemer, of the Rues Madame, Jacob, Tombe Issoire, and Notre-Dame des Champs, before the triumphant Galsworthy had finished his next sentence. . . . For that was the real triumph of his radiant personality, that not one of the fierce beasts quivering under his lash so much as raised a protest. No other man in the world could have brought that off!

BEFORE THE WARS

PORTRAIT OF THE ARTIST AS A DANDY

You are to think of me then as rather a dandy. I was going through that phase. It lasted perhaps eight years—until Armageddon made one dress otherwise. Every morning about eleven you would see me issue from the door of my apartment. I should be wearing a very long morning coat, a perfectly immaculate high hat, lavender trousers, a near-Gladstone collar, and a black satin stock. As often as not, at one period, I should be followed by a Great Dane. The dog actually belonged to Stephen Reynolds but he disliked exercising it in London because he was nervous at crossings. But a policeman will always stop the traffic for a Great Dane to cross. I carried a malacca cane with a gold knob.

I would walk up Holland Park Avenue as far as the entrance to Kensington Gardens, diagonally across them to Rotten Row where I would cross to St James's Park and the Green Park, cross them and reach one or other of my clubs about half-past twelve, read the papers and my letters until one. Then I would lunch at the club or the Carlton and take a hansom—later a taxi—back to my apartment which I would reach about half-past two. At five I would go to or give a tea-party. Before dinner I would take a bath and a barber would come in and shave me. I dined out every day, but very occasionally, for someone special I would cook a dinner myself in my own flat, putting a chef's coat over my evening things. I had two boasts, the one that no one had ever seen me work, the other that I walked four miles every day on grass. That was in crossing the parks. In Central Park, New York, I had been apostrophized by a policeman who said:

'Get off the grass, same as you would in any other civilized country.' I used my second boast usually on New Yorkers, of whom I saw a good many.

My father used to say that he was the laziest man in the world, yet he had done more work than any man living. I could almost say as much of myself. I fancy that for ten years—say from 1904 to 1914—I never took a complete day's rest. I worked even on the trains in America at a time when that was less usual than it is to-day. My record in the British Museum Catalogue fills me with shame; it occupies page on page with the mere titles of my printed work. Even at that it is not a complete record; it omits several books published only in America. I do not imagine that anyone not a daily journalist has written as much as I have and I imagine that few daily journalists have written more.

I do not say that I am proud of the record. If I had written less I should no doubt have written better. Of the fifty-two odd separate books there catalogued probably forty are out of print. There is only one of those forty that I should care to re-publish and of the remaining twelve there are not more than six of which I should much regret the disappearance.

This great body of work was produced without any feeling of fatigue. At the time of which I am writing I used to work with great regularity from nine to eleven when I went out to lunch and from half-past two to half-past four when I would go out to tea. After I was eighteen I never wrote at night and except for a week or so before the publication of the first number of the *English Review* I never did any work at all—even editing or proof correcting—after dinner. In the four hours of work I turned out exactly 2,000 words. Of these I would condemn about half. This left about 1,000 words for the day. A thousand words a day is 365,000 for the year—enough to make over four novels. Of course I never published four novels in any one year. Only twice indeed have I published as many as two. The usual tale was one novel and one book of the type called in England 'serious.' There the novel can never be heralded as 'serious.' It would give the public cause to think the writer was in earnest which to the Englishman is insupportable. In the United States books that are not novels are classed as 'non-fiction.' The classification is perhaps not accurate but it is more complimentary to the novelist. That I suppose is why I have latterly published more books to the west than to the east of the Atlantic. Earnestness *will* come creeping into what I write.

A LITERARY PARTY

The year was 1903. Those digits added up to thirteen. No one should have done anything in that year. Or it was perhaps because the house I then took was accursed. It was a monstrous sepulchre—and not even whitened. It was grey with the greyness of withered bones. It was triangular in ground plan: the face formed the nose of a blunted redan, the body tapered to a wedge in which there was a staircase like the corkscrew staircases of the Middle Ages. The façade was thus monstrous, the tail ignoble. It was seven stories in height and in those days elevators in private houses were unknown. It was what housemaids call: 'A Murderer.'

The happenings in that house come back to me as gruesome and bizarre. I daresay they were merely normal. They were mere episodes in the chain of disasters, suicides, bankruptcies, and despairs that visited its successive tenants and owners. My first party was distinguished by Conrad's attack on the unfortunate Mr Charles Lewis Hind. This violent encounter took place in a circle of half-gay, half-morose celebrities. Mr James had brought Mrs Humphry Ward; Mrs Clifford, who could be as awful as Mrs Ward,

had brought some mild and decorous young American—I
should think it was Mr Owen Wister. Mr Watts-Dunton
had brought a message from Swinburne, blessing me because he had known me as a baby. This he repeated *à tort
et à travers* at the oddest and most inconvenient moments.
He was deaf and accustomed to speaking to Swinburne
who was deafer. I found myself distracted at odd moments
by his rather snuffling, elevated voice exclaiming:

'Swinburne said in excusing himself for not attending
this party of our gifted young host. . . .'

He was a little dark man with an immense waterfall of
grey moustache. Finally he settled himself on, I think, the
always patient Mr Galsworthy and repeated over and over
again the message with which he was charged. Then I was
aware that Conrad had hold of Lewis Hind's tie and was
dragging him towards the door that gave on to the corkscrew staircase. If he had thrown Hind down it the poor
man would have been killed. I managed to separate them
but I haven't forgotten and don't suppose I ever shall
forget the look of polite incredulity of the more august
guests. Mrs Humphry Ward looked like a disgusted sheep.
Mrs Clifford, who loved the society of reviewers, was
openly distressed at the disappearance of Mr Hind. Mr
Hind was the editor of the *Academy*. The *Academy* was
a rather livelier *Athenaeum*. A great lady of the Court of
His Majesty put her lorgnettes up to her proud nose and
weary eyes and exclaimed to me afterwards:

'Haw! Very interesting. But awkward for you . . . I suppose all literary parties are like that.'

She added:

'I wonder you give 'em. I shouldn't. I once gave one but
it did not work. Yet one tries to encourage . . . ah . . . these
things!'

The court in those days had to be interested in
Literature because Edward VII wanted to be told about
books. I know this because I had at that date a secretary
who was very highly connected. Her name was Smith and
she was the daughter of a very famous soldier. She was

one day sitting with the beautiful Lady Londonderry who was her cousin. Lady Londonderry was dying of a painful disease, but lay on a sofa. The King came in. Miss Smith was the shyest human being I have ever known. She desired to sink into the ground and made for the door. Lady Londonderry told her to stay and pour tea for them. Lady Londonderry presented her as 'Miss Smith, the daughter of the famous soldier.' The King said:

'Smith ... ah we all know *that* name.' Royal politenesses must exact a certain lack of the sense of humour....

Well; the King asked Lady Londonderry if he might touch the bell and ask the footman for some very dry toast as he was banting. Miss Smith poured tea. As she was finally escaping the King said:

'Miss Smith. Lady Londonderry tells me you are interested in literature. I like books. I like boys' books ... Captain Marryat now. I have read all Captain Marryat. But I find it very difficult to get books like that.' He said that he had asked all the Court but no one could tell him of books like that. He added:

'If in the course of your researches at the British Museum, Miss Smith, you should come across any such books, I should be very much obliged if you would jot their names down on a postcard and send it to me, at Buckingham Palace.'

Miss Smith said it seemed to her curious that he should think she did not know his address.

STARTING A REVIEW

There entered then into me the itch of trying to meddle in English literary affairs. The old literary gang of the *Athenaeum-Spectator-Heavy Artillery* order was slowly decaying. Younger lions were not only roaring but making carnage of their predecessors. Mr Wells was then growing a formidable mane, Arnold Bennett if not widely known was at least known to and admired by me. Mr Wells had given me Bennett's first novel—*A Man From The North*. Experimenting in forms kept Conrad still young. Henry James was still 'young James' for my uncle William Rossetti and hardly known of by the general public. George Meredith and Thomas Hardy had come into their own only very little before, Mr George Moore was being forgotten as he was always being forgotten, Mr Yeats was known as having written the *Isle of Innisfree*. It seemed to me that if that nucleus of writers could be got together with what undiscovered talent the country might hold a Movement might be started. I had one or two things I wanted to say. They were about the technical side of novel writing. But mostly I desired to give the writers of whom I have spoken as it were a rostrum. It was with that idea that I had returned from America. England, I knew, would always regard me as, rather comically and a little suspiciously—too damn in earnest. The others it might listen to and I might slip a word in now and then.

The nature of the periodical to be started gave me a good deal of thought. To imagine that a magazine devoted to imaginative literature and technical criticism alone would find more than a hundred readers in the United Kingdom was a delusion that I in no way had. It must therefore of necessity be a hybrid, giving at least half its space to current affairs. Those I did not consider myself fit to deal with. I knew either nothing about them or I knew so much that I could not form any opinions. The only public matter as to which I was determined to take a line was that of female suffrage.

I dallied with the idea for some time. Then I came across the politician who had insisted on telling me his life history. I do not remember if he approached me or I him. At any rate we quickly came to an agreement. He was a virulent Tory of the new school and he wanted an organ of his own. He was to provide half of the capital necessary which we agreed was to be £5,000, I the other half. He was to edit half the magazine, which was to be a monthly, I the other half. Being a businessman as well as a politician he was to manage the business affairs of the concern, I to see to its make up, proof-reading, and other details of publication. It was a good arrangement. I liked him very much. He was too brilliant to like me extremely but he tolerated me more than he tolerated most people. He had an exaggerated idea of my omniscience and political influence.

I had arranged with the house of Duckworth to publish the *Review* and had commissioned a number of stories, poems, and critical articles. He came to me one day and said he could not supervise the business affairs of the concern. That was rather a heavy blow because I knew enough about business to know that I should make a muddle of that side of it. I sighed, cabled to Byles who was then in Japan to come back and take on the business of the *Review*, and consented to continue to enterprise. A little later my friend came to me and said that he could not undertake to do half the editing. A General Election was in the offing; he had neglected his constituency; he would have to go perpetually into the North to kick off footballs, open flower shows, subscribe to fox-hounds, and utter verbal coruscations. He suggested that I might find some one else of his school of thought to direct the political policy of the *Review*; I sighed again and consented. For that Marwood was indicated. He was an Old, rather than a New Tory and he was incurably indolent. But he consented to suggest from Winchelsea the sort of article that should go into the *Review* and in most cases to indicate the writers who should be invited to contribute. My political friend proposed in fairness that if so much of the labour was to fall on me he should increase the amount of capital that he found whilst I should retain my full half share of the control of the periodical. I was glad of that because I had lately had rather serious financial reverses.

The dummy of the first number approached completion; I had announced the name of the periodical, *The English Review*, in the press. It was Conrad who chose the title.

He felt a certain sardonic pleasure in the choosing so national a name for a periodical that promised to be singularly international in tone, that was started mainly in his not very English interest and conducted by myself who was growing every day more and more alien to the normal English trend of thought, at any rate in matters of literary technique. And it was matters of literary technique that almost exclusively interested both him and myself. That was very un-English.

A couple of presumably needy journalists, both of very great ability, conceived the idea of making me, who was presumed to be rolling in wealth, pay for the use of that title. They registered it as soon as I had announced it in the press and then asked me to pay a prodigious sum for its use. I offered them half a sovereign a piece. They then published a single-sheet broad-sheet under the title of *The English Review*. Its letterpress consisted of virulent attacks on Lord Northcliffe and myself, promising extraordinary revelations as to both of us in their next number. I fancy they imagined that Lord Northcliffe was financing the review. The main allegation against myself was that I was a 'multiple reviewer.' The charge was true enough but only as far as one book was concerned. That was Charles Doughty's *Dawn in Britain*—an epic poem in twelve books and four volumes. I had a great admiration for Doughty, who was the author also of *Arabia Deserta* and I read his poem entirely through with a great deal of pleasure. No reviewer in London had leisure for that task. The book looked as if it might go unreviewed, so I asked a number of those gentlemen to let me review it for them. Others, hearing that I had volunteered to do it, also asked me to relieve them of the task. I do not remember how many reviews I wrote: it was a considerable number and some of them were quite long. I pleased myself by finding that I could do them all without once repeating a sentence or even an idea. At any rate I was quite unrepentant. I do not see why you should not write more than one review of a book for which you have a great admiration. I have written several times about *Ulysses*.

I continued to take no notice of the other *English Review*. My telephone became a constant worry because those two gentlemen rang me up at all hours of the night asking me to buy the title for sums that gradually descended from a thousand pounds to five. Lord Northcliffe on the other hand applied for an injunction against my rivals in one of the courts—I forget which. The injunction was granted and the other *English Review* disappeared. The real joke was that I had lent one of those lively persons the money with which he paid for his broadsheet. At any rate, just before he printed it, I had met him looking very destitute in Fleet Street and had lent him exactly the sum with which he paid his printer's and papermaker's bill.

A little later I went to a Trench dinner. A Trench dinner was a Dutch treat presided over by Herbert Trench, the Irish poet. They were agreeable affairs and attended by most of the brilliant people in London. I was only asked to one. On this occasion I was set at a round table with Mr Hilaire Belloc, Mr Gilbert Chesterton, Mr Maurice Baring, and Mr H. G. Wells. My politician was at another table with Mr Trench, the Marchioness of Londonderry and other notables.

Amongst all these celebrities I felt nervous. Celebrities are always rude to me. That has been the case from my tenderest years. I can hardly think of one that has not, at one time or another, said rude things to me. I ought to except politicians. I can hardly remember a politician who has not said nice things to me about my books—as soon as he heard that I was a writer. I suppose they learn that when canvassing for votes. Mr Balfour once asked me to send him my books as they came out. I did for years. He always wrote politely thanking me for the volume 'from the reading of which he anticipated much pleasure.' The letters were always marked: 'Not for publication.'

I knew I should not get through that dinner without

discomfort. It came. Mr Belloc was late. I had written an article about him a day or two before. It had been published that morning. I had classed him among the brilliant *jeunes* of the day and had expressed the really great admiration I felt for his wit, sincerity, and learning. He hurried in, saw me, stopped as if he had been shot, thrust his hand through his forelock, gave one more maledictory glance at me with his baleful, pebble-blue eyes and then sank wearily into his chair next to Mr Maurice Baring. He looked anywhere but at me and began an impassioned monologue about the misfortunes of historians. They wore themselves out searching for matter in the British Museum Library and other stuffy places; they toiled till far into the night putting the results of their researches on paper. After infinite tribulation they published their books. Then along came the cold-eyed critic.

I forget what Mr Belloc said that the cold-eyed critic did to the historian but I realized that it was my eyes that were frigid in his. In my eulogy of him I had amiably found fault with some gigantic exaggeration in, I think, a book about the Cromwell family. What exactly Thomas Cromwell had done to our co-religionists or how Oliver had sinned against the Church of Rome I forget. Heaven forbid that I should set myself down as good a Papist as Mr Belloc, but I dislike to think of myself as a worse. I consider that there are only two human organizations that are nearly perfect for their disparate functions. They are the Church of Rome and His Britannic Majesty's Army. I would cheerfully offer my life for either if it would do them any good and supposing them not to be arrayed the one against the other. But I could not see that the cause of the Church was advantaged by gigantically exaggerating the confiscations from which she has suffered any more than it would help the Old Contemptibles to represent them as having been without exception teachers in Sunday Schools. I had said this mildly in my article. As a matter of fact I wished that Mr Belloc would write novels and leave propaganda to the less gifted.

The affair ended dramatically in nothing, for before ending his monologue Mr Belloc suddenly burst out to some one whom I could not see at the chairman's table beside us:

'Our Lord! What do you know about Our Lord? Our Lord was a gentleman.'

After that I escaped notice in the shadow of Mr Chesterton. Mr Chesterton and Mr Belloc were one on each side of Mr Baring. They occupied themselves for some time in trying in vain to balance glasses of Rhine Wine on the skull of Mr Baring. That gentleman comes back to me as having been then only a little less bald than an egg. The floor and his shirt front received the wine in equal quantities. . . .

Suddenly Mr Belloc was at me again. He said that I would not dare to print in my *Review* any article that he sent me just as it stood. I said I would. He repeated that I would not and I that I would. He was in those days almost as vigorous a muck-raker as S. S. McClure and hardly anyone had the courage to print him in his more coruscating moments. I may say that I did print his article but, since it contained the most amazing accusations against bishops, keepers of the Crown jewels, West Indian Governors and other apparently unoffending and unimportant beings, I made the printer black out the names and functions of everybody concerned. Those pages of the *Review* startlingly resembled newspapers in Russia after they had received the attention of the censor. They startled Mr St Loe Strachey, the Editor of the *Spectator*, to some purpose. He confused my *English Review* with the broad-sheet promoted by the two journalists and supposed that either I or Mr Belloc intended to threaten the owners of the blacked out names with exposure in another number if we were not bought off. Solemnly and weightily he protested against this growing tendency in British journals. He seemed to me to be a mild and doting old gentleman, so I wrote to him amiably and told him that he had accused me of being a blackmailer and would he kindly refute himself in the next number of his journal. He did so and wrote me a very agitated letter, saying that he had meant nothing of the sort. He did not say what he *had* meant.

That Trench dinner, different as it was from the Trench dinners that we afterwards ate, came also to an end. I was going towards the Piccadilly Tube. It was pouring and Mr Belloc was begging me not to believe that he was in fact the light-hearted being that he appeared. Actually he was filled with the woes of all the world.

I was beginning to assure him that from then on I would regard his as a figure of the deepest tragedy. We were just turning into the Tube Station when my politician, ex-fellow editor and business manager came running up rather breathlessly and caught hold of the arm of mine that Mr Belloc was not imprisoning. He said:

'Fordie, I'm very sorry. I can't find my half share of the capital for the *Review*.'

I said:

'That will be all right.' He disappeared and I went on assuring Mr Belloc of my appreciation of his pessimism.

It appeared subsequently that my friend was suffering from the same financial disaster that had hit hard not only myself but many other people. It was the case of a disappearance abroad with an expensive young woman of a man the bearer of a very honoured name in whose faith too many had reposed their trust. He subsequently committed suicide.

There seemed to be nothing to do but to close down that periodical, pay off the contributors whom I had already commissioned and realize my dream of retiring to a little farm in Provence. I had of course to tell Marwood who was by that time as enthusiastic about the *Review* as he could be about anything.

He agreed with me. There was nothing to do but to shut it down. He made a good many caustic remarks about Young Tories in general and my friend in particular. I disagreed with him. That politician was no more guilty than I. Marwood, however, was certain that he had never intended to find the money.

I returned from Winchelsea to Aldington where I had by now bought a cottage. There remained, it seemed, nothing for it but to emigrate to Provence and there seemed to be nowhere else to emigrate to. As the world then appeared to me I could support living in London if I had the *Review*. Without it, I couldn't.

I was writing to a friend I had in Tarascon—a *notaire* —to ask about small farms that might be for sale in his neighbourhood. It was a Sunday. Marwood was suddenly on the terrace. He was pale with indignation and brandished a crumpled newspaper. He panted:

'You've got to carry on that *Review*.'

I had never seen him agitated before—and I never did again. He must have got up at four that morning to catch the train from Winchelsea to Aldington.

The newspaper announced that the *Cornhill Magazine* had refused to print, on the score of immorality, a poem of Thomas Hardy called *A Sunday Morning Tragedy*. All the other heavy and semi-heavy monthlies, all the weeklies, all the daily papers in England had similarly refused. Marwood said:

'You must print it. We can't have the country made a laughing stock.' He was of opinion that the rest of the world must guffaw if it heard that Hardy could not find a publisher in England. Marwood was accustomed to say that nothing worth the attention of a grown man had been written in England since the eighteenth century. Clarendon's *History of the Great Rebellion* and the Jacobean poets were his reading. He made a great concession to modernity when he read Maine's *Ancient Law* and Doughty's *Arabia Deserta*. Yet there he was mad to spend several thousand pounds in order to publish one poem by a modern poet who as poet was hardly known at all. For, of course, he found the money that hadn't been found by my other friend.

That was *my* Sunday morning tragedy. But for that I should have been saved a great deal of labour, a number of enemies. I should have been, now, twenty years instead of only six months, a kitchen-gardener in Provence.

ENTER EZRA POUND

When I first knew him his Philadelphian accent was comprehensible if disconcerting; his beard and flowing locks were auburn and luxuriant; he was astonishingly meagre and agile. He threw himself alarmingly into frail chairs, devoured enormous quantities of your pastry, fixed his pince-nez firmly on his nose, drew out a manuscript from his pocket, threw his head back, closed his eyes to the point of invisibility and looking down his nose would chuckle like Mephistopheles and read you a translation from Arnaut Daniel. The only part of that *aubade* that you would understand would be the refrain:

> *'Ah me, the darn, the darn it comes toe sune!'*

We published his *Ballad of the Goodly Fere*, which must have been his first appearance in a periodical except for contributions to the *Butte Montana Herald*. Ezra, though born there in a caravan during the great blizzard of—but perhaps I ought not to reveal the year. At any rate Ezra left Butte at the age of say two. The only one of his poems written and published there that I can remember had for refrain:

> *'Cheer up, Dad!'*

As a reaction against a sentiment so American he shortly afterwards became instructor in Romance languages at the University of Pennsylvania. His history up to the date of his appearance in my office which was also my drawing-room comes back to me as follows: Born in the blizzard his first meal consisted of kerosene. That was why he ate such enormous quantities of my tarts, the flavour of kerosene being very enduring. It accounted also for the glory of his hair. Where he studied the Romance languages I could not gather. But his proficiency in them was considerable when you allowed for the slightly negroid accent that he adopted when he spoke Provençal or recited the works of Bertran de Born.

His grandfather I understood was an unsuccessful candidate for the Presidency in the time of Blaine, his father assayer to the Mint in Philadelphia, a function requiring almost incredible delicacy of touch. His grandfather, as was the habit of millionaires in the America of that day, made and lost fortunes with astonishing rapidity and completeness. He had promised to send Ezra to Europe. Ezra was just making his reservations when his grandfather failed more finally and more completely than usual.

Ezra therefore came over on a cattle boat. Many poets have done that. But I doubt if any other ever made a living by showing American tourists about Spain without previous knowledge of the country or language. It was, too, just after the Hispano-American war when the cattle-boat dropped him in that country.

It was with that aura of romance about him that he appeared to me in my office drawing-room. I guessed that he must be rather hard up, bought his poem at once and paid him more than it was usual to pay for ballads. It was not a large sum but Ezra managed to live on it for a long time—six months, I think—in unknown London. Perhaps my pastry helped.

... AND D. H. LAWRENCE

In the year when my eyes first fell on words written by
Norman Douglas, G. H. Tomlinson, Wyndham Lewis,
Ezra Pound, and others, amongst whom was Stephen
Reynolds, who died too young and is much too forgotten
—upon a day I received a letter from a young school
teacher in Nottingham. I can still see the handwriting—
as if drawn with sepia rather than written in ink, on grey-
blue notepaper. It said that the writer knew a young man
who wrote, as she thought, admirably but was too shy to
send his work to editors. Would I care to see some of
his writing?

In that way I came to read the first words of a new
author:

> 'The small locomotive engine, Number 4, came
> clanking, stumbling down from Selston with seven
> full wagons. It appeared round the corner with loud
> threats of speed, but the colt that it startled from
> among the gorse which still flickered indistinctly
> in the raw afternoon, outdistanced it in a canter.
> A woman walking up the railway line to Underwood,
> held her basket aside and watched the footplate of
> the engine advancing.'

I was reading in the twilight in the long eighteenth-
century room that was at once the office of the *English
Review* and my drawing-room. My eyes were tired; I
had been reading all day so I did not go any further with
the story. It was called *Odour of Chrysanthemums*. I laid
it in the basket for accepted manuscripts. My secretary
looked up and said:

'You've got another genius?'

I answered: 'It's a big one this time,' and went upstairs
to dress. . . .

Miss E.T. in her little book on the youth of Lawrence —and a very charming and serviceable little book it is— seems to be under the impression that she sent me as a first instalment only poems by Lawrence. Actually she first asked me if I would care to see anything—and then should it be poetry or prose. And I had replied asking her to send both, so that she had sent me three poems about a schoolmaster's life ... and *Odour of Chrysanthemums*. I only mention this because I found the poems, afterwards, to be nice enough but not immensely striking. If I had read them first I should certainly have printed them—as indeed I did; but I think the impact of Lawrence's personality would have been much less vivid. ... Let us examine, then, the first paragraph of *Odour of Chrysanthemums*.

The very title makes an impact on the mind. You get at once the knowledge that this is not, whatever else it may turn out, either a frivolous or even a gay, springtime story. Chrysanthemums are not only flowers of the autumn; they are the autumn itself. And the presumption is that the author is observant. The majority of people do not even know that chrysanthemums have an odour. I have had it flatly denied to me that they have, just as, as a boy, I used to be mortified by being told that I was affected when I said that my favourite scent was that of primroses, for most people cannot discern that primroses have a delicate and as if muted scent.

Titles as a rule do not matter much. Very good authors break down when it comes to the effort of choosing a title. But one like *Odour of Chrysanthemums* is at once a challenge and an indication. The author seems to say: Take it or leave it. You know at once that you are not going to read a comic story about someone's butler's omniscience. The man who sent you this has, then, character, the courage of his convictions, a power of observation. All these presumptions flit through the mind. At once you read:

'The small locomotive engine, Number 4, came clanking,

stumbling down from Selston,' and at once you know that this fellow with the power of observation is going to write of whatever he writes about from the inside. The 'Number 4' shows that. He will be the sort of fellow who knows that for the sort of people who work about engines, engines have a sort of individuality. He had to give the engine the personality of a number.... 'With seven full wagons'.... The 'seven' is good. The ordinary careless writer would say 'some small wagons.' This man knows what he wants. He sees the scene of his story exactly. He has an authoritative mind.

'It appeared round the corner with loud threats of speed.'... Good writing; slightly, but not *too* arresting.... 'But the colt that it startled from among the gorse... outdistanced it at a canter.' Good again. This fellow does not 'state.' He doesn't say: 'It was coming slowly,' or—what would have been a little better—'at seven miles an hour.' Because even 'seven miles an hour' means nothing definite for the untrained mind. It might mean something for a trainer of pedestrian racers. The imaginative writer writes for all humanity; he does not limit his desired readers to specialists.... But anyone knows that an engine that makes a great deal of noise and yet cannot overtake a colt at a canter must be a ludicrously ineffective machine. We know then that this fellow knows his job.

'The gorse still flickered indistinctly in the raw afternoon....' Good too, distinctly good. This is the just-sufficient observation of Nature that gives you, in a single phrase, landscape, time of day, weather, season. It is a raw afternoon in autumn in a rather accented countryside. The engine would not come round a bend if there were not some obstacle to a straight course—a watercourse, a chain of hills. Hills, probably, because gorse grows on dry, broken-up waste country. They won't also be mountains or anything spectacular or the writer would have mentioned them. It is, then, just 'country.'

Your mind does all this for you without any ratiocination on your part. You are not, I mean, purposely sleuthing. The engine and the trucks are there, with the white smoke blowing away over hummocks of gorse. Yet there has been practically none of the tiresome thing called descriptive nature, of which the English writer is as a rule so lugubriously lavish. . . . And then the woman comes in, carrying her basket. That indicates her status in life. She does not belong to the comfortable classes. Nor, since the engine is small, with trucks on a dud line, will the story be one of the Kipling-engineering type, with gleaming rails, and gadgets, and the smell of oil warmed by the bearings, and all the other tiresomenesses.

You are, then, for as long as the story lasts, to be in one of those untidy, unfinished landscapes where locomotives wander innocuously amongst women with baskets. That is to say, you are going to learn how what we used to call 'the other half'—though we might as well have said other ninety-nine hundredths—lives. And if you are an editor and that is what you are after, you know that you have got what you want and you can pitch the story straight away into your wicker tray with the few accepted manuscripts and go on to some other occupation. . . . Because this man knows. He knows how to open a story with a sentence of the right cadence for holding the attention. He knows how to construct a paragraph. He knows the life he is writing about in a landscape just sufficiently constructed with a casual word here and there. You can trust him for the rest. . . .

I cannot say that I liked Lawrence much. He remained too disturbing even when I got to know him well. He had so much need of moral support to take the place of his mother's influence that he kept one—everyone who at all came into contact with him—in a constant state of solicitude. He claimed moral support imperiously—and physical care too. I don't mean that he whined. He just ordered you to consider that there he was in Croydon subject to the drag of the minds of the school-children for hours of every day in a fetid atmosphere. . . . And that is the great curse and plague of the schoolmaster's life . . . the

continuous drag of the minds of the pupils pulling you
down ... and then with the tired mind to write masterpieces in the odd moments of silence.

And then came the scourge! He was pronounced tuber-
cular. I don't know how we knew that he had been so
pronounced. I don't think he ever mentioned it to me;
perhaps he did not to anyone. It was a subject that he
was always shy of mentioning. But Galsworthy and
Masterman and even the solid, stolid Marwood—and
of course several ladies—went about for some time with
worried faces because Lawrence was writing masterpieces
and teaching in a fetid atmosphere. He had to be got out
of it. He ought to be allowed to resign his job and be
given a pension so that he could go on writing his masterpieces. That was where Masterman, who was a Minister
of the Crown and supposed to be scheduled as the next
Liberal Prime Minister, came in. He was to use his influence on the educational authorities to see that Lawrence got a pension as having contracted tuberculosis in
the service.

Alas, alas, Croydon was not within the Administrative
County of London. The London County Council gave
pensions to invalided school teachers. But the Surrey County
Council did not. Not even the Crown could coerce a
county into doing what it did not want to do. ... In the
end, I think he was allotted a small lump sum. But one
had had a good deal of anxiety.

There had been no difficulty in finding a publisher
for him. The odd, accidental, as if *avant la lettre* notoriety
that he had gained ... made several publishers be anxious
to compete for his suffrages. They even paid him good
little sums for his first books. He didn't have then, if
ever, any very serious difficulties. And the London of those
days was a kind place to people who were reputed to be
writing masterpieces. There were kind, very rich people
who asked nothing better than to be nice to young men
of gifts. So that in a very short time Lawrence was writing
home exultantly that he had dined with two Royal

Academicians, several *Times* reviewers, Cabinet Ministers, and Ladies of Title, galore, galore. I don't mean that the exultation was snobbish delight at mingling with the Great. No, it was delight at seeing himself by so far on the road ... towards the two thousand a year. ...

In the course of a good many Saturday afternoon or Sunday walks in the Gardens or Park, there came home to me a new side of Lawrence that was not father-mother derived—that was pure D.H. It was his passionate—as it were an almost super-sex-passionate—delight in the opening of flowers and leaves. He would see in the black-ish grass of Kensington Gardens a disreputable, bedrag-gled specimen of a poor relation of the dandelion whose name I have forgotten. ... Oh, yes, the coltsfoot—the most undistinguished of yellow ornaments of waste places and coal dumps. ... And immediately Lawrence, who had been an earnest *jeune homme pauvre* with a fox-coloured poll, drawing wisdom from a distinguished, rather portly editor, would become a half-mad, woodland creature, darting on that poor thing come there by acci-dent, kneeling before it, feeling with his delicate, too white and beautiful fingers, the poor texture of its petals. And describing how, the harbinger of spring, it covered with its sheets of gold the slag-heaps and dumps of his native countryside. ... With a really burning language!

And it was not the starved rapture of the Cockney poets to whom flowers were mysteries. He knew the name and the habits and the growths of every flower of the country-sides and of stoats and weasels and foxes and thrushes. Because of course Nottingham, for all its mining suburbs, was really in and of the country, and a great part of the time—the parts of his time when he had really lived—had been spent on the farms that surrounded his home. ... That, of course, you can gather from his books. ...

Above all from his books. The nature passages of the ordinary English novelist are intolerable—the Dartmoors and Exmoors and Woodlands and the bearded tits and comfreys and the rest. (I am not talking of naturalists.)

But the nature passages of Lawrence run like fire through his books and are exciting—because of the life that comes into his writing even at moments when he is becoming rather tiresomely introspective. So that at times when you read him you have the sense that there really was to him a side that was supernatural ... in tune with deep woodlands, which are queer places. I rather dislike writing just that because it sounds like the fashionable writing about Lawrence which gloomingly identifies him with Pan—or Priapus or Pisces or phalluses—which you don't find in Nottinghamshire woodlands. . . .

Well. . . . He brought me his manuscripts—those of *The White Peacock* and *Sons and Lovers*. And he demanded, imperiously, immensely long sittings over them ... insupportably long ones. And when I suggested breathing spaces for walks in the Park he would say that that wasn't what he had sacrificed his Croydon Saturday or Sunday for. And he held my nose down over this passage or that passage and ordered me to say *why* I suggested this emendation or that. And sometimes he would accept them and sometimes he wouldn't ... but always with a good deal of natural sense and without *parti pris*. I mean that he did not stick obstinately to a form of words because it was his form of words, but he required to be convinced before he would make any alteration. He had learned a great deal from reading other writers—mostly French—but he had a natural sense of form that was very refreshing to come across—and that was perhaps his most singular characteristic. His father was obviously not a dancing teacher and minor craftsman for nothing.

And then one day he brought me half the MS. of *The Trespassers*—and that was the end. It was a *Trespassers* much—oh, but much!—more phallic than is the book as it stands and much more moral in the inverted-puritanic sense. That last was inevitable in that day, and Lawrence had come under the subterranean fashionable influences that made for Free Love as a social and moral arcanum. So that the whole effect was the rather dreary one of a schoolboy larking among placket-holes, dialoguing with a Wesleyan minister who has been converted to Ibsen. It gave the effect that if Lawrence had not met that sort of religion he might have been another ... oh, say, Congreve. As it was it had the making of a thoroughly bad hybrid book and I told him so.

I never saw him again ... to talk to. But he did, in successive re-writings, change the book a good deal ... at least I suppose there were successive re-writings. ... And I suppose I hurt his feelings a good deal. Anyhow I am glad I did not have to go through his manuscripts any more. I don't—and I didn't then—think that my influence was any good to him. His gift for form, in his sort of long book, was such that I could suggest very little to him and the rest of his gift was outside my reach. And, as I have said, he is quite good enough as he is— rich and coloured and startling like a mediaeval manuscript.

THE MARCONI COMMISSION

The only time I wrote about anything political was during the Marconi case. Of that I attended the hearings fairly regularly and I was shocked at the deterioration that appeared to have begun in English public life since the Boer War and the death of Queen Victoria. Before that time a Minister of the Crown was expected to—and usually did—lay down office a poorer man than when he entered public life. That was true too of Germany. Both Bismarck and Gladstone had died poorer than they had been on coming into their inherited wealth. A number of ministers of the first Asquith administration did not however see why a Minister should not use government information when making their investments. They did not indeed see why they should not let their friends in on a good thing. I mean that they really did not see it. Nor did they see any necessity for concealment. Their relatives and intimates called inside financial information one to the other up the very staircases of their clubs.

There was nothing very wonderful in that. After the South African War a wave of financial gambling overcame the country. The great houses in Park Lane fell into the hands of the Randlords as South African speculators who had made good were called. They were received familiarly at Court, became intimates of the highest in the land, won classic races and became national heroes.

I suppose it was no affair of mine. But perhaps the certainty that the poor old Queen was turning in her grave got on my nerves. At any rate I wrote some impassioned articles backing up Mr F. W. Wilson, the financial editor of the *Outlook*. It was he who really brought about the exposure of the Marconi Affair.

The Postmaster-General was at that date negotiating with the Marconi Company to make a network of Marconi Stations connecting the dominions of the Empire. That much was known to the public and the shares of the Marconi Company rose sympathetically or fell according as the negotiations progressed or stood still. When therefore the relatives and intimates of the Postmaster-General put it about with very little caution among *their* relatives and intimates that the Chancellor of the Exchequer—who ought to be a financial expert—was buying shares in a company subsidiary to the Marconi Company proper the shares of everything connected with wireless telegraphy began extraordinarily to boom and Mr Wilson began his attacks on the Chancellor of the Exchequer, the Post-master-General and a number of their relatives. The Government at first pooh-poohed the matter. But the agitation spread to other papers and quarters. It became so intense that they had to appoint a Royal Commission to enquire into the whole matter of the sales of Marconi shares.

As I have said, I attended a number of the sittings

of this body. I had before then attended, usually as a witness, a few Royal Commissions. They were non-political and seemed to be conducted with decorum and a fairly efficient if somnolent desire to obtain information. But the Marconi Commission must have been one of the most farcical bodies that ever met. There were seven Liberals and five Tories who voted with the unanimity of the clockwork soldiers of the Russian ballet, each party against the other. The Tories voted that any evidence that could be helpful to the ministers concerned should not be heard, the Liberals that it should. When evidence unfavourable to the ministers was being heard all the Liberals went to sleep in a body; when anything that could be dug up to be favourable to them all the Tories seemed to have been drugged. In addition, Lord Robert Cecil, who presumably suffered from a bad throat, constantly took out an atomiser and opened his mouth extraordinarily wide. The noise of the spray and his vocal garglings would extremely disconcert any ministerial witness.

The evidence was extraordinarily prolix, the repetitions interminable. Gentleman after gentleman swore that he had heard ministerial relatives shouting financial information up the marble staircase of the National Liberal Club; gentleman after gentleman swore that he had not. Financial experts deposed that the shares of companies subsidiary to the parent company would be advantaged by the Postmaster-General's giving a contract to that parent company; financial experts deposed that they would not be in the least advantaged. Everyone in London or New York who had ever heard of anyone else purchasing anything called after Marconi was examined by one side or the other.

At last came the turn of the editor of, I think, the *Financial News*, the journal and its editor having the greatest possible weight in the City. His evidence was not immensely important, mainly because he had been in South America during the greater part of the time when the case had been brewing. When he had finished,

the President of the Commission put to him the formal
question: Had he anywhere, at any time or in any circumstances heard the name of any other minister who
was said to have bought shares in any company connected
with Marconi? The editor said that he had not. The chairman, who was bald, white-headed and stout, repeated with
extraordinary solemnity, whilst all the Tories snored:

'You have never—at any time, in *any* circumstances,
in any place heard mention of any Minister except those
whose conduct is here under enquiry as having purchased
any shares in any company in any remotest way connected
with Marconi's?'

The editor said that he had of course heard idle gossip
naming one Minister. But he had means of knowing the
names of all purchasers of such stock and knew the gossip
was absolutely untrue. All the Liberal members became
at once as if galvanised. They insisted on having the name
of the accused Minister.

The editor energetically refused to give it. The gossip
was perfectly irresistible. He had heard it in a bar in
Buenos Aires from a person who in the nature of events
could not have private information about the case. And
he repeated that he knew the allegation was absolutely
untrue.

The Liberals went on pressing him. A Conservative,
Mr Amory, made a pointed and impassioned remark about
the waste of the Commission's time. The editor refused
still. He said he could not as a gentleman be asked to
give currency to gossip that he regarded as pestilential
lying by the worst type of bar-loafer. His emotion was
impressive. The Liberals continued to press him, the
Tories to protest. At last the room was cleared for the
Commission to put the matter to the vote. The seven
Liberals voted for the evidence, the five Tories against
its being heard.

The editor was pallid. He protested against being
coerced into dishonouring himself. It was no good. He
was threatened with the Speaker's writ committing him

to the Clock Tower. The whole room hung on his lips
in an intense silence. Lord Robert Cecil's spray sounded
like artillery; his hanging open jaw gave him the appearance of being about to die. At last the witness said:

'The name was that of Mr Winston Churchill. ... But
I protest. ...'

That Committee Room at once became like pandemonium. At last the Chairman could be heard to say:

'Mr Churchill must be written to to attend before us,'
and we all adjourned to lunch. When we came back there
was a long pause, some minutes being inaudibly read.
Suddenly there was a roar like that of a charging wild
boar. Mr Churchill was pushing aside the people in the
doorway as if he had been a forward in a game of football
and near the goal. His top hat was pressed down over his
ears, his face was as pallid as wax: whiter than the paper
on which this is written. His features were so distorted
that he was almost unrecognizable. He dashed himself at
the chair that was in the horse-shoe shaped space before
the Commissioners. He shouted:

'If any man has dared to say that I would do such a
damned swinish thing as to buy any share in any filthy
company in any way connected with any Governmental
action. ... If any man has dared. ...'

The chairman said:

'There, there Mr Winston we all know your admirable
record.' The Tories hissed in unison: 'An outrage. ...'

Mr Churchill slammed his fist violently on the table
before him and began again:

'If I could get my hands on his throat. ... To say that
I could be capable of such infamy. ...'

Mr Lloyd George's private secretary dashed up behind
him and whispered in his ear. Mr Churchill said:

'I don't care. ... *Infamy!* ...' Other ministers' secretaries had a try at him, the humour of the scene being
added to by the fact that there was a gangle of acrimonious
divorce cases going on among the ministers' secretaries.
Mr Asquith was having a great deal of trouble and putting

himself to some expense in order to prevent charges and
cross-charges making a very pretty scandal and to provide
incomes denied to erring partners by recalcitrant and disagreeable parties. I had not considered till then that it was
part of the Prime Minister's duties to provide for the lame
ducks and divorced wives of his more immediate supporters. But apparently Mr Asquith took the view that it
was and behaved with great generosity and kindness. I
know this because I was engaged to persuade one of the
more unreasonable parties to one of the cases to behave
with some moderation.

The final comic relief to the situation was provided by
one of the Liberal members who, having begun life by
pushing a costermonger's barrow, had lately been en-
nobled. This knight, who was very handsome in a dark
and bearded way, had a singularly sentimental manner and
a singular accent. He leaned romantically over the table
towards Mr Churchill and made an elaborate oratorical
effort. He begged Mr Churchill to be sure that no one in
that assembly could so much as most distantly suspect
Mr Churchill of financial irregularity. How, he said, could
any suspicion of dishonour attach to one descended from
the heroic John Churchill, Duke of Marlborough, and one
of the greatest generals the world had ever seen?

John Churchill, Duke of Marlborough, had to the
common knowledge been one of the greatest eighteenth-
century exponents of the art of what is to-day called
grafting. So the handsome knight's speech proved too
much for the gravity of the meeting and the sitting broke
up in some disorder after Mr Churchill with tremendous
emphasis had assured the members that, since his taking
the smallest office under the Crown, he had not bought a
single share in any company whose destinies could be
affected by government and before taking such office he
had disposed of every such share as happened to be in his
possession.

Mr George's speech of exculpation was one of the
most marvellous feats of oratorical pathos that could be

imagined. Certainly I have never heard on the stage or read in any book anything much more moving. He made no attempt to deny having purchased shares that he ought strictly speaking not to have bought, but he said he had bought them in the usual course of investment and on the advice of his usual financial adviser. He had had nothing to do with any attempts to influence the market. And was, he said, a career of sedulous devotion to the service of his country to be broken because of a mistake that any one not born to opportunities of great experience in the manipulations of shares might easily make?

As he went on he moved the House to deep emotion. A great many of the members—Mr Balfour was one—were moved to tears. I know that I came very near crying myself and in that matter I was as bitter an opponent as Mr George ever had. After the first five minutes of the speech there could be no doubt that the division would be a triumph for him. And it was. He carried practically the whole House with him.

The Marconi Commission had been a grotesque affair and after the sitting which I have described it was summarily brought to an end. But it did undoubtedly have the effect of restoring English public standards to their earlier strictness. I do not believe that any Minister of the Crown has since bought any shares which could in any way be questioned. The horror of having such a body sit interminably on one's case must be enough to deter you from the most minute of irregularities.

A SHAMEFUL EPISODE

I had been then to the Empire to see Miss Génée dance, at a time when seeing Miss Génée dance was one of the great pleasures of my life. There used to be, next door to

the old Café Royal, a German beer house called Gam-
brinius'. There I always went after the theatre, at least
when—as I usually was—I was alone. It was vast,
decorated with antlers, helmets, *morgensterns*, owls the
light of whose eyes went in and out, and the usual decora-
tions that made for a simple Teutonic atmosphere. There
was an end, giving on Glasshouse Street, that was rather
smart and an end towards Regent Street that was rather
Bohemian. When I was in one mood I would go to one
end, at other times to the other.

I was sitting then towards the Regent Street end about
one in the morning. Towards the other end of the place
there was a group of perhaps six or seven waiters and the
proprietor, Mr Oddenino, and a member of the public.
They were moving chairs, displacing guests, and looking
carefully on the floor. I observed near my feet what looked
like a large fragment of a beer mug—a dull piece of glass
in the sawdust. Then I saw, after I had poked it with my
stick, that it was faceted. I picked it up. It seemed duller
in my hand than on the ground. It seemed too large to be
valuable. I had two regular waiters under whom I sat in
that place, the one at one end, the other at the other. The
one on the Regent Street side was old, North German,
and extremely ugly, the one towards Glasshouse Street
was young, Austrian, and cherubic. I asked the old man
what the group at the far end were looking for. He said:

'The gentleman has lost a diamond out of his tie-pin.'

I got up and strolled over to that civilian. I say 'civilian'
because waiters always impress me as being military over-
lords of their domains. I held my open hand towards him.
I said I supposed that what was in my palm was what he
had lost. He jumped at it, as it were, and for a moment
was too excited, showing it to the waiters. His tie-pin was
noticeable as being, on top of its stick, a large, empty
circlet of gold. At last he said to me, quite inoffensively:

'I suppose I could not offer you anything for finding it?'

I said he could not. Then he asked me to sit down and

have a drink with him. I said I would prefer not to. I do not think I ever took a drink with a stranger. Then he said:

'You *must* have a drink with me. Do you know what that stone is? It is the . . . diamond.'

It comes back to me as having been the Hope diamond but I daresay it wasn't. It was at any rate one of the famous diamonds of the world of that day. I said that having held the . . . diamond in my hand was sufficient reward for having strolled across the café to restore it to him. He said:

'Then come back to Claridge's with me and taste my champagne. I've got some. . . .' He named some fabulous brand and vintage year.

When I still refused he said:

'But I'm Harriman.' He added: 'T. E. Harriman.'. . . I think those were the initials. At any rate they were those of the then railway king of the United States. I said I was as glad to have seen him as to have seen his diamond but that champagne disagreed with me. As a matter of fact I dislike champagne almost more than any other fluid.

I strolled back to my place. But here is the point: I was not half across the café when my little Austrian waiter ran after me and said:

'How could you do it? How *could* you do it? How could you?'

I expressed astonishment. He said, almost crying:

'Why did you give him the diamond? Of course you could not take a reward. But if you had given it to me to give him he must have given me three—four—five hundred pounds, by law. Then I could have opened my café in Wien and married and been happy for ever.'

I was never so ashamed of myself. I have not got over being ashamed of it. Since then I have eaten I suppose the majority of my meals at restaurants—and that lesson I have never forgotten. Waiters, I mean, are human beings and the wise man remembers it.

ALAS!

Two years ago I happened to find in New York my engagement book for 1914. As I had made up my mind to make that city my headquarters from then on I had taken a number of old papers over there in order to sort them out and store them. The engagement book was by chance among them. It was tied up with the soiled, soaked translation into French of my one novel. I had begun to make it in Bécourt-Bécordel wood in July 1916.

The engagement book was an amazing, packed affair. From the middle of May to the end of June, except for the week-ends which I spent either at Selsey where I lived next to Masterman and the editor of the *Outlook* or at other people's country houses—there were only six days on which I did not have at least three dinner and after-dinner dates. There would be a dinner, a theatre or a party, a dance. Usually a breakfast at four after that. Or Ezra and his gang carried me off to their night club which was kept by Mme. Strindberg, decorated by Epstein and situate underground.

London was adorable then at four in the morning after a good dance. You walked along the south side of the park in the lovely pearl-grey coolness of the dawn. A sparrow would chirp with a great volume of distinct sound in the silence. Another sparrow, another—a dozen, a hundred, ten thousand. They would be like the violins of an orchestra. Then the blackbirds awakened, then the thrushes, then the chaffinches. It became the sound of an immense choir with the fuller notes of the merle family making obligatos over the chattering counterpoint of the sparrows. Then, as like as not, you turned into the house of some one who had gone before you from the dance to grill sausages and make coffee. Then you breakfasted— usually on the lead roof above a smoking room, giving on to a deep garden. There would be birds there too. Those who cannot remember London then do not know what life holds. Alas. . . .

THE HEART
OF THE COUNTRY

'MEARY'

THOSE brown, battered men and women of an obscure Kentish countryside come back to me as the best English people I ever knew. I do not think that, except for the parson and the grocer, any one of them could read or write but I do not believe that one of them ever betrayed either me or even each other. If, as I undoubtedly do, I love England with a deep love, though I grow daily more alien to the Englishman, it is because of them. Here are some of them:

About twenty-five years ago I wanted some mushroom catsup. Bonnington was in a scattered, little-populated village of the south of England. The village stood on what had formerly been common land; running all down the side of a range of hills. But this common land had been long since squatted on, so that it was a maze of little hawthorn hedges surrounding little closes. Each close had a few old apple- or cherry-trees, a patch of potato ground, a cabbage patch, a few rows of scarlet runners, a few plants of monthly roses, a few plants of marjoram, fennel, borage, or thyme. And in each little patch there stood a small dwelling. Mostly these were the original squatters' huts built of mud, whitewashed outside and crowned with old thatched roofs on which there grew grasses, house-leeks, or even irises. There were a great many of these little houses beneath the September sunshine and it was all a maze of the small green hedges.

I had been up to the shop in search of my catsup, but though they sold everything from boots and straw hats to darning needles, bacon, haricot beans, oatmeal, and British wines, they had no catsup. I was wandering desultorily homewards among the small green hedges down hill, looking at the distant sea seven miles away over the marsh. Just beyond a little hedge I saw a woman digging potatoes in the dry, hot ground. She looked up as I passed and said:

'Hullo, Measter!'

I answered: 'Hullo, Missus!' and I was passing on when it occurred to me to ask her whether she knew anyone who sold catsup. She answered:

'Naw! Aw doan't knaw no one!'

I walked on a little farther and then sat down on a stile for half an hour or so; enjoying the pleasant weather and taking a read in the country paper which I had bought in the shop. Then I saw the large, stalwart old woman coming along the stony path carrying two great trugs of the potatoes that she had dug up. I had to get down from the stile to let her pass. And then seeing that she was going my way, that she was evidently oldish and was probably tired, I took the potato trugs from her and carried them. She strode along in front of me between the hedges. She wore an immense pair of men's hob-nailed boots that dragged along the stones of the causeway with metallic sounds, an immense shawl of wool that had been beaten by the weather until it was of a dull liver colour, an immense skirt that had once been of lilac cotton print, but was now a rusty brown, and an immense straw hat that had been given her by some one as being worn out and that had cost twopence when it was new. Her face was large, as round and much the same colour as a copper warming-pan. Her mouth was immense and quite toothless except for one large fang, and as she smiled cheerfully all the time, her great gums were always to be seen. Her shoulders were immense and moved with the roll and heave of those of a great bullock. This was the wisest and upon the whole the most estimable human being that I ever knew at all well. Her hands were enormous and stained a deep blackish green over their original copper colour by the hops that it was her profession to tie.

As we walked along she told me that she was exactly the same age as our Queen who was then just seventy. She told me also that she wasn't of those parts but was a Paddock Wood woman by birth, which meant that she came from the true hop country. She told me also that her husband had died fifteen years before of the sting of a viper, that his poor old leg went all like green jelly up to his thigh before he died, and that he had been the best basket-maker in all Kent. She also told me that we can't all have everything and that the only thing to do is to 'keep all on gooing.'

I delivered up her trugs to her at her garden gate and she said to me with a cheerful nod:

'Well I'll do the same for you mate, when you come to be my age.' She shambled over the rough stone of her garden path and into her dark door beneath the low thatch that was two yards thick. Her cottage was more dilapidated than any that I have ever seen in my life. It stood in a very long narrow triangle of ground, so that the hedge that I walked along must have been at least eighty yards in length, while at its broadest part the potato patch could not have measured twenty spade breadths. But before I was come to the end of the hedge her voice was calling out after me:

'Measter! Dun yo really want ketchup?'

I replied that I really did.

She said:

'Old Meary Spratt up by Hungry Hall wheer ye see me diggin'—she makes ketchup.'

I asked her why she had not told me before and she answered,

'Well, ye see the Quality do be asking foolish questions, I thought ye didn't really want to know.'

I learnt afterwards it wasn't only the dislike of being asked foolish questions. In Meary Walker's long, wise life she had experienced one thing—that no man with a collar and a tie is to be trusted. She had had it vaguely in her mind that, when I asked the question, I might be some sort of excise officer trying to find out where illicit distilling was carried on. She didn't know that the making of catsup was not illegal. She had heard that many of her poor neighbours had been fined heavily for selling bottles of home-made sloe-gin or mead. She had refused to answer, out of a sense of automatic caution for fear she should get poor old Meary Spratt into trouble.

But next morning she turned up at my cottage carrying two bottles of Meary Spratt's catsup in an old basket covered with a cloth. And after that, seeing her rather often at the shop on Saturday nights when all the world came to buy its Sunday provisions, and because she came in to heat the bake-oven with faggots once a week, and to do the washing—in that isolated neighbourhood, among the deep woods of the Weald, I got to know her as well as I ever knew anybody. This is her biography:

She was the daughter of a day labourer among the hop-fields of Paddock Wood. When she had been born, the youngest of five, her own mother had died. Her father had brought a stepmother into the house. I never discovered that the stepmother was notably cruel to Meary. But those were the Hungry 'Forties. The children never had enough to eat. Once, Meary cut off one of her big toes. She had jumped down into a ditch after a piece of turnip peel. She had of course had no shoes or stockings and there had been a broken bottle in the ditch.

So her childhood had been a matter of thirst, hunger, and frequent chastisements with the end of a leather strap that her father wore round his waist. When she was four-teen she was sent to service in a great house where all the maids slept together under the roof. Here they told each other legends at night—odd legends that exactly resembled the fairy tales of Grimm—legends of princes and prin-cesses, of castles, or of travelling companions on the road. A great many of these stories seemed to hinge upon the price of salt which at one time was extravagantly dear in the popular memory, so that one princess offered to have her heart cut out in order to purchase a pound of salt that should restore her father to health.

From this house Meary Walker ran away with a gipsy— or at least he was what in that part of the world was called a 'pikey'—a user of the turnpike road. So, for many years they led a wandering existence, until at last they settled down in this village. Until the date of that settlement Meary had not troubled to marry her Walker. Then a parson insisted on it, but it did not trouble her much either way.

Walker had always been a man of weak health. He had what is called the artistic temperament—a small, dark, delicate man whose one enthusiasm was his art of making baskets. In that he certainly excelled. But he was lazy and all the work of their support fell on Meary. She tied hops— and this is rather skilled work,—she picked them in the autumn; she helped the neighbours with baking and brewing. She cleaned up the church once a week. She planted the potatoes and cropped them. She was the first cottager in East Kent to keep poultry for profit. In her biography you could find traces of great benevolence and of considerable heroism. Thus, one hard winter, she supported not only herself and her husband, but her old friend Meary Spratt, at that time a widow with six children. Meary Spratt was in bed with pneumonia and its after effects, from December to March. Meary Walker nursed her, washed and tended the children, and made the livings for all of them.

Then there came the time when she broke her leg and had to be taken against her will to the hospital which was seven miles away. She did not want to be in the hospital; she was anxious to be with Walker who was then dying of gangrene of the leg. She was anxious too about a sitting hen; one of her neighbours had promised her half a crown for a clutch of chickens. She used to lie in hospital, patting her broken knee under the bedclothes and exclaiming:

'Get well, get well, oh do get well quickly!' And even twenty years afterwards when she rehearsed these scenes and these words there would remain in the repetition a whole world of passionate wistfulness. But indeed, she translated her passion into words. One night, driven beyond endurance by the want of news of Walker and of her sitting hen she escaped from the hospital window and crawled on her hands and knees the whole seven miles from the hospital to her home. She found when she arrived in the dawn that Walker was in his coffin. The chickens however were a healthy brood. Her admiration for Walker, the weak and lazy artist in basket-making, never decreased. She treasured his best baskets to the end of her life as you and I might treasure Rembrandts. Once, ten years after, she sat for a whole day on his grave. The old sexton, growing confused with years, had made a mistake and was going to inter another man's wife on top of Walker. Meary stopped that.

For the last twenty-six years or so of her life she lived in the mud hut which I had first seen her enter. She went on as before, tying hops, heating ovens, picking up stones, keeping a hen or two. She looked after, fed and nursed— for the love of God—a particularly disagreeable old man called Purdey who had been a London cab-driver. He sat all day in a grandfather's chair, grumbling and swearing at Meary whenever she came in. He was eighty-two. He had no claim whatever upon her and he never paid her a penny of money.

So she kept on going all through life. She was always cheerful: she had always on her tongue some fragment of peasant wisdom. Once, coming back from market, she sat down outside a public-house and a soldier treated her to a pot of beer. Presently there rode up the Duke of Cambridge in his field-marshal's uniform and beside him there was the Shah of Persia. They were watching a sham fight in the neighbourhood. Meary raised her pot of beer towards these royal personages and wished them health. They nodded in return.

'Well,' Meary called out to the Duke, 'you're only your mother's son like the rest of us.'

Once, Batalha Reis amiably told her that, in his language, bread was 'pom.' She expressed surprise, but then she added:

'Oh, well poor dear, when you're hungry you've got to eat it, like the rest of us, whatever you call it.'

She was sorry for him because he had to call bread by such an outlandish name. She could not think how he remembered the word. Yet she knew that *Brot* was the German for bread and *Apfel* for apples, because, during the Napoleonic Wars, the Hanoverian Legion had garrisoned that part of the country and there remained until the accession of Queen Victoria. One of what she called the jarman legions had murdered his sweetheart, who had been a friend of her mother's, and when he was hung for it at Canterbury he asked for *Brot* and *Apfel* on the scaffold. She saw him hung, a pleasant fair boy, and when she looked down at her hands she said they were white as lard.

So she worked on until she was seventy-eight. One day she discovered a swelling under her left breast. It gave her no pain but she wanted to know what it was. So she put a hot brick to it. She knew that if it was cancer that was a bad thing to do, but she wanted to get it settled. The swelling became worse. So she walked to the hospital—the same hospital that she had crawled away from. They operated on her next morning—and she was dead by noon. Her last words were:

'Who's going to look after old Purdey?'

CAREW AND OTHER TRAMPS

It puzzled me for many years to know what castles in Spain a tramp built—what was *his* particular Island of the Blest; and after getting over the first shyness of accosting these slightly repellent bundles of clothes (for it is, after all, the clothes that repel us), I pursued this ideal with some diligence. It was Carew, the tramp, who got me most easily over my shyness. He was a man of no particular book-learning, though he said that hardly a day passed without his picking up a paper. He was the son of a Guardsman and a prostitute, and his professional tale had it that he had been bred up as a tooth-comb maker; machines had destroyed *that* occupation. He carried a comb in his pocket; but I fancy that he delighted to comb his long golden beard, and had the comb for that purpose, inventing the profession to fit the implement. I have met him in Regent's Park, on the Sussex Downs, in Cornwall, and in the Strand; but he always carried his boots under his arm—I never knew quite why. I fancy it was on account of some superstition: he did not like boots, but a sort of luck, I imagine, clung to this particular pair. An odd mixture of sardonic candour and savage reticence, he would admit to having been in every gaol in the south of England, but he would never reveal what he was afraid of on the roads at night. He always crept into the shelter of some house at nightfall, and he had once, he told me, been arrested for following a young lady five miles across Salisbury Plain in the moonlight—with no other evil purpose than the desire to keep a human being in sight.

In spite of the comb, he said he had never done a day's work in his life, and never meant to. He lay by the roadside, and sometimes he had been so magnificently lazy that he had gone without food for two days rather than beg. 'You get sick of people's faces at times,' he said.

But Carew, as far as I can discover, built no castles in Spain. He supposed that pneumonia would carry him off one of these days, probably in China, as he styled Lewes gaol. He called the various prisons by the names of countries, and nick-named workhouses after the great cities of the world. Thus Eachend Hill Union was Paris with him, and Bodmin, Rome; though this caused confusion, because, of course, London itself is Rome in the lingo of the hedgerows. His crimes, as far as I know, were limited to sleeping out; in this flagrant offence he was very frequently taken because of the nervous tendency which made him sleep in stack-yards near cattle, or in farm stables near horses, for the sake of company. He exhibited with a pride a small sheaf of newspaper cuttings which recorded his convictions, and his insolent retorts to magistrates. He was delighted with these; but he seemed to have no further ambitions. He was as contented with a 'bob' as with a 'quid' if I gave it him, and apparently contented with a 'brown.' He let life roll by in front of him, and took from it as little as he gave.

If you stay for any time at an inn looking down on one of the great tramp highways, you will see the same faces, the same clothes, the same battered hats, the same splay feet, pass and repass your window at intervals of a day or two; for many of these tramps, having found a string of two or three comfortable wards, will spend, like summer ghosts, the whole of the warm season haunting the same countryside. Congenital lack of candour, the desire to please their interlocutor, sheer muzziness of brain, or sheer ferocity, make it difficult to discover what may be the ideal of this brown flotsam. Their universal and official shibboleth has it that if they could only get a steady job and a nice little cottage they would settle down with the missus and kids and live respectable under the parson for evermore. The more candid of the men, when they were assured that their reply would make no difference in the number of coppers destined for them, confessed almost without exception that their ideal was to have a pension like a soldier. This appeared to be, as it were, the good establishment that every middle-class man wishes for his daughter. As a matter of fact, a very considerable percentage of the innumerable old soldiers who solicit alms along the road do have such pensions, and for perhaps three glorious nights out of the month are kings of the earth—kings over draggled and carneying subjects, as aware as their monarch himself of when pay-day comes round, and where the floodgates of oblivion will be let loose.

One very hot day last month, on a high-road broad and parched, stretching out level and without end beneath an empty sky, on a day so hot that the very larks were silent, and the twittering duologue of the linnets sounded as if it came from dusty little throats, I sat down in the long grass under the hedge by the side of a very inviting and swarthy tramp. He suddenly brought out in a rich soft voice, without any inquiry of mine—

'Lord! I'd like to be a workhouse master. I'd like to be the master of a workhouse! Wouldn't I give the casuals champagne and porterhouse steaks one day, and wouldn't I wollup them the next!'

A little time before I had walked along the same road in a drenching rain with a German tramp, tiny, wizened, ferret-faced, and with the extravagant gestures of an actor. With his right hand he held firmly to my sleeve, and from a great scroll of manuscript in his left he read passages from a poem about the beauties of nature abounding in the forest near the town of Carlsruhe in Baden. His whole being was engrossed in his work, he saw neither road, sky, nor sea; only from time to time he broke off to exclaim, 'This is very pleasant, you will like this very much!' His life-history, varied and unromantic as it was, would occupy too much space in the telling, but *his* consoling thought was that Wagner had been too poor to possess an overcoat whilst he was writing his music drama of *Rienzi*; and hope, ardour, confidence, and romance were in his eyes and voice when, at saying farewell to me, he uttered the words: 'There is a Russian author, I forget his name, who has just bought an estate on the Volga for 700,000 marks; once he was only a tramp like me.' He was quite illiterate and his poem was atrocious, but he said that people on the road were very kind to him; one gentleman at Brighton had given him board and lodging for three nights.

Thus between the fragrant hedgerows the townsman newly come into his heart of the country will see this vast body of dun-coloured units driven backwards and forwards like ghosts upon the tides of the winds. For him, indeed, they must remain ghosts; as a rule he will feel the repulsion that we must all feel for those who are outside our world, outside our life, outside our praise, outside our banning or our cursing.

They are as much outside pity or regret as are the innumerable dead; they have gone back into the heart of the country and have become one with the ravens, the crows, the weasels, and the robins, picking up the things that we have no use for, from such small parcels of grounds as we have not enclosed.

To the really inveterate townsman every weather-beaten man or woman that he passes along the road is a tramp. It is as difficult for him to distinguish a genuine waggoner from a fraudulent tooth-comb maker as to tell rye grass from permanent pasture, or the mistle from the song-thrush. But gradually as he sinks deeper into the life of the country, passes during weeks and months between hedgerows and begins to note differences between the songs of birds, he will acquire a sort of instinctive knack of distinguishing between one sort and the other. The differences lie in minute things, in the poise of the head, the way of setting down the foot, the glance of the eye in passing. The townsman may make experiments in reclaiming the tramp—like Hercules he will wrestle with death for possession of one soul—but once the man is really dead there is no recalling him. He may set him up and endow him with tools, clothes, a place to live in, and all the fair simulacra of our corporate life; he may keep him propped up for a day, for a week, for a month, for a year, but sooner or later the body will collapse and the soul once more be at one with the Maker of the hedgerow. To try preventing the real tramp from following out his life is like attempting to stifle the words of a poet or the sighs of a miserable lover. But if he ever come to examine meticulously, the townsman will discover that amongst these ghosts there whirl past some that still cling to life, that claim our pity and need such helping hands as the gods will let us give. Once, when I lived on a hillside below a common, I came home in the evening down through the furze and saw a faded old man and a faded old woman, with the usual perambulator of the traveller, encamped in a small sandpit. They were both painfully clean, and beneath an arbour of gorse bushes had an odd air of being Philemon and Baucis cast upon an unsympathetic world, where the very twilight of the gods had passed away. But what struck me most and most disagreeably was to see my own favourite yellow Orpington cock dancing up and down in front of the old man full a quarter of a mile away from my gate. I imagined that he was one of those people who can whisper poultry out of a field, just as gipsies are said to do with stallions. But on reaching home I saw my cock contentedly dusting himself in an ash-heap, and when I went a couple of hours later to the post, passing the old people's settlement, I saw that the yellow cock had been reinforced by a gigantic lop-eared rabbit, an aged tortoise-shell cat, and a battered accordion. These were the Lares and Penates of this ancient couple, the signs that, evil days having fallen upon them and the hatred of the workhouse having forced them to take the road, they still clung desperately to as much as they could carry in a perambulator of their former householder's dignity; they still clung desperately to life, the old man still hoping for fruit-trees to prune, the old woman still cherishing her ideal of many beehives to look after.

TABLE TALK

MYSELF

IN A mild way I should call myself a sentimental Tory and a Roman Catholic.

GOOD FRIDAY

Good Friday before last I gave a lunch to four men at my London club. I passed the meat as a matter of habit, of good manners, of what you will. What was my astonishment to discover that each of my guests passed the meat. In short each of us five was actually a Roman Catholic of a greater or less degree of earnestness. Yet, although we were all five fairly intimate, meeting frequently and talking of most of the things that men talk about, we were not any one of us aware of the other's religious belief. This, I think, would be impossible anywhere but in London, and it is just for that reason that London of to-day is such a restful place to live in.

ROSSETTI'S INVERNESS CAPE

Upon Rossetti's death, his inverness, which was made in the year 1869, descended to my grandfather. Upon my grandfather's death it descended to me, it being then twenty-three years old. I wore it with feelings of immense pride as if it had been—and indeed was it not?—the mantle of a prophet. And such approbation did it meet with in my young friends of that date that this identical garment was copied seven times, and each time for the use of a gentleman whose works, when Booksellers Row still existed, might ordinarily be found in the Twopenny Box. So this garment spread the true tradition, and indeed it was imperishable and indestructible, though what has become of it by now I do not know. I wore it for several years until it must have been aged probably thirty, when, happening to wear it during a visit to my tailor's, and telling that gentleman its romantic history, I was distressed to hear him remark, looking over his pince-nez:

'Time the moths had it!'

This shed such a light upon the garment from the point of view of tailors that I never wore it again. It fell, I am afraid, into the hands of a family with little respect for relics of the great, and I am fairly certain that I observed its capacious folds in the mists of an early morning upon Romney Marsh some months ago, enveloping the limbs of an elderly and poaching scoundrel called Slingsby.

A FABIAN DEBATE

I remember being present at a Fabian debate as to the attributes of the Deity. I forget what it was all about, but it lasted a very considerable time. Towards the end of the meeting an energetic lady arose—it was, I think, her first attendance at a Fabian meeting—and remarked:

'All this talk is very fine, but what I want to know is, whether the Fabian Society does, or does not, believe in God?'

A timid gentleman rose and replied:

'If Mrs Y—— will read Fabian Tract 312, she will discover what she ought to think upon this matter.'

THE MUSIC STOPPED

The other day I was at a wedding reception—there was a very large crowd. In one corner an excellent quintette discussed selections from the *Contes d'Hofmann*. We were all talking twenty to the dozen. My *vis-à-vis* was telling me something that did not interest me, when the voice of a man behind me said: 'So they left him there in prison with a broken bottle of poison in his pocket.' And then the music stopped suddenly and I never heard who the man was, or what he had done to get into prison, or why he had broken the bottle of poison.

STRAWBERRY JAM AND OYSTERS

The other day I attended a concert consisting mainly of the Song Cycles of Debussy, setting the words of Verlaine. They were sung by an Armenian lady who had escaped from a Turkish harem and had had no musical training. She was a barbaric creature who uttered loud howls, and the effect was to me disagreeable in the extreme; all the same, the audience was large and enthusiastic and the most enlightened organ of musical opinion of to-day spoke of the performance with a chastened enthusiasm. I happened to meet the writer of the notice in the course of the following afternoon, and I asked him what he really got for himself out of that singular collocation of sounds. He said airily: 'Well, you see, one gets emotions!'

I said: 'Good God! what sort of emotions?'

He answered: 'Well, you see, if one shuts one's eyes one can imagine that one is eating strawberry jam and oysters in a house of ill-fame, and a cat is rushing violently up and down the keyboard of the piano with a cracker tied to its tail.'

I said: 'Then why in the world didn't you say so in your notice?'

He smiled blandly:

'Well, you see, an ignorant public might take such a description for abuse, and we cannot afford to abuse anything now.'

PRE-RAPHAELITE LOVE

Love, according to the Pre-Raphaelite canon, was a great but rather sloppy passion. Its manifestations would be Paolo and Francesca, or Launcelot and Guinevere. It was a thing that you swooned about on broad, general lines, your eyes closed, your arms outstretched. It excused all sins, it sanctified all purposes and, if you went to hell over it, you still drifted about amongst snow-flakes of fire with your eyes closed and in the arms of the object of your passion. For it is impossible to suppose that when Rossetti painted his picture of Paolo and Francesca in hell, he, or any of his admirers, thought that these two lovers were really suffering. They were not. They were suffering perhaps with the malaise of love which is always an uneasiness, but an uneasiness how sweet! And the flakes of flames were descending all over the rest of the picture, but they did not fall upon Paolo and Francesca. No, the lovers were protected by a generalized, swooning passion that formed, as it were, a moral and very efficient macintosh all over them. And no doubt what D. G. Rossetti and his school thought was that, although guilty lovers have to go to hell for the sake of the story, they will find hell pleasant enough because the aroma of their passion, the wings of the great god of love and the swooning intensity of it all will render them insensible to the inconveniences of their lodgings. As much as to say that you do not mind the bad cooking of the Brighton hotel if you are having otherwise a good time of it.

ON OBSOLETE WORDS

I remember once hearing Stephen Crane—the author of *The Red Badge of Courage* and of *The Open Boat*, which is the finest volume of true short stories in the English language—I remember hearing him, with his wonderful eyes flashing and his extreme vigour and intonation, comment upon a sentence of Robert Louis Stevenson that he was reading. The sentence was: 'With interjected finger he delayed the motion of the timepiece.' 'By God, poor dear!' Crane exclaimed. 'That man put back the clock of English fiction fifty years.' I do not know that this is exactly what Stevenson did do. I should say myself that the art of writing in English received the numbing blow of a sandbag when Rossetti wrote, at the age of eighteen, *The Blessed Damozel*. From that time forward and until to-day—and for how many years to come!—the idea has been inherent in the mind of the English writer that writing was a matter of digging for obsolete words with which to express ideas for ever dead and gone. Stevenson did this, of course, as carefully as any Pre-Raphaelite, though instead of going to mediaeval books he ransacked the seventeenth century. But this tendency is unfortunately not limited to authors misusing our very excellent tongue. The other day I was listening to an excellent Italian *conférencier* who assured an impressed audience that Signor D'Annunzio is the greatest Italian stylist there has ever been, since in his last book he has used over 2,017 obsolete words which cannot be understood by a modern Italian without the help of a mediaeval glossary.

MR RUSKIN'S EPITHET

On one page of one of Mr Ruskin's books I have counted the epithet 'golden' six times. There are 'golden days,' 'golden-mouthed,' 'distant golden spire,' 'golden peaks' and 'golden sunset,' all of them describing one picture by Turner in which the nearest approach to gold discernible by a precise eye is a mixture of orange red and madder brown.

MIXING UP NAMES

Nothing can prevent my mixing up names. I suppose I inherit the characteristic from my grandfather, who had it to a dangerous degree. I would come in and say to him:

'Grandpa, I met Lord Leighton in the Park and he sent his regards to you.' He would exclaim with violence: 'Leighton! How dare you be seen talking to him? And how dare he presume to send messages to me? He is the scoundrel who...' I would interrupt:

'But, Grandpa, he is the President of the Royal Academy....' He would interrupt in turn: 'Nonsense. I tell you he is the fellow who got seven years for....' A few minutes after he would exclaim:

'Leighton? Oh, Leighton? Why didn't you say Leighton if you meant Leighton. I thought you said Fothergill-Bovey Haines. Of course there is no reason why you should not be civil to Leighton.'

WALTER CRANE'S GLOVES

I moved back to the Pent which I had let to an artist then of some fame. His name being Crane he had painted a bird of that species on the front door which gave on to the stockyard beyond a narrow strip of terrace and lawn. He had also painted numbers on all the room-doors. There were thirteen. His family used to take baths on the lawn which worried and astonished the stockmen and shepherds in the yards below. When they left there remained behind them an extraordinary number of gloves. In every drawer of the bedrooms there were old, soiled and crumpled gloves. I have remained wondering to this day what they can have been wanting with so many. Is there a *maladie de gants* as there is said to be of boots? At any rate we used them all to manure the roots of a vine that covered the front of the house. Leather is the best of all manures for vines and also for figs. Indeed if you want to plant a fig tree you should plant it with its roots in an old leather portmanteau. You will have wonderful figs.

THE CITY OF DREADFUL NIGHT

Those were grim enough times for artists—the 'eighties and early 'nineties. I don't know that they are any better now. There was a blind poet called Philip Bourke Marston. He was not a very striking poet, but because he was blind he occupied a position of some note amongst the minor Pre-Raphaelite group. He was bearded like an elder states-man of those days and, with his down-glancing eyes, was of noble appearance. Members of the group used to take it in turns to read to him in his gloomy room in the Euston Road. One day another poet of much greater repu-tation came in. He threw a fit of delirium tremens and imagined himself a Bengal tiger; he fell upon poor Mars-ton and mauled him rather severely, the blind man being unable to defend himself at all. William Sharpe came in and found them struggling on the floor. He pulled off the dipsomaniac who immediately burst a blood vessel, his blood pouring all over both Marston and Fiona Macleod. Sharpe ran around to the nearby hospital to fetch a doctor. The physician in charge immediately cried out that Sharpe must be arrested for murder. He was drunk. In the mean-time, the dipsomaniac bled to death and Marston nearly went out of his mind. . . . Yes, grim times in that city of dreadful night!

MAUPASSANT AND THE NAKED LADY

Mr James recounted that once, when Mr James had been invited to lunch with him, Maupassant had received him, not, be assured, in a dressing-gown, but in the society of a naked lady wearing a mask.... And Maupassant assured the author of *The Great Good Place* that the lady was a *femme du monde*. And Mr James believed him.... Fortune could go no further than *that*! ...

A NOVELIST'S CREDO

The first thing the novelist has to learn is self-effacement —that first and that always. Not for him flowing locks, sombreros, flaming ties, eccentric pants. If he gets himself up like a poet humanity will act towards him as if he were a poet ... disagreeably. That would not matter were it not that he will see humanity under a false aspect. Then his books will be wrong.

His effort should be to be at one with his material. Without that he will not understand the emotions and reactions of his human renderings. Superstitions, belief in luck, premonitions, play such a great part in human motives that a novelist who does not to some extent enter into those feelings can hardly understand and will certainly be unable to render to perfection most human affairs. Yes, you must sacrifice yourself. You must deny yourself the pleasure of saying to your weaker brothers and sisters: 'Haw! No superstitions about me.' Indeed you must deny yourself the pleasure of high-hatting anybody about anything. You must live merrily and trust to good letters.

POEMS

ON HEAVEN

To V.H., who asked for a working Heaven

I

That day the sunlight lay on the farms;
On the morrow the bitter frost that there was!
That night my young love lay in my arms,
  The morrow how bitter it was!

And because she is very tall and quaint
And golden, like a *quattrocento* saint,
I desire to write about Heaven;
To tell you the shape and the ways of it,
And the joys and the toil in the maze of it,
For these there must be in Heaven,
Even in Heaven!

For God is a good man, God is a kind man,
And God's a good brother, and God is no blind man,
And God is our father.

I will tell you how this thing began:
How I waited in a little town near Lyons many years,
And yet knew nothing of passing time, or of her tears,
But, for nine slow years, lounged away at my table in the
    shadowy sunlit square
Where the small cafés are.

The *Place* is small and shaded by great planes,
Over a rather human monument
Set up to *Louis Dixhuit* in the year
Eighteen fourteen; a funny thing with dolphins
About a pyramid of green-dripped, sordid stone.
But the enormous, monumental planes
Shade it all in, and in the flecks of sun

359

Sit market women. There's a paper shop
Painted all blue, a shipping agency,
Three or four cafés; dank, dark colonnades
Of an eighteen-forty *Maîrie*. I'd no wish
To wait for her where it was picturesque,
Or ancient or historic, or to love
Over well any place in the land before she came
And loved it too. I didn't even go
To Lyons for the opera; Arles for the bulls,
Or Avignon for glimpses of the Rhône.
Not even to Beaucaire! I sat about
And played long games of dominoes with the *maîre*,
Or passing *commis-voyageurs*. And so
I sat and watched the trams come in, and read
The *Libre Parole* and sipped the thin, fresh wine
They call Piquette, and got to know the people,
The kindly, southern people . . .

Until, when the years were over, she came in her swift
    red car,
Shooting out past a tram; and she slowed and stopped and
    lighted absently down,
A little dazed, in the heart of the town;
And nodded imperceptibly.
With a sideways look at me.

So our days here began.

And the wrinkled old woman who keeps the café,
And the man
Who sells the *Libre Parole*,
And the sleepy gendarme,
And the fat *facteur* who delivers letters only in the shady,
Pleasanter kind of streets;
And the boy I often gave a penny,
And the *maîre* himself, and the little girl who loves toffee
And me because I have given her many sweets;
And the one-eyed, droll

Bookseller of the *rue Grand de Provence*,—
Chancing to be going home to bed,
Smiled with their kindly, fresh benevolence,
Because they knew I had waited for a lady
Who should come in a swift, red, English car,
To the square where the little cafés are.
And the old, old woman touched me on the wrist
With a wrinkled finger,
And said: 'Why do you linger?—
Too many kisses can never be kissed!
And comfort her—nobody here will think harm—
Take her instantly to your arm!
It is a little strange, you know, to your dear,
To be dead'!

But one is English,
Though one be never so much of a ghost;
And if most of your life has been spent in the craze to
        relinquish
What you want most,
You will go on relinquishing,
You will go on vanquishing
Human longings, even
In Heaven.

God! You will have forgotten what the rest of the world
        is on fire for—
The madness of desire for the long and quiet embrace,
The coming nearer of a tear-wet face;
Forgotten the desire to slake
The thirst, and the long, slow ache,
And to interlace
Lash with lash, lip with lip, limb with limb, and the fingers
        of the hand with the hand
And . . .

You will have forgotten . . .
                                    But they will all awake;

Aye, all of them shall awaken
In this dear place.
And all that then we took
Of all that we might have taken,
Was that one embracing look,
Coursing over features, over limbs, between eyes, a making
    sure, and a long sigh,
Having the tranquillity
Of trees unshaken,
And the softness of sweet tears,
And the clearness of a clear brook
To wash away past years.
(For that too is the quality of Heaven,
That you are conscious always of great pain
Only when it is over
And shall not come again.
Thank God, thank God, it shall not come again,
Though your eyes be never so wet with the tears
Of many years!)

II

And so she stood a moment by the door
Of the long, red car. Royally she stepped down,
Settling on one long foot and leaning back
Amongst her russet furs. And she looked round . . .
Of course it must be strange to come from England
Straight into Heaven. You must take it in,
Slowly, for a long instant, with some fear . . .
Now that *affiche*, in orange, on the kiosque:
'*Six Spanish bulls will fight on Sunday next
At Arles, in the arena*' . . . Well, it's strange
Till you get used to our ways. And, on the *Maîrie*,
The untidy poster telling of the *concours
De vers de soie*, of silkworms. The cocoons
Pile, yellow, all across the little Places
Of ninety townships in the environs

Of Lyons, the city famous for her silks.
What if she's pale? It must be more than strange,
After these years, to come out here from England
To a strange place, to the stretched-out arms of me,
A man never fully known, only divined,
Loved, guessed at, pledged to, in your Sussex mud,
Amongst the frost-bound farms by the yeasty sea.
Oh, the long look; the long, long searching look!
And how my heart beat!

                    Well, you see, in England
She had a husband. And four families—
His, hers, mine, and another woman's too—
Would have gone crazy. And, with all the rest,
Eight parents, and the children, seven aunts
And sixteen uncles and a grandmother.
There were, besides, our names, a few real friends,
And the decencies of life. A monstrous heap!
They made a monstrous heap. I've lain awake
Whole aching nights to tot the figures up!
Heap after heaps, of complications, griefs,
Worries, tongue-clackings, nonsenses and shame
For not making good. You see the coil there was!
And the poor strained fibres of our tortured brains,
And the voice that called from depth in her to depth
In me ... my God, in the dreadful nights,
Through the roar of the great black winds, through the
      sound of the sea!
Oh agony! Agony! From out my breast
It called whilst the dark house slept, and stairheads creaked;
From within my breast it screamed and made no sound;
And wailed ... And made no sound.
And howled like the damned ... No sound! No sound!
Only the roar of the wind, the sound of the sea,
The tick of the clock ...
And our two voices, noiseless through the dark.
O God! O God!

(That night my young love lay in my arms ...

There was a bitter frost lay on the farms
In England, by the shiver
And the crawling of the tide;
By the broken silver of the English Channel,
Beneath the aged moon that watched alone—
Poor, dreary, lonely old moon to have to watch alone,
Over the dreary beaches mantled with ancient foam
Like shrunken flannel;
The moon, an intent, pale face, looking down
Over the English Channel.

But soft and warm She lay in the crook of my arm,
And came to no harm since we had come quietly home
Even to Heaven;
Which is situate in a little old town
Not very far from the side of the Rhône,
That mighty river
That is, just there by the Crau, in the lower reaches,
Far wider than the Channel.)

But, in the market place of the other little town,
Where the Rhône is a narrower, greener affair,
When she had looked at me, she beckoned with her long,
      white hand,
A little languidly, since it is a strain, if a blessed strain, to
      have just died.
And, going back again,
Into the long, red, English racing car,
Made room for me amongst the furs at her side.
And we moved away from the kind looks of the kindly
      people
Into the wine of the hurrying air.
And very soon even the tall grey steeple
Of Lyons cathedral behind us grew little and far
And then was no more there . . .
And, thank God, we had nothing any more to think of,
And, thank God, we had nothing any more to talk of;
Unless, as it chanced, the flashing silver stalk of the pampas
Growing down to the brink of the Rhône,

On the lawn of a little chateau, giving onto the river.
And we were alone, alone, alone . . .
At last alone . . .

The poplars on the hill-crests go marching rank on rank,
And far away to the left, like a pyramid, marches the ghost
    of Mont Blanc.
There are vines and vines and vines, all down to the
    river bank.
There will be a castle here,
And an abbey there;
And huge quarries and a long, white farm,
With long thatched barns and a long wine shed,

As we ran alone, all down the Rhône.
And that day there was no puncturing of the tyres to fear;
And no trouble at all with the engine and gear;
Smoothly and softly we ran between the great poplar alley
All down the valley of the Rhône.
For the dear, good God knew how we needed rest and to
    be alone.
But, on other days, just as you must have perfect shadows
    to make perfect Rembrandts,
He shall afflict us with little lets and hindrances of His own
Devising—just to let us be glad that we are dead . . .
Just for remembrance.

III

Hard by the castle of God in the Alpilles,
In the eternal stone of the Alpilles,
There's this little old town, walled round by the old, grey
    gardens . . .
There were never such olives as grow in the gardens of
    God,
The green-grey trees, the wardens of agony
And failure of gods.
Of hatred and faith, of truth, of treachery

They whisper; they whisper that none of the living prevail;
They whirl in the great mistral over the white, dry sods,
Like hair blown back from white foreheads in the enormous
  gale
Up to the castle walls of God . . .

But, in the town that's our home,
Once you are past the wall,
Amongst the trunks of the planes,
Though they roar never so mightily overhead in the day,
All this tumult is quieted down, and all
The windows stand open because of the heat of the night
That shall come.
And, from each little window, shines in the twilight a light,
And, beneath the eternal planes
With the huge, gnarled trunks that were aged and grey
At the creation of Time,
The Chinese lanthorns, hung out at the doors of hotels,
Shimmering in the dusk, here on an orange tree, there on
  a sweet-scented lime,
There on a golden inscription: 'Hotel of the Three Holy
  Bells.'
Or 'Hotel Sublime,' or 'Inn of the Real Good Will.'
And, yes, it is very warm and still,
And all the world is afoot after the heat of the day,
In the cool of the even in Heaven . . .
And it is here that I have brought my dear to pay her all
  that I owed her,
Amidst this crowd, with the soft voices, the soft footfalls,
  the rejoicing laughter.
And after the twilight there falls such a warm, soft darkness,
And there will come stealing under the planes a drowsy
  odour,
Compounded all of cyclamen, of oranges, or rosemary and
  bay,
To take the remembrance of the toil of the day away.

So we sat at a little table, under an immense plane,
And we remembered again

The blisters and foments
And terrible harassments of the tired brain,
The cold and the frost and the pain,
As if we were looking at a picture and saying: 'This is true!
Why this is a truly painted
Rendering of that street where—you remember?—I
    fainted.'
And we remembered again
Tranquilly, our poor few tranquil moments,
The falling of the sunlight through the panes,
The flutter for ever in the chimney of the quiet flame,
The mutter of our two poor tortured voices, always
    a-whisper
And the endless nights when I would cry out, running
    through all the gamut of misery, even to a lisp, her
    name;
And we remembered our kisses, nine, maybe, or eleven—
If you count two that I gave and she did not give again.

And always the crowd drifted by in the cool of the even,
And we saw the faces of friends,
And the faces of those to whom one day we must make
    amends,
Smiling in welcome.
And I said: 'On another day—
And such a day may well come soon—
We will play dominoes with Dick and Evelyn and Frances
For a whole afternoon.
And, in the time to come, Genée
Shall dance for us, fluttering over the ground as the sun-
    light dances.'
And *Arlésiennes* with the beautiful faces went by us,
And gipsies and Spanish shepherds, noiseless in sandals of
    straw, sauntered nigh us,
Wearing slouch hats and old sheep-skins, and casting
    admiring glances
From dark, foreign eyes at my dear . . .
(And ah, it is Heaven alone, to have her alone and so near!)

So all this world rejoices
In the cool of the even
In Heaven . . .
And, when the cool of the even was fully there,
Came a great ha-ha of voices.
Many children run together, and all laugh and rejoice and
    call,
Hurrying with little arms flying, and little feet flying, and
    little hurrying haunches,
From the door of a stable,
Where, in an *olla podrida*, they had been playing at the
    corrida
With the black Spanish bull, whose nature
Is patience with children. And so, through the gaps of the
    branches
Of jasmine on our screen beneath the planes,
We saw, coming down from the road that leads to the
    olives and Alpilles,
A man of great stature,
In a great cloak,
With a great stride,
And a little joke
For all and sundry, coming down with a hound at his side.
And he stood at the cross-roads, passing the time of day
In a great, kind voice, the voice of a man-and-a-half!—
With a great laugh, and a great clap on the back,
For a fellow in black—a priest I should say,
Or may be a lover,
Wearing black for his mistress's mood.
'A little toothache,' we could hear him say; 'but that's so
    good
When it gives over.' So he passed from sight
In the soft twilight, into the soft night,
In the soft riot and tumult of the crowd.

And a magpie flew down, laughing, holding up his beak
    to us.

And I said: 'That was God! Presently, when he has walked
    through the town
And the night has settled down,
So that you may not be afraid,
In the darkness, he will come to our table and speak to us.'
And past us many saints went walking in a company—
The kindly, thoughtful saints, devising and laughing and
    talking,
And smiling at us with their pleasant solicitude.
And because the thick of the crowd followed to the one
    side God,
Or to the other the saints, we sat in solitude.
In the distance the saints went singing all in chorus,
And our Lord went by on the other side of the street,
Holding a little boy.
Taking him to pick the musk-roses that open at dusk,
For wreathing the statue of Jove,
Left on the Alpilles above
By the Romans; since Jove,
Even Jove,
Must not want for his quota of honour and love;
But round about him there must be,
With all its tender jollity,
The laughter of children in Heaven,
Making merry with roses in Heaven.

Yet never he looked at us, knowing that that would be
    such joy
As must be over-great for hearts that needed quiet;
Such a riot and tumult of joy as quiet hearts are not able
To taste to the full . . .

. . . And my dear one sat in the shadows; very softly she
    wept:—
Such joy is in Heaven,
In the cool of the even,
After the burden and toil of the days,
After the heat and haze

In the vine-hills; or in the shady
Whispering groves in high passes up in the Alpilles,
Guarding the castle of God.

And I went on talking towards her unseen face:
'So it is, so it goes, in this beloved place,
There shall be never a grief but passes; no, not any;
There shall be such bright light and no blindness;
There shall be so little awe and so much loving-kindness;
There shall be a little longing and enough care,
There shall be a little labour and enough of toil
To bring back the lost flavour of our human coil;
Not enough to taint it;
And all that we desire shall prove as fair as we can paint it.'
For, though that may be the very hardest trick of all
God set Himself, who fashioned this goodly hall.
Thus He has made Heaven;
Even Heaven.

For God is a very clever mechanician;
And if He made this proud and goodly ship of the world,
From the maintop to the hull,
Do you think He could not finish it to the full,
With a flag and all,
And make it sail, tall and brave,
On the waters, beyond the grave?
It should cost but very little rhetoric
To explain for you that last, fine, conjuring trick;
Nor does God need to be a very great magician
To give to each man after his heart,
Who knows very well what each man has in his heart:
To let you pass your life in a night-club where they dance,
If that is your idea of heaven; if you will, in the South of
    France;
If you will, on the turbulent sea; if you will, in the peace
    of the night;
Where you will; how you will;
Or in the long death of a kiss, that may never pall:

He would be a very little God if He could not do all this,
And He is still
The great God of all.

For God is a good man; God is a kind man;
In the darkness He came walking to our table beneath the
    planes,
And spoke
So kindly to my dear,
With a little joke,
Giving Himself some pains
To take away her fear
Of His stature,
So as not to abash her,
In no way at all to dash her new pleasure beneath the planes,
In the cool of the even
In Heaven.

That, that is God's nature.
For God's a good brother, and God is no blind man,
And God's a good mother and loves sons who're rovers,
And God is our father and loves all good lovers.
He has a kindly smile for many a poor sinner;
He takes note to make it up to poor wayfarers on sodden
    roads;
Such as bear heavy loads
He takes note of, and of all that toil on bitter seas and
    frosty lands,
He takes care that they shall have good at His hands;
Well He takes note of a poor old cook,
Cooking your dinner;
And much He loves sweet joys in such as ever took
Sweet joy on earth. He has a kindly smile for a kiss
Given in a shady nook.
And in the golden book
Where the accounts of His estate are kept,
All the round, golden sovereigns of bliss,
Known by poor lovers, married or never yet married,

Whilst the green world waked, or the black world quietly
    slept;
All joy, all sweetness, each sweet sigh that's sighed—
Their accounts are kept,
And carried
By the love of God to His own credit's side.
So that is why He came to our table to welcome my dear,
    dear bride,
In the cool of the even
In front of a café in Heaven.

1914

ANTWERP

I

Gloom!
An October like November;
August a hundred thousand hours,
And all September,
A hundred thousand, dragging sunlit days,
And half October like a thousand years . . .
And doom!
That then was Antwerp . . .

In the name of God,
How could they do it?
Those souls that usually dived
Into the dirty caverns of mines;
Who usually hived
In whitened hovels; under ragged poplars;
Who dragged muddy shovels, over the grassy mud,
Lumbering to work over the greasy sods . . .
Those men there, with the appearances of clods
Were the bravest men that a usually listless priest of God
Ever shrived . . .
And it is not for us to make them an anthem.
If we found words there would come no wind that would
      fan them
To a tune that the trumpets might blow it,
Shrill through the heaven that's ours or yet Allah's
Or the wide halls of any Valhallas.
We can make no such anthem. So that all that is ours
For inditing in sonnets, pantoums, elegiacs, or lays
Is this:
In the name of God, how could they do it?'

II

For there is no new thing under the sun,
Only this uncomely man with a smoking gun

In the gloom . . .
What the devil will he gain by it?
Digging a hole in the mud and standing all day in the rain
  by it
Waiting his doom,
The sharp blow, the swift outpouring of the blood,
Till the trench of grey mud
Is turned to a brown purple drain by it.
Well, there have been scars
Won in many wars . . .
Punic,
Lacedæmonian, wars of Napoleon, wars for faith, wars for
  honour, for love, for possession,
But this Belgian man in his ugly tunic,
His ugly round cap, shooting on, in a sort of obsession,
Overspreading his miserable land,
Standing with his wet gun in his hand . . .
Doom!
He finds that in a sudden scrimmage,
And lies, an unsightly lump on the sodden grass . . .
An image that shall take long to pass!

III

For the white-limbed heroes of Hellas ride by upon their
  horses
For ever through our brains.
The heroes of Cressy ride by upon their stallions;
And battalions and battalions and battalions—
The Old Guard, the Young Guard, the men of Minden
  and of Waterloo,
Pass, for ever staunch,
Stand for ever true;
And the small man with the large paunch,
And the grey coat, and the large hat, and the hands behind
  the back,

Watches them pass
In our minds for ever . . .
But that clutter of sodden corses
On the sodden Belgian grass—
That is a strange new beauty.

IV

With no especial legends of marchings or triumphs or duty,
Assuredly that is the way of it,
The way of beauty . . .
And that is the highest word you can find to say of it.
For you cannot praise it with words
Compounded of lyres and swords,
But the thought of the gloom and the rain
And the ugly coated figure, standing beside a drain,
Shall eat itself into your brain.
And that shall be an honourable word;
'Belgian' shall be an honourable word,
As honourable as the fame of the sword,
As honourable as the mention of the many-chorded lyre,
And his old coat shall seem as beautiful as the fabrics
    woven in Tyre.

V

And what in the world did they bear it for?
I don't know.
And what in the world did they dare it for?
Perhaps that is not for the likes of me to understand.
They could very well have watched a hundred legions go
Over their fields and between their cities
Down into more southerly regions.
They could very well have let the legions pass through
    their woods,

And have kept their lives and their wives and their
  children and cattle and goods.
I don't understand.
Was it just love of their land?
Oh poor dears!
Can any man so love his land?
Give them a thousand thousand pities
And rivers and rivers of tears
To wash off the blood from the cities of Flanders.

VI

This is Charing Cross;
It is midnight;
There is a great crowd
And no light.
A great crowd, all black that hardly whispers aloud.
Surely, that is a dead woman—a dead mother!
She has a dead face;
She is dressed all in black;
She wanders to the bookstall and back,
At the back of the crowd;
And back again and again back,
She sways and wanders.

This is Charing Cross;
It is one o'clock.
There is still a great cloud, and very little light;
Immense shafts of shadows over the black crowd
That hardly whispers aloud . . .
And now! . . . That is another dead mother,
And there is another and another and another . . .
And little children, all in black,
All with dead faces, waiting in all the waiting-places,
Wandering from the doors of the waiting-room
In the dim gloom.

These are the women of Flanders.
They await the lost.
They await the lost that shall never leave the dock;
They await the lost that shall never again come by the
    train
To the embraces of all these women with dead faces;
They await the lost who lie dead in trench and barrier and
    foss,
In the dark of the night.
This is Charing Cross; it is past one of the clock;
There is very little light.

There is so much pain.

L'Envoi.
And it was for this that they endured this gloom;
This October like November,
That August like a hundred thousand hours,
And that September,
A hundred thousand dragging sunlit days,
And half October like a thousand years . . .
Oh poor dears!

                           1915

VIEWS

I

Being in Rome I wonder will you go
Up to the Hill. But I forget the name ...
Aventine? Pincio? No: I do not know.
I was there yesterday and watched. You came.

The seven Pillars of the Forum stand
High, stained and pale 'neath the Italian heavens,
Their capitals linked up form half a square;
A grove of silver poplars spears the sky.
You came. Do you remember? Yes, you came,
But yesterday. Your dress just brushed the herbs
That nearly hide the broken marble lion ...
And I was watching you against the sky.
Such light! Such air! Such prism hues! and Rome
So far below; I hardly knew the place.
The domed St Peter's; mass of the Capitol;
The arch of Trajan and St Angelo ...
Tiny and grey and level; tremulous
Beneath a haze amidst a sea of plains ...
But I forget the name, who never looked
On any Rome but this of unnamed hills.

II

Tho' you're in Rome you will not go, my You,
Up to that Hill ... But I forget the name,
Aventine? Pincio? No, I never knew ...
I was there yesterday. You never came.

I have that Rome; and you, you have a Me,
You have a Rome and I, I have my You;
My Rome is not your Rome: my you, not you
                    ... For, if man knew woman

378

I should have plumbed your heart; if woman, man
Your me should be true I . . . If in your day—
You who have mingled with my soul in dreams,
You who have given my life an aim and purpose,
A heart, an imaged form—if in your dreams
You have imagined unfamiliar cities
And me among them, I shall never stand
Beneath your pillars or your poplar groves . . .
Images, simulacra, towns of dreams
That never march upon each other's borders
And bring no comfort to each other's hearts!

III

Nobly accompanied am I—Since you,
You—simulacrum, image, dream of dreams,
Amidst these images and simulacra
Of shadowy house fronts and these dim, thronged streets
Are my companion!
              Where the pavements gleam
I have you alway with me: and grey dawns
In the far skies bring you more near—more near
Than City sounds can interpenetrate.
All vapours form a background for your face
In this unreal town of real things,
And my you stands beside me and makes glad
All my imagined cities and thence walks
Beside me towards yet unimagined hills . . .
Being we two, full surely we shall go
Up to that Hill . . . some synonym for Home.
Avalon? Grave? or Heaven? I do not know . . .
But one day or today, the day may come,
When I may be your I, your Rome my Rome.

1910

'WHEN THE WORLD WAS IN BUILDING...'

Thank Goodness, the moving is over,
They've swept up the straw in the passage
And life will begin...
This tiny, white, tiled cottage by the bridge!...
When we've had tea I will punt you
To Paradise for the sugar and onions...
We will drift home in the twilight,
The trout will be rising...

1918